INTRODUCTION TO OPTIMAL CONTROL

INTRODUCTION TO
OPTIMAL CONTROL

IAN McCAUSLAND

Associate Professor of Electrical Engineering
University of Toronto

JOHN WILEY & SONS, INC.

NEW YORK · LONDON · SYDNEY · TORONTO

Library of Congress Catalog Card Number: 68–30918
SBN 471 58160 7
Printed in the United States of America

Preface

I have written this book in order to provide a simple introduction to the field of optimal control. I am not attempting here to provide advanced knowledge about any of the various specialized techniques available for optimal control but rather to provide introductory information in general. The examples and problems are chosen to illustrate the various methods as simply as possible, without becoming too much involved with computational difficulties. A rigorous mathematical treatment has not been attempted; I hope, however, that the method of presentation may enable the student to develop some insight into optimization methods by studying these straightforward examples. In short, one of the principal aims of this book is ease of use, and it should be realized that the knowledge gained here is only a small part of the knowledge required to become an expert in the field of optimal control. As a guide to more advanced study, suggestions for further reading are included.

The background knowledge necessary for the comprehension of the material in this book is relatively modest. A prior knowledge of classical control theory or linear system theory, including the use of the Laplace transform, is assumed. Knowledge of simple matrix algebra, including the multiplication and inversion of matrices, is taken for granted, and some acquaintance with probability theory will be helpful. The book is intended for a first-year graduate course or for advanced undergraduate study. I hope that it also may be useful to engineers who have no access to university graduate courses and who wish to study the subject for themselves.

I start by introducing some of the earlier examples of optimization in control systems: the choice of optimum values of system parameters to minimize the integral squared error for a transient input or the mean squared error for a stationary random input. A brief discussion of classical Wiener filtering and an uncomplicated introduction to Kalman filter theory are also included. I then discuss the state representation of systems, a topic that is fundamental to most of the modern developments in control theory. The calculus of variations is introduced in a simple, nonrigorous way, with emphasis on control problems, and the maximum principle and dynamic programming are also introduced. A brief discussion of some of the basic principles of computational methods of optimization is also included.

Relationships between different methods of optimization are pointed out, and sample problems are solved by different methods to illustrate these relationships. Geometrical interpretations of various results are given, in an attempt to provide insight into the mathematical results.

I am grateful to the colleagues and students who, by their comments and suggestions, have helped in the preparation of this book. The constructive criticisms and suggestions of several reviewers have been of great value; I am especially grateful (without implicating them in the imperfections of the book) to Professor P. Dorato of the Polytechnic Institute of Brooklyn and Professor W. R. Perkins of the University of Illinois. I also thank F. T. Man and P. J. McLane for reading the final manuscript, and J. W. Zaleski for suggesting some of the examples and problems.

Toronto
February, 1968

Ian McCausland

Contents

Notation and Symbols

GENERAL NOTATION

Throughout this book, a superscript dot represents differentiation with respect to time. A straight horizontal bar over a quantity represents its time average, while a wavy bar represents the ensemble average (Chapter 3). An asterisk represents the optimum value of a quantity. The symbol F_x represents the partial derivative of F with respect to x.

VECTOR NOTATION

Boldface lower-case letters, such as $\mathbf{x}$ and $\mathbf{u}$, normally represent column vectors (although the components may appear in the text as a row in the form $x_1, \ldots, x_n$). Boldface capital letters, such as $\mathbf{A}$ and $\mathbf{B}$, normally represent matrices. In certain rare cases, however, a boldface capital of the form $\mathbf{X}(s)$ represents the Laplace transform of the vector $\mathbf{x}(t)$; these can be identified by the s in parentheses appearing after the boldface capital. The symbol $\mathbf{A}'$ represents the transpose of the matrix $\mathbf{A}$. Different vectors are represented by superscripts, and the components of a vector are represented by subscripts; for example, $\mathbf{x}^1$ and $\mathbf{x}^2$ are vectors, and x_1 and x_2 are components of the vector $\mathbf{x}$. The symbols $x_1{}^2$ and $x_2{}^2$ may represent components of the vector $\mathbf{x}^2$ or the squares of the quantities x_1 and x_2; the correct interpretation will be obvious from the context in any particular case. In the following rare cases, which are specifically pointed out where they appear in the text, a boldface letter appears with a subscript: in Section 4.10, the symbol $\mathbf{c}_j$ represents the jth row of a matrix $\mathbf{C}$, and in certain parts of Chapters 4 and 7 the symbol $\mathbf{x}_{n+1}$ is used to denote the vector $(x_1, \ldots, x_n, x_{n+1})$, the symbol $^0\mathbf{x}$ to denote the vector $(x_0, x_1, \ldots, x_n)$, and the symbol $^0\mathbf{x}_{n+1}$ to denote the vector $(x_0, x_1, \ldots, x_n, x_{n+1})$. The scalar product of two vectors is denoted by the symbol $\mathbf{a} \cdot \mathbf{b}$, representing $\sum_{i=1}^n a_i b_i$.

LIST OF PRINCIPAL SYMBOLS

A, B, C, D	Matrices of System parameters
B	Damping parameter
C	Capacitance
$d(t)$	Desired value of a function (Chapter 3)
e	Servomechanism error
e	Base of natural logarithms
e	Vector representing an ensemble of errors (Chapter 3)
$F(n)$	Fibonacci numbers
$F, \mathscr{F}$	Augmented integrand in calculus of variations
$H, \mathscr{H}, \tilde{\mathscr{H}}$	Hamiltonian function
I	Unit matrix
j	$\sqrt{-1}$
J	Moment of inertia
k, K	Gain
L	Inductance
$\mathscr{L}$	Laplace transform
$\mathscr{L}^{-1}$	Inverse Laplace transform
p	Adjoint vector or costate vector
R	Resistance
s	Laplace transform variable
$S_n(x), S(t, x), \mathcal{S}$	Cost function
t	Time
T	Time interval, time constant, sampling period
u	Control input vector $u_1, \ldots, u_r$
$w(t)$	Impulse response
x	State vector $x_1, \ldots, x_n$
y	Output vector $y_1, \ldots, y_p$
$\delta(t)$	Dirac delta function
ζ	Damping factor
$\boldsymbol{\theta}$	An eigenvector
$\boldsymbol{\Theta}$	A matrix of eigenvectors
θ	Phase angle
λ	An eigenvalue
$\boldsymbol{\Lambda}$	Diagonal matrix of eigenvalues
τ	Time shift
$\phi_{xx}(\tau)$	Autocorrelation function of x
$\Phi_{xx}(j\omega)$	Power-density spectrum of x
$\boldsymbol{\Phi}(t), \boldsymbol{\Phi}(t, \tau)$	Fundamental matrix, transition matrix
$\boldsymbol{\Psi}(t, \tau)$	Transition matrix of adjoint system
ω	Angular velocity or frequency

$\triangleq$	Equals by definition
$\simeq$	Is approximately equal to
$\neq$	Is not equal to
$[t_0, t_1]$	Closed interval $t_0 \leq t \leq t_1$
(t_0, t_1)	Open interval $t_0 < t < t_1$
$(t_0, t_1]$	Semiclosed interval $t_0 < t \leq t_1$
$[t_0, t_1)$	Semiclosed interval $t_0 \leq t < t_1$
sgn	Signum function

$$\text{sgn}[x] = \begin{cases} +1 & \text{for } x > 0 \\ -1 & \text{for } x < 0 \\ \text{undefined} & \text{for } x = 0 \end{cases}$$

1

Introduction

During the last few years a large proportion of the research in the field of control theory has been on the subject of optimal control. Most of the published work on this subject is at a very high mathematical level, beyond the reach of most engineers. The purpose of this book is to provide a simple introduction to the field of optimal control, in a non-rigorous form, at a level that should be understandable by the average graduate engineer.

The theory of optimal control may be considered to be a combination of the theory of automatic control and the theory of maxima and minima, and it is taken for granted that the reader has had some background courses in both of these areas. For example, the reader is assumed to have studied an introductory course in feedback control systems, including the use of the Laplace transformation. It is also assumed that the reader has studied simple problems involving the finding of maximum and minimum values of functions, such as the typical problems used as examples in the study of differential calculus.

A typical maximization problem, which the student will already have encountered, is the problem of finding the dimensions of the rectangle of specified perimeter which encloses the maximum possible area. If it is assumed that increase in area is desirable, the case of maximum area represents the optimum result. This problem has two essential features of an optimization problem, namely:

1. There is a clearly-defined quantity which is to be maximized (minimized). In this case the area is to be maximized.

2. There are restrictions which prevent this quantity from being made as large (as small) as we might wish. In this case, the prescribed length of perimeter and the stipulation that the figure be rectangular are restrictions which limit the area which can be attained.

In all the problems considered in this book, optimization will be taken to

1

mean the maximization or minimization[1] of some scalar quantity. This is not to say, however, that the stipulation of the quantity to be maximized or minimized is easily done. On the contrary, this may be the most difficult part of the problem, and the finding of an "optimal" result may have little value if the wrong criteria are used to decide what result should be sought [1].[2]

For example, in a certain chemical process it may be possible to say that an increase in output is a desirable result. However, if we find that the method used to increase the output causes an increase in the pollution of the environment, it may be very difficult to decide what is the best result. As we take a broader view of a situation, the decision as to what is optimal usually involves subjective criteria which may have to be resolved in a somewhat arbitrary fashion. This book does not offer any guidance for deciding what is optimal; it has the more humble purpose of showing how to achieve the maximum or minimum value of the chosen figure of merit.[3]

The following is a brief summary of the material covered in the remainder of the book.

CHAPTER 2   OPTIMIZATION OF A SIMPLE SERVOMECHANISM

This chapter introduces an optimization problem based on the transient response of a simple servomechanism. This is a very simple extension of feedback control theory and is an attempt to relate simple optimization problems to the reader's knowledge of control theory.

CHAPTER 3   STATISTICAL DESIGN OF LINEAR SYSTEMS

This is a study of the classical Wiener optimization theory for a linear system with a stationary random input. More modern developments such as the Kalman filter are also treated briefly. A knowledge of basic probability theory is assumed here. If the reader is not interested in statistical optimization, this chapter may be omitted without significant loss of continuity.

---

[1] Any optimization problem which can be represented as a maximization problem can equally well be represented by a minimization problem. For example, if the symbol A is used to represent the area which is to be maximized, we can treat the problem as a minimization of $-A$ if desired. Throughout this book, any results obtained for a maximization apply equally well for a minimization.

[2] Numbers in square brackets refer to the list of references at the end of the chapter.

[3] Various names have been used to denote the quantity to be maximized or minimized when optimizing a control system. Some of these are: figure of merit, performance index, performance criterion, criterion function, cost function, profit function, return function, penalty function, objective function, and payoff function.

CHAPTER 4　STATE REPRESENTATION OF SYSTEMS

This chapter deals with the state representation of systems, which is fundamental to modern control theory. The state of a system is represented by a vector, and the system differential equations are written in terms of this vector. A knowledge of simple matrix operations is assumed.

CHAPTER 5　CALCULUS OF VARIATIONS

This simple introduction to the classical calculus of variations does not attempt to provide a detailed and rigorous treatment of the subject, about which many books have been written; instead it attempts to relate the theory to control examples where possible.

CHAPTER 6　THE MAXIMUM PRINCIPLE

An explanation of the maximum principle gives simple examples to illustrate the use of the method. The method is presented as an extension or generalization of the calculus of variations.

CHAPTER 7　DYNAMIC PROGRAMMING

The discussion of dynamic programming embodied in this chapter attempts to help the reader to understand its fundamental nature. It is shown that there is a close relationship between dynamic programming and the maximum principle.

CHAPTER 8　COMPUTATIONAL METHODS OF OPTIMIZATION

Here we have a brief summary of some of the basic features of methods of direct computation of optimal solutions. Because the computation of optimal solutions may be considered to be an art rather than a science, only the basic principles involved are discussed.

REFERENCES

Selected references for further reading are provided at the end of each chapter. Only literature in English, or which is readily available in English translation, is cited. While this may not give a fully representative selection, it will provide sufficient material for further study.

For the reader who has not studied control theory before, there are many books available, such as reference [2]. An excellent mathematical reference, which provides most of the background mathematics required, is reference [3].

REFERENCES

[1] Zadeh, L. A., "What is Optimal?" *IRE Trans. Inform. Theory*, Vol. I.T.-4, No. 1 (March 1958), p. 3.
[2] Clark, R. N., *Introduction to Automatic Control Systems*, Wiley, New York, 1962.
[3] Pipes, L. A., *Applied Mathematics for Engineers and Physicists*, 2nd ed., McGraw-Hill, New York, 1958.

2

Optimization of a Simple Servomechanism

In this chapter we shall use a simple second-order linear servomechanism as an example to illustrate a simple type of optimization problem. The integral of the square of the error, in response to a step input, will be taken as the performance criterion, and the optimization will be achieved by varying parameters of the system.

2.1 DESCRIPTION OF THE SIMPLE SERVOMECHANISM

Consider the simple servomechanism or position-control system shown in Fig. 2.1. This is a very well-known type of control system, which is analyzed in detail in books such as references [1,2]. In the diagram, J and B_0 represent the polar moment of inertia and the viscous-damping parameter of the load. The load is driven by a separately excited direct-current motor with its armature energized by a power amplifier. The amplifier input voltage is equal to the difference of potential between the movable contacts of the two potentiometers, one of which is driven by the reference or input shaft, and the

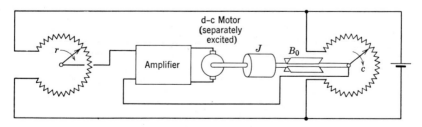

Fig. 2.1. A simple servomechanism.

other by the controlled or output shaft. The variables r and c represent the angular positions of the reference and controlled shafts, respectively, and it is assumed that these are measured with respect to corresponding positions on the potentiometers in such a way that the amplifier input voltage is directly proportional to the difference $r - c$. If the system error is defined to be $r - c$ (the difference between the reference variable and the controlled variable), the amplifier input voltage is directly proportional to the error. Provided that the interconnections of the system have the appropriate polarities, the system will tend to act in such a way as to reduce the error.

Let us now derive the equations which characterize the behavior of this feedback control system. Let us simplify the analysis by assuming that the system is linear, that the inductance of the motor armature is zero, that the amplifier has infinite input impedance and zero output impedance, and that the torque required to drive the potentiometers is zero. Let us use the following symbols to represent the various variables and parameters of the system.

J = Polar moment of inertia (kilogram-meter^2)
B_0 = Viscous damping parameter (newton-meters per radian per second)
e_a = Amplifier output voltage (volts)
i_a = Motor armature current (amperes)
R = Armature resistance (ohms)
T_m = Motor torque (newton-meters)
k_p = Potentiometer constant (amplifier input voltage per radian of error)
k = Amplifier voltage gain
k_m = Motor torque constant (newton-meters per ampere)
k_m = Motor voltage constant (volts per radian per second)

The last two constants are the same, if the MKS system of units is used. If another system is used, they differ only by a constant factor. The equations of the system may be written as follows:

$$e_a = kk_p(r - c) \tag{2.1}$$

$$i_a = \frac{e_a - k_m\dot{c}}{R} \tag{2.2}$$

where the superscript dot represents differentiation with respect to time t.

$$T_m = k_m i_a \tag{2.3}$$

$$T_m = J\ddot{c} + B_0\dot{c} \tag{2.4}$$

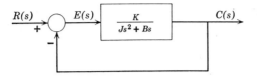

Fig. 2.2. Block diagram of simple servomechanism.

Combining Equations 2.1 to 2.4, we obtain the following differential equation relating the controlled or output variable c to the reference or input variable r.

$$J\ddot{c} + B_0\dot{c} = \frac{k_m[kk_p(r - c) - k_m\dot{c}]}{R} \tag{2.5}$$

Equation 2.5 can be written in the form

$$J\frac{d^2c}{dt^2} + B\frac{dc}{dt} + Kc = Kr \tag{2.6}$$

where

$$B \overset{\Delta}{=}{}^1 B_0 + \frac{k_m{}^2}{R}$$

and

$$K \overset{\Delta}{=} \frac{k_m kk_p}{R}$$

The system can be represented by the transfer-function block diagram shown in Fig. 2.2. In the diagram, s is the Laplace transform variable, $R(s)$ and $C(s)$ are the Laplace transforms of the time functions $r(t)$ and $c(t)$, and $E(s)$ is the Laplace transform of the error $e(t)$, where $e(t) \overset{\Delta}{=} r(t) - c(t)$.

2.2 THE PERFORMANCE CRITERION

Now suppose that some of the system parameters are adjustable, and let us study the problem of finding an optimum set of values for the adjustable parameters. To begin with, therefore, we must specify the performance criterion by which we shall decide whether the system is optimal. Let us define our performance criterion as follows: Consider the response of the system to a unit step input starting at $t = 0$, with the initial values of c and

---

[1] The symbol "$\overset{\Delta}{=}$" means "equals by definition."

its time derivative $\dot{c}$ both zero. Find the value of the resulting integral squared error, defined by the expression

$$I = \int_0^\infty [e(t)]^2 \, dt \tag{2.7}$$

The optimum set of values of the adjustable parameters will be defined as the set of values which makes the expression I of Equation 2.7 take on the minimum possible value.

Our problem will be more easily solved if we can express the integral squared error in terms of frequency-domain quantities. This can be done by using Parseval's theorem (see Appendix A), which allows us to write

$$\int_{-\infty}^\infty [x(t)]^2 \, dt = \frac{1}{2\pi j} \int_{-j\infty}^{j\infty} X(s)X(-s) \, ds \tag{2.8}$$

where $X(s)$ is the Laplace transform of the time function $x(t)$, and $j = \sqrt{-1}$. If $E(s)$ is the Laplace transform of the error $e(t)$, where $e(t)$ is zero for all t less than zero, we can express the integral squared error in the form

$$I = \int_0^\infty [e(t)]^2 \, dt = \frac{1}{2\pi j} \int_{-j\infty}^{j\infty} E(s)E(-s) \, ds \tag{2.9}$$

The value of the right-hand integral in Equation 2.9 can easily be found from published tables, such as the table quoted in Appendix D, provided that $E(s)$ can be written in the form $c(s)/d(s)$, where

$$c(s) \triangleq c_0 + c_1 s + \cdots + c_{n-1} s^{n-1} \tag{2.10}$$

and

$$d(s) \triangleq d_0 + d_1 s + \cdots + d_n s^n \tag{2.11}$$

and where $d(s)$ has zeros in the left half only of the complex plane. For example, for $n = 1$ in Equations 2.10 and 2.11, we find from Appendix D that

$$I_1 = \frac{c_0^2}{2d_0 d_1} \tag{2.12}$$

where the subscript associated with I indicates the value of n in Equation 2.11. Similarly, for $n = 2$ we obtain

$$I_2 = \frac{c_1^2 d_0 + c_0^2 d_2}{2d_0 d_1 d_2} \tag{2.13}$$

From the block diagram (Fig. 2.2) we can write down the transfer function relating the input and the error in the form

$$\frac{E(s)}{R(s)} = \frac{Js^2 + Bs}{Js^2 + Bs + K} \tag{2.14}$$

Accordingly, if the input $r(t)$ is a unit step function with Laplace transform $1/s$, the transform of the error may be expressed in the form

$$E(s) = \frac{B + Js}{K + Bs + Js^2} \tag{2.15}$$

We can now use expression 2.13 to find the value of the integral I_2. By virtue of Equation 2.9, this integral gives the value of the integral squared error. The values of the coefficients in expressions 2.10 and 2.11 are as follows:

$$\begin{aligned} c_0 &= B \\ c_1 &= J \\ d_0 &= K \\ d_1 &= B \\ d_2 &= J \end{aligned} \tag{2.16}$$

Using these values, the value of the integral squared error is given by Equation 2.13 to be

$$I = \frac{JK + B^2}{2KB} \tag{2.17}$$

Equation 2.17 gives the integral squared error for a unit step input, in terms of the system parameters J, B, and K. It should be noted that J, B, and K must not be negative, because the use of the table for the evaluation of the integral is not valid unless $Js^2 + Bs + K$ has zeros in the left half only of the complex plane.

We are now in a position to find the values of the adjustable parameters which give a minimum of the integral squared error. One rather obvious result is obtained if only J is adjustable, in that the best result is obtained if J is zero. In practice, however, J is unlikely to be adjustable to that extent because there is some load to be driven and its parameters are likely to be unalterable.

2.3 ADJUSTABLE DAMPING

As a more realistic assumption, let us suppose that the damping parameter B is adjustable. This adjustment could be achieved in practice by the connection of an auxiliary rate-feedback loop to the basic system. If we assume for the present that K and J are both fixed, we would find the value of B for minimum integral squared error by differentiating expression 2.17 with respect to B and setting the result to zero. This gives the optimum value of B to be

$$B^* = \sqrt{JK} \tag{2.18}$$

where the asterisk is used to denote the optimum value. This optimum value of B can be expressed in terms of a damping factor, if we rewrite the system differential Equation 2.6 in the standardized form

$$\frac{d^2c}{dt^2} + 2\zeta\omega_n \frac{dc}{dt} + \omega_n{}^2 c = \omega_n{}^2 r \tag{2.19}$$

where the damping factor ζ is defined by

$$\zeta \triangleq \frac{B}{2\sqrt{JK}} \tag{2.20}$$

and the undamped natural frequency ω_n is defined by

$$\omega_n \triangleq \sqrt{\frac{K}{J}} \tag{2.21}$$

Comparison of Equations 2.18 and 2.20 shows that, if K and J are fixed, the optimum value of B corresponds to a damping factor of 0.5. This is a well-known result [3].

2.4 ADJUSTABLE GAIN

Let us now suppose that both J and B are fixed, and that K is adjustable. This could be achieved in practice by adjusting the amplifier gain, or the voltage supply to the potentiometers. If we differentiate expression 2.17 with respect to K, we find that the derivative approaches zero only as K approaches

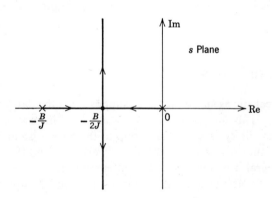

Fig. 2.3. Loci of roots of characteristic equation as K increases.

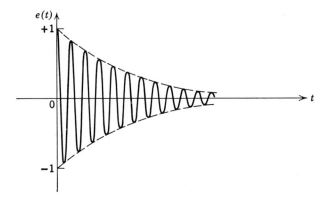

Fig. 2.4. Transient error for large K (not to scale).

infinity. If we take the limit of the value of I in (2.17) as K approaches infinity, we find it to be

$$\lim_{K \to \infty} I = \frac{J}{2B} \tag{2.22}$$

We can explain this result by considering the transient response of the system. The loci of the roots of the characteristic equation (the zeros of $Js^2 + Bs + K$), as K varies, are of the form shown in Fig. 2.3 (where the arrows indicate the direction of increasing K). The loci are such that, no matter how large K becomes, the envelope of the decaying sinusoidal transient response is always of the form $A \exp(-Bt/2J)$, where A is some constant. For very large K, the transient error will be of the form sketched in Fig. 2.4. The starting points of the envelope approach $+1$ and -1 as K approaches infinity, and the frequency of oscillation approaches infinity. Now, since the mean square value of a sine wave is half the square of the peak value, we can say that in the limit the integral squared error is given by the expression

$$\lim_{K \to \infty} I = \frac{1}{2} \int_0^\infty [e^{-Bt/2J}]^2 \, dt = \frac{J}{2B} \tag{2.23}$$

which is the same result as that given by expression 2.22, derived from the table of integrals.

2.5 TWO ADJUSTABLE PARAMETERS

If both B and K were variable, the conditions for a minimum value of the integral squared error would be found by taking the partial derivatives of expression 2.17, with respect to B and K, and setting both of these partial derivatives to zero. This would give two equations from which the required values of B and K could be found. In the present case we would find that B and K would both approach infinity while maintaining the relationship described by Equation 2.18, and that the error would approach zero.

In practice there would be some limitations on the magnitudes of the parameters K and B. Let us consider a constraint which, while it does not necessarily represent a practical situation, provides a simple illustration of a method of dealing with constraints. Suppose that K and B are limited by the condition

$$KB = C \qquad (2.24)$$

where C is some positive constant (it will be recalled that K and B are both assumed to be positive).

In this case, probably the simplest method of finding the conditions for the constrained minimum is to express K in terms of B from Equation 2.24 and then express the integral squared error in terms of B and J only. This gives the integral squared error to be

$$I_c = \frac{JC/B + B^2}{2C} \qquad (2.25)$$

where I_c represents the integral squared error subject to the constraint (Equation 2.24). If we now differentiate Equation 2.25 with respect to B, remembering that C and J are constant, we find that the condition for zero derivative is given by

$$2B^3 = JC \qquad (2.26)$$

Recalling that $C = KB$, we find that the optimum constrained value of B is given by

$$B_c{}^* = \sqrt{\frac{JK}{2}} \qquad (2.27)$$

The corresponding value of the damping factor ζ turns out to be $1/2\sqrt{2}$ or approximately 0.353.

2.6 THE METHOD OF LAGRANGE MULTIPLIERS

Although it does not simplify the work in this particular example, it would be possible to obtain the relationships for the constrained minimum by using a Lagrange multiplier [4]. The method would proceed as follows. We would augment the quantity to be minimized, I, by a constant λ (the Lagrange multiplier) multiplied by the quantity to be kept constant, namely, KB. We would obtain the expression

$$F = \frac{JK + B^2}{2KB} + \lambda KB \qquad (2.28)$$

where the value of the Lagrange multiplier λ is still to be found. The introduction of λ allows us to treat the minimization of F as an unconstrained minimization problem, and the values of the three unknowns are obtained from the three equations

$$\frac{\partial F}{\partial B} = 0$$

$$\frac{\partial F}{\partial K} = 0 \qquad (2.29)$$

$$KB = C$$

Verification that these equations provide the correct result is left to the reader. The use of a Lagrange multiplier is in many cases the simplest method of solving a constrained optimization problem, and these multipliers will be encountered frequently throughout this book.

2.7 GRAPHICAL INTERPRETATION OF THE MINIMIZATION PROCESS

We can illustrate the relationship between the integral squared error and the parameters B and K by a plot of contour lines of I (lines of equal magnitude of I) on the B-K plane. If the value of I is a constant D, we can use Equation 2.17 to express K as a function of B in the form

$$K = \frac{B^2}{2BD - J} \qquad (2.30)$$

Contour lines for various values of D are sketched in Fig. 2.5, the lower curves corresponding to higher values of D. The dotted curve shows the locus of the unconstrained optimum values B^*, for various values of K, as given by Equation 2.18. This locus is a parabola. $B^* = \sqrt{JK}$

The constrained minimum of the integral squared error, with the constraint $KB = C$, can be interpreted in terms of a contour map as follows. Figure 2.6 shows a typical contour line of constant I, together with a curve illustrating the relationship $KB = C$. The latter curve is a rectangular hyperbola. The point P, at which the curve representing $BK = C$ touches the contour line, represents the optimum values of B and K subject to the constraint $BK = C$.

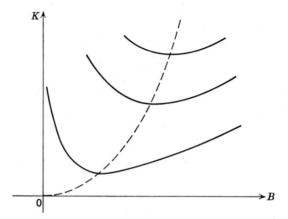

Fig. 2.5. Contour lines of integral squared error in *B-K* plane (not to scale).

We see from Fig. 2.6 that, if the constraint (Equation 2.24) had been written in the form $KB \leqslant C$, the result would have been the same. In other words, the point P in Fig. 2.6 represents the best result that can be obtained if KB is constrained to be equal to or less than C. Points below the curve $KB = C$ represent points where $KB < C$, and cannot give a better value of I than that corresponding to the point P.

Figure 2.6 suggests a further method of finding the conditions for the constrained optimum. At the point P, two conditions are satisfied: (1) the contour line and the line $BK = C$ meet, and (2) the two curves have the same

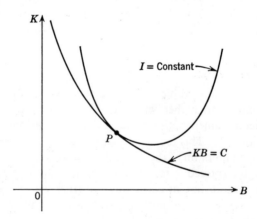

Fig. 2.6. Illustration of the conditions for a constrained minimum (not to scale).

slope. Applying these two conditions we obtain two equations in the two unknowns B and K as follows. Applying condition (1), we obtain

$$K = \frac{C}{B} = \frac{B^2}{2BD - J} \tag{2.31}$$

Applying condition (2), we obtain

$$\frac{dK}{dB} = \frac{-C}{B^2} = \frac{2B(BD - J)}{(2BD - J)^2} \tag{2.32}$$

Verification that these equations provide the correct values of B and K is left to the reader.

SUMMARY

In this chapter a method of optimizing the parameters of a simple servo-mechanism has been presented as a simple extension of classical control theory. The minimum of a function of two variables has been obtained by partial derivatives, and the use of a Lagrange multiplier in the solution of a constrained optimization problem has been illustrated.

For a more thorough treatment of the optimization of the transient response of a linear system, reference [3] is recommended.

REFERENCES

[1] Brown, G. S., and D. P. Campbell, *Principles of Servomechanisms*, Wiley, New York, 1948.
[2] Clark, R. N., *Introduction to Automatic Control Systems*, Wiley, New York, 1962.
[3] Newton, G. C., L. A. Gould, and J. F. Kaiser, *Analytical Design of Linear Feedback Controls*, Wiley, New York, 1957.
[4] Smith, L. P., *Mathematical Methods for Scientists and Engineers*, Dover Pub., New York, 1961.

PROBLEMS

1. In the system described in this chapter, suppose that it is desired to adjust the system so as to obtain the smallest possible integral squared error in response to a unit step input, without allowing the integral squared value of the output acceleration to exceed a certain value. The integral squared value of the output acceleration is defined to be

$$I_A \triangleq \int_0^\infty [\ddot{c}(t)]^2 \, dt \tag{2.33}$$

Assuming that J is fixed, and that I_A is not to exceed a certain constant M, find the values of K and B which give the minimum value of the integral squared error to a unit step input.

2. In the system described in this chapter, suppose that it is desired to limit the output acceleration by taking as the performance criterion the sum of the integral squared error and the integral squared acceleration. Assuming that J is fixed, and that the input is a unit step function, find the values of K and B which minimize $I + I_A$, where I and I_A are defined by Equations 2.7 and 2.33.

3. The system shown in Fig. 2.7 is compensated by a lead network as shown. Find the value of T such that the integral squared error, in response to a step input, is minimum.

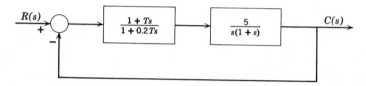

Fig. 2.7

4. Figure 2.8 shows a linear system with an impulse response e^{-at}, and with an input e^{-t} ($t \geqslant 0$). Find the value of a such that the output $y(t)$ is as close as possible to the input, in the integral-squared-error sense.

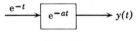

Fig. 2.8

5. The input to the system shown in Fig. 2.9 is a unit step function, and it is desired to minimize the integral squared error. Find the optimum value of K, and the optimum value of integral squared error, for the two cases (a) $T = 0$, and (b) $T = 0.8$.

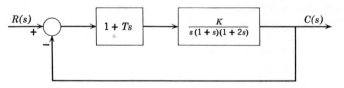

Fig. 2.9

3

Statistical Design of Linear Systems

This chapter is devoted to a study of some of the problems of designing a linear control system which will respond in an optimum way to a random input. Statistical optimization, as first described by Wiener [1], was the first significant development in the field of optimization-of control systems. The chapter includes a brief study of the Kalman filtering technique. It is thought by the author, however, that a detailed study of Kalman filter theory is beyond the scope of this book and should be treated as a subject for more advanced study by the reader after finishing this book. If the student so desires, this chapter may be omitted without significant loss of continuity.

Because the system inputs considered in this chapter are indeterminate, we can only consider the optimization of the system in a statistical sense based on the average or expected value of some quantity such as the square of the error. To be specific, we shall take as our criterion of optimality (at least in the earlier part of this chapter) the minimization of the mean squared error, that is, the time average of the square of the error. It is fairly obvious that the system parameters which give optimum performance with one particular input will not necessarily be best for other random inputs. Accordingly, it is necessary to be able to describe the random input signal in such a way that the essential properties of the signal, from the point of view of its effects on the mean squared error, are revealed.

3.1 STATISTICAL DESCRIPTION OF RANDOM SIGNALS

It will be assumed that the random input is a member function of a stationary random process.[1] A random process is an infinitely large set, or

---

[1] The reader who is not familiar with the statistical representation of signals should still be able to follow the work of this chapter quite easily, by accepting the definitions of correlation functions given here. Various works dealing with the statistical design of linear systems can be found in the list of references at the end of this chapter, for example references [1, 4, 6, 9].

ensemble, of signals having statistical properties in common, and a random input to a control system may be considered as a member chosen at random from such an ensemble. For a stationary process, statistical measures taken over all the signals of the ensemble (for example, the average of the instantaneous values of all signals at a single instant of time t) are independent of the time t at which the statistical measure is considered.

For signals which are members of a stationary random process, it will be shown that the required descriptions of signals are their correlation functions, which are defined below.

AUTOCORRELATION FUNCTIONS

For a random signal $x(t)$, the autocorrelation function may be defined as

$$\phi_{xx}(\tau) = \lim_{T \to \infty} \frac{1}{2T} \int_{-T}^{T} x(t)x(t + \tau) \, dt \qquad (3.1)$$

That is, the autocorrelation function is the average (over all time) of the value of the function at a particular instant multiplied by its value after a time shift of τ seconds. For convenience, we shall denote the time average by a bar over the quantity, as shown in Equation 3.2

$$\phi_{xx}(\tau) = \overline{x(t)x(t + \tau)} \qquad (3.2)$$

It is immediately obvious that $\phi_{xx}(0)$ is the mean squared value of the signal $x(t)$. It is also obvious that, as the average of the product is taken over all time, a shift of the same amount in the opposite sense will give the same average product. That is, the autocorrelation function $\phi_{xx}(\tau)$ is an even function of time shift τ, which may be expressed by the relationship

$$\phi_{xx}(-\tau) = \phi_{xx}(\tau) \qquad (3.3)$$

It should be noted that, although there is a unique autocorrelation function for a given random signal, there are infinitely many signals corresponding to the same autocorrelation function.

As an example of an autocorrelation function, let us consider the signal

$$x(t) = A \sin(\omega t + \theta) \qquad (3.4)$$

This signal may be considered to be a member of an ensemble of signals in which the phase angle is (uniformly) randomly distributed between 0 and 2π radians [2]. For this signal, the value of the product of the value of the function and its own value τ seconds later is given by

$$x(t)x(t + \tau) = A^2 \sin(\omega t + \theta) \sin(\omega t + \theta + \omega \tau) \qquad (3.5)$$

In this case, the average over all time is the same as the average over one complete cycle, which is given by

$$\overline{x(t)x(t + \tau)} = \frac{A^2}{2T} \int_0^T [\cos \omega\tau - \cos (2\omega t + 2\theta + \omega\tau)] \, dt \qquad (3.6)$$

where T is the period of the sine wave. This leads to the following expression

$$\phi_{xx}(\tau) = \overline{x(t)x(t + \tau)} = \frac{A^2}{2} \cos \omega\tau \qquad (3.7)$$

The autocorrelation is a cosine wave of the same frequency as the original sine wave. As we should expect, due to the averaging over all time, the phase angle of the original sine wave does not appear in the expression for the autocorrelation function. In other words, the position of the time origin is irrelevant.

As another example of an autocorrelation function, let us consider a random square wave $x(t)$ as shown in Fig. 3.1, defined as follows:

1. The signal $x(t)$ takes on only the values $+A$ and $-A$, and remains constant on intervals of T seconds.
2. The value of the signal $x(t)$ during the next interval is determined by the toss of an unbiased coin (that is, the values $+A$ and $-A$ are equally probable).

To find the value of $\overline{x(t)x(t + \tau)}$, we proceed as follows. First, we consider two values of the function, separated in time by an amount $\tau > T$. If we multiply these two values together, we shall obtain either $+A^2$ or $-A^2$, the

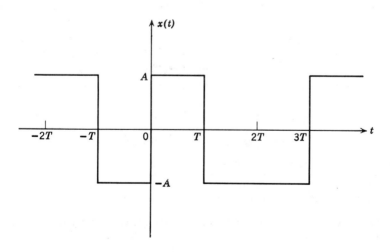

Fig. 3.1. A random square wave.

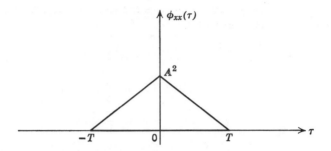

Fig. 3.2. Autocorrelation function of random square wave.

two possibilities being equally likely. If we average the product over all time, the result is therefore zero.

Next, we consider values of the function shifted by an amount $\tau < T$. If $\tau = 0$, the product of the two values is always $+A^2$. As τ increases from zero, the likelihood that both t and $t + \tau$ are in the same T-second interval, and therefore that the product of the two values is $+A^2$, becomes less. The likelihood that the product is $-A^2$ becomes greater. If we imagine a rigid rod sliding at uniform speed along the horizontal axis of the diagram in Fig. 3.1 (imagining that the diagram extends to infinity in both directions), and if we suppose that the rod has a length corresponding to the magnitude of the interval τ which is less than T, then the proportion of the time of motion in which both ends are in different T-second intervals is τ/T. Therefore the proportion of the total time in which both ends are in the same interval is $1 - (\tau/T)$. As the product of the function values at the two ends of the rod is averaged over the whole function, and as the average will be zero for the proportion of the time when the two ends are in different T-second intervals and $+A^2$ when they are in the same interval, we shall obtain an average of $A^2(1 - \tau/T)$. Because of the property that the autocorrelation function is even, this autocorrelation function can be written in the form

$$\phi_{xx}(\tau) = A^2\left(1 - \frac{|\tau|}{T}\right) \qquad \text{for } |\tau| \leqslant T$$
$$= 0 \qquad \text{for } |\tau| > T$$

(3.8)

The graph of this function is shown in Fig. 3.2.

CROSS-CORRELATION FUNCTION OF TWO RANDOM SIGNALS

If there are two random signals $x(t)$ and $y(t)$, the cross-correlation function $\phi_{xy}(\tau)$ is defined by the equation

$$\phi_{xy}(\tau) = \overline{x(t)y(t + \tau)}$$

(3.9)

Note that the order of subscripts is significant, and that $\phi_{xy}(\tau)$ is not an even function of τ. It is easy to show, however, that

$$\phi_{xy}(-\tau) = \phi_{yx}(\tau) \tag{3.10}$$

3.2 MEAN SQUARED ERROR IN TERMS OF CORRELATION FUNCTIONS

The correlation functions defined above were introduced in order to provide descriptions of random signals which would reveal their effect on the mean squared error in a control system. It will now be shown that these descriptions do satisfy this requirement.

Consider the time-invariant linear system shown in Fig. 3.3. The linear system is assumed to have an impulse response or weighting function $w(t)$, and to be subjected to a random input $x(t)$, giving an output $y(t)$. It is further assumed that there is a desired output $d(t)$ to which $y(t)$ is required to correspond as closely as possible. The quantity $e(t)$, the error, is defined as the difference between the desired output $d(t)$ and the actual output $y(t)$, that is,

$$e(t) \overset{\Delta}{=} d(t) - y(t) \tag{3.11}$$

In order to find the mean squared error $\overline{e^2(t)}$, we first write the expression for the system output $y(t)$ in terms of the input $x(t)$ and the impulse response $w(t)$. This expression is the convolution integral.

$$y(t) = \int_{-\infty}^{\infty} x(t - u)w(u)\,du \tag{3.12}$$

The mean squared error can be written as

$$\overline{e^2(t)} = \overline{[d(t) - y(t)]^2} \tag{3.13}$$

Substituting Equation 3.12 in Equation 3.13, we obtain

$$\overline{e^2(t)} = \overline{\left[d(t) - \int_{-\infty}^{\infty} x(t - u)w(u)\,du \right]^2} \tag{3.14}$$

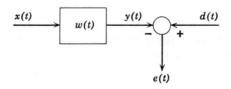

Fig. 3.3. A linear system with random input $x(t)$.

Expanding the squared sum, we obtain

$$\overline{e^2(t)} = \overline{d^2(t)} - \overline{2\,d(t)\int_{-\infty}^{\infty} x(t-u)w(u)\,du}$$

$$+ \overline{\int_{-\infty}^{\infty} x(t-u)w(u)\,du \int_{-\infty}^{\infty} x(t-v)w(v)\,dv} \qquad (3.15)$$

Interchanging the operations of integration and averaging,[2] we obtain

$$\overline{e^2(t)} = \overline{d^2(t)} - 2\int_{-\infty}^{\infty} \overline{x(t-u)\,d(t)}w(u)\,du$$

$$+ \int_{-\infty}^{\infty}\int_{-\infty}^{\infty} \overline{x(t-u)x(t-v)}w(u)w(v)\,du\,dv \qquad (3.16)$$

Inserting the notation of correlation functions where appropriate, we obtain the expression

$$\overline{e^2(t)} = \phi_{dd}(0) - 2\int_{-\infty}^{\infty} \phi_{xd}(u)w(u)\,du$$

$$+ \int_{-\infty}^{\infty}\int_{-\infty}^{\infty} \phi_{xx}(u-v)w(u)w(v)\,du\,dv \qquad (3.17)$$

The meaning of expression 3.17 is as follows: For a given linear system, a given random input, and a specified desired output, the mean squared error is determined by the correlation functions of these signals. That is, for the purpose of obtaining an optimum design of a linear system, with the criterion of minimum mean squared error, the signals are sufficiently described by their correlation functions.

3.3 FREQUENCY-DOMAIN CHARACTERISTICS OF RANDOM SIGNALS

The correlation functions introduced in Section 3.1 are functions of a time-shift variable. It turns out that, as in the case of Laplace and Fourier transformable functions of time, it is often useful to be able to use frequency-domain representations of these functions. We can, for example, use the

---

[2] This interchange is valid in most cases of practical interest. See reference [3] for further comments.

bilateral Laplace transformation[3] to define a frequency-domain function corresponding to the autocorrelation function of the signal $x(t)$ as follows[4]

$$\Phi_{xx}(s) \triangleq \int_{-\infty}^{\infty} \phi_{xx}(\tau) e^{-s\tau} \, d\tau \tag{3.18}$$

For the particular case where $s = j\omega$, the function defined in Equation 3.18 is known as the power-density spectrum or spectral density of the random signal $x(t)$. By similar reasoning we can define a cross-spectral density of two random signals by the expression

$$\Phi_{xy}(s) \triangleq \int_{-\infty}^{\infty} \phi_{xy}(\tau) e^{-s\tau} \, d\tau \tag{3.19}$$

If the frequency-domain function $\Phi_{xx}(s)$ is known, the autocorrelation function $\phi_{xx}(\tau)$ may be found by the inverse Laplace transformation

$$\phi_{xx}(\tau) = \frac{1}{2\pi j} \int_{c-j\infty}^{c+j\infty} \Phi_{xx}(s) e^{\tau s} \, ds \tag{3.20}$$

In particular, the mean squared value of x, which is the value of $\phi_{xx}(\tau)$ for $\tau = 0$, can be found from the expression

$$\phi_{xx}(0) = \frac{1}{2\pi} \int_{-\infty}^{\infty} \Phi_{xx}(j\omega) \, d\omega \tag{3.21}$$

The function $\Phi_{xx}(j\omega)$, the Fourier transform of the autocorrelation function, or the power-density spectrum of the random signal, is purely real. This can be shown by observing that $\Phi_{xx}(j\omega)$, obtained by substituting $j\omega$ for s in Equation 3.18, can be expressed in the form

$$\Phi_{xx}(j\omega) = \int_{-\infty}^{\infty} \phi_{xx}(\tau)(\cos \omega\tau - j \sin \omega\tau) \, d\tau \tag{3.22}$$

Because $\phi_{xx}(\tau)$ is an even function of τ, the imaginary part disappears when the integration is performed, thus making $\Phi_{xx}(j\omega)$ a real function. The expression 3.21 is therefore merely an integral of a real function. The fact that the integral (Equation 3.21) gives the mean squared value of the time function $x(t)$ will be used in computation of the mean squared error in a control system, and in the optimization of the system by minimization of that measure of the error.

---

[3] It is assumed that the reader is familiar with the unilateral Laplace transformation. Some remarks on the bilateral transformation, insofar as it applies to the present development, are found in Appendix B.

[4] It should be noted that there are variations throughout the literature in the constant multipliers used in the definition of $\Phi_{xx}(s)$ and the inverse transformation. No confusion arises provided the same definition is used consistently.

Let us now consider a simple example to illustrate the finding of the frequency-domain function. Suppose that the autocorrelation function of a random function $x(t)$ is given by

$$\phi_{xx}(\tau) = e^{-a|\tau|} \tag{3.23}$$

where a is a positive real constant. The Laplace transform of this function may be obtained from Equation B.8 of Appendix B and is given by

$$\Phi_{xx}(s) = \frac{1}{s + a} - \frac{1}{s - a} = \frac{2a}{a^2 - s^2} \tag{3.24}$$

By a study of the method suggested in Appendix B for finding the Laplace transform of a negative-time function, we see that, if there is a pole (or zero) of $\Phi_{xx}(s)$ at some value s, there is also a pole (or zero) of $\Phi_{xx}(s)$ at the value $-s$. For this reason, the function $\Phi_{xx}(s)$ is normally a rational function of s^2.

Let us now discuss methods of evaluating the integral squared value of a time function by integration of the appropriate frequency-domain function.

3.4 FREQUENCY-DOMAIN COMPUTATION OF MEAN SQUARED VALUES OF RANDOM FUNCTIONS

As shown above in Equation 3.21, the value of $\phi_{xx}(0)$, which is the same as the mean squared value of $x(t)$, is given by

$$\phi_{xx}(0) = \overline{x^2(t)} = \frac{1}{2\pi} \int_{-\infty}^{\infty} \Phi_{xx}(j\omega) \, d\omega \tag{3.25}$$

or by the form given in Equation 3.20, with $\tau = 0$:

$$\phi_{xx}(0) = \overline{x^2(t)} = \frac{1}{2\pi j} \int_{-j\infty}^{j\infty} \Phi_{xx}(s) \, ds \tag{3.26}$$

Methods of evaluating the integrals of Equation 3.25 or Equation 3.26 are as follows:

1. By graphical integration.
2. By numerical integration.
3. By contour integration.
4. By a table of integrals.

Methods 1 and 2 can be used because the function $\Phi_{xx}(j\omega)$ which appears in Equation 3.25 is purely real. No particular comment is required on these methods; standard methods of numerical integration can be found in a textbook on numerical analysis.

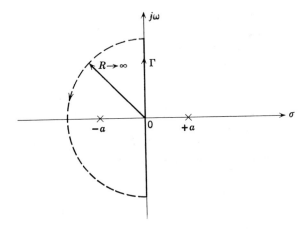

Fig. 3.4. Poles of $\Phi_{xx}(s)$ in the complex plane.

Method 3 may be illustrated briefly by considering the mean squared value of the function $x(t)$ used in the example of the previous section, where the power-density spectrum is given by Equation 3.24. The poles of this function are shown in the complex plane in Fig. 3.4. The value of the integral (Equation 3.26) can be found by finding the integral around the Γ contour shown in Fig. 3.4, in the counterclockwise direction, and subtracting the contribution due to the dotted semicircle, which is assumed to have a very large radius. It is easy to show that, because $\Phi_{xx}(s)$ behaves as $-2a/s^2$ as s approaches infinity, the integral around the large semicircle is zero. Similar reasoning would apply if the large semicircle were in the right-half plane instead of the left. As the integral around the closed contour is $2\pi j$ multiplied by the sum of the residues at the poles enclosed by the contour, the mean squared value as given by Equation 3.26 turns out to be unity because the residue at the pole at $s = -a$ is unity. We see that this gives the correct value of $\phi_{xx}(0)$, as given by Equation 3.23.

Method 4 may be used by factoring $\Phi_{xx}(s)$ into two factors, one with all the poles and zeros in the left-half plane, and one with all poles and zeros in the right-half plane. Assuming that $\Phi_{xx}(s)$ is a rational function of s^2, we then obtain Equation 3.26 in the form

$$\overline{x^2(t)} = I_n = \frac{1}{2\pi j} \int_{-j\infty}^{j\infty} \frac{c(s)c(-s)}{d(s)d(-s)} \, ds \tag{3.27}$$

where $c(s)$ and $d(s)$ are given by the expressions

$$c(s) = c_0 + c_1 s + \cdots + c_{n-1} s^{n-1}$$
$$d(s) = d_0 + d_1 s + \cdots + d_n s^n \tag{3.28}$$

Here $c(s)$ and $d(s)$ are assumed to have zeros in the left-half plane only,[5] and the subscript n in (3.27) indicates the highest power of s appearing in $d(s)$. The situation is very similar to the evaluation of integral squared error in Chapter 2 by consulting a table of integrals; instead of having $E(s)E(-s)$ as the integrand (as in Equation 2.9), we have the function $\Phi_{xx}(s)$ which is of similar form. The table used for evaluation of the integral in Equation 2.9, and quoted in Appendix D, can also be used to evaluate the integral in Equation 3.26 in exactly the same way. Let us illustrate this by using as an example once again the function $\Phi_{xx}(s)$ given by Equation 3.24. For the purpose of this method, we express $\Phi_{xx}(s)$ in the form

$$\Phi_{xx}(s) = \left(\frac{\sqrt{2a}}{a+s}\right)\left(\frac{\sqrt{2a}}{a-s}\right) \tag{3.29}$$

We use that portion of the table already quoted as expression 2.12, with the following values of the constants

$$\begin{aligned} c_0 &= \sqrt{2a} \\ d_0 &= a \\ d_1 &= 1 \end{aligned} \tag{3.30}$$

As expected, we find the value of the integral to be unity.

3.5   OPTIMIZATION OF THE PARAMETERS OF A SYSTEM

Let us now use the theory we have developed in the previous sections to study a simple problem of finding the optimum values of the adjustable parameters of a simple linear system with a statistical input.

Suppose that we have a situation of the type illustrated in Fig. 3.3, with the input $x(t)$ being a message $m(t)$ contaminated by additive noise $n(t)$. That is, the input signal $x(t)$ is given by

$$x(t) = m(t) + n(t) \tag{3.31}$$

Suppose also that the desired output of the system is the message $m(t)$. In other words, the system is required to act as a filter to separate the message from the noise.

Let us suppose that the power-density spectrum of $m(t)$ is given by

$$\Phi_{mm}(s) = \frac{3}{1-s^2} \tag{3.32}$$

---

[5] Actually, as pointed out in Appendix D, it is not *necessary* for $c(s)$ to have zeros in the left-half plane only. That is, however, the usual situation in dealing with power spectra.

Let us suppose also that the noise $n(t)$ is so-called white noise, meaning noise which is equally distributed over the whole frequency spectrum, with a power-density spectrum given by

$$\Phi_{nn}(s) = 1 \tag{3.33}$$

We shall suppose also that the message and the noise are uncorrelated; in other words

$$\phi_{mn}(\tau) = 0 \tag{3.34}$$

for all τ.

Let us suppose that the transfer function of the system, or filter, is of the form

$$W(s) = \frac{K}{1 + TS} \tag{3.35}$$

We shall further suppose that the performance criterion is minimum mean squared error between the system output $y(t)$ and the message $m(t)$, and we shall find out how we should adjust K or T, or both, in order to obtain the best possible result. The procedure is as follows:

We first note that the error in this case is made up of two components, namely:

a. The error in the output caused by the noise input to the filter.

b. The error in the output caused by the distortion of the message component of the input.

Because the message and noise are uncorrelated, we can find the total mean squared error by finding components a and b separately and adding the two results.[6]

Component a. The contribution of component a can be found as follows. If we consider the filter with noise input only, with no message component, the output of the filter is wholly erroneous. The block diagram Fig. 3.5 illustrates this situation.

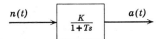

Fig. 3.5. Linear filter with noise input.

---

[6] By using relationships derived in Appendix C it is possible to show that, if two uncorrelated inputs are applied to a linear system, the two components of output so obtained are themselves uncorrelated with each other.

It is shown in Appendix C that, if a random signal $x(t)$ is applied to a linear system with transfer function $W(s)$, the output $y(t)$ will have a power-density spectrum given by

$$\Phi_{yy}(s) = W(s)W(-s)\Phi_{xx}(s) \tag{3.36}$$

In view of Equation 3.36 and the fact that $\Phi_{nn}(s) = 1$, the power-density spectrum of component a of the error can be written as

$$\Phi_{aa}(s) = \left(\frac{K}{1 + Ts}\right)\left(\frac{K}{1 - Ts}\right) \tag{3.37}$$

The total mean squared error due to component a can therefore be found by using the table of integrals as before. We see that the values to be substituted in Equation 2.12 for I_1 are

$$\begin{aligned} c_0 &= K \\ d_0 &= 1 \\ d_1 &= T \end{aligned} \tag{3.38}$$

The value of the integral is given by

$$I_1 = \frac{K^2}{2T} \tag{3.39}$$

Component b. This is the component caused by distortion of the message component of the input by the linear filter, and can be expressed as the mean squared value of the quantity $b(t)$ in Fig. 3.6. The transfer function from $m(t)$ to $b(t)$ can be written as

$$\frac{B(s)}{M(s)} = 1 - \frac{K}{1 + Ts} = \frac{1 - K + Ts}{1 + Ts} \tag{3.40}$$

Therefore, in view of the power-density spectrum of $m(t)$, as given by Equation 3.32, we can write the power-density spectrum of $b(t)$ in the form

$$\Phi_{bb}(s) = \left(\frac{1 - K + Ts}{1 + Ts}\right)\left(\frac{1 - K - Ts}{1 - Ts}\right)\left(\frac{\sqrt{3}}{1 + s}\right)\left(\frac{\sqrt{3}}{1 - s}\right) \tag{3.41}$$

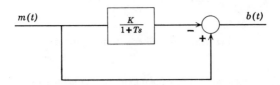

Fig. 3.6. Linear filter with input $m(t)$.

We can evaluate the mean squared error of component b by evaluating integral I_2, using the tabulated result as given in Equation 2.13 with the following coefficients.

$$
\begin{aligned}
c_0 &= \sqrt{3}(1 - K) \\
c_1 &= \sqrt{3}T \\
d_0 &= 1 \\
d_1 &= 1 + T \\
d_2 &= T
\end{aligned}
\tag{3.42}
$$

The mean squared value of component b is therefore given by

$$
I_2 = \frac{3T^2 + 3(1 - K)^2 T}{2T(1 + T)}
\tag{3.43}
$$

Hence the total mean squared error, recalling that $m(t)$ and $n(t)$ are uncorrelated, is the sum of the two components

$$
\overline{e^2(t)} = \frac{K^2}{2T} + \frac{3T^2 + 3(1 - K)^2 T}{2T(1 + T)}
\tag{3.44}
$$

For a particular value of T, we can easily differentiate the expression 3.44 with respect to K, and find the value of K which makes $\overline{e^2(t)}$ a minimum.

If we suppose that both K and T are allowed to be adjusted, we can find the optimum values of both of these parameters by taking the partial derivatives of Equation 3.44 with respect to K and to T, and setting both of these equal to zero. This gives two equations from which we find the values of K and T to be

$$
\begin{aligned}
K &= 0.5 \\
T &= 0.5
\end{aligned}
\tag{3.45}
$$

3.6 USE OF TRANSIENT SIGNALS TO FIND THE MEAN SQUARED ERROR FOR A RANDOM INPUT

Because of the great similarity of the mathematical expressions for the integral squared error to a transient input and the mean squared error to a random input, it is possible to obtain data for a system with a random input by studying the response of the system to a transient input. We shall now study this method of approach.

Let us assume that we have a linear system, and suppose we represent the error as one of the outputs of the system, with a transfer function $W(s)$ from input to error, as shown in Fig. 3.7.

Let us consider the following two cases: 1. where $x(t)$ is a random input, and 2. where $x(t)$ is a transient input starting at $t = 0$.

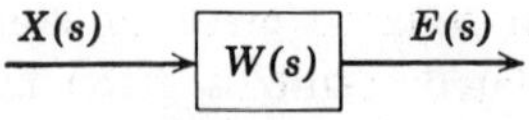

Fig. 3.7. Linear system with the error shown as an output.

Case 1. From Equation 3.26 we have

$$\overline{e^2(t)} = \frac{1}{2\pi j} \int_{-j\infty}^{j\infty} \Phi_{ee}(s) \, ds \tag{3.46}$$

which may be expressed as

$$\overline{e^2(t)} = \frac{1}{2\pi j} \int_{-j\infty}^{j\infty} \Phi_{xx}(s) W(s) W(-s) \, ds \tag{3.47}$$

Substituting $j\omega$ for s and simplifying, we obtain

$$\overline{e^2(t)} = \frac{1}{2\pi} \int_{-\infty}^{\infty} \Phi_{xx}(j\omega) |W(j\omega)|^2 \, d\omega \tag{3.48}$$

Case 2. From Equation 2.9 we have

$$\int_0^\infty e^2 \, dt = \frac{1}{2\pi j} \int_{-j\infty}^{j\infty} E(s) E(-s) \, ds \tag{3.49}$$

which may be expressed as

$$\int_0^\infty e^2 \, dt = \frac{1}{2\pi j} \int_{-j\infty}^{j\infty} X(s) W(s) X(-s) W(-s) \, ds \tag{3.50}$$

Substituting $j\omega$ for s and simplifying, we obtain

$$\int_0^\infty e^2 \, dt = \frac{1}{2\pi} \int_{-\infty}^{\infty} |X(j\omega)|^2 |W(j\omega)|^2 \, d\omega \tag{3.51}$$

On comparing Equations 3.48 and 3.51 we see that, if we have a random signal and a transient signal so related that $\Phi_{xx}(j\omega)$ for the random signal is exactly the same as $|X(j\omega)|^2$ for the transient signal for all values of ω, then the mean squared error in a given linear system to the random signal is the same as the integral squared error in the same system for the transient signal, no matter what the transfer function of the system may be. This may be very helpful if we wish to design a system by analogue-computer simulation, because it may be much easier to apply a certain transient signal to the system over and over again, making suitable adjustments of parameters between trials, than to apply a random signal over and over again, because optimization in the statistical sense may require a very long time of trial to ensure consistent results. These useful relationships were pointed out in a paper by Etkin [5], and similar methods are discussed by Laning and Battin [6].

As an example of a pair of signals which are related in this way, consider a random function whose autocorrelation is given by

$$\phi_{xx}(\tau) = e^{-a|\tau|} \tag{3.52}$$

The power-density spectrum is given by

$$\Phi_{xx}(s) = \frac{2a}{(a + s)(a - s)} \tag{3.53}$$

If we consider the transient signal given by

$$x(t) = \sqrt{2a}e^{-at} \; (t > 0) \tag{3.54}$$

the Laplace transform of this function is given by

$$X(s) = \frac{\sqrt{2a}}{(a + s)} \tag{3.55}$$

and the product

$$X(s)X(-s) = \frac{2a}{(a + s)(a - s)} \tag{3.56}$$

is the same as $\Phi_{xx}(s)$ given by Equation 3.53. This means that the transient signal 3.54 would give the same magnitude of integral squared error, when applied to any linear system, as the magnitude of the mean squared error in the same system when a random signal whose autocorrelation function is given by Equation 3.52 is applied to that system.

3.7 OPTIMIZATION OF IMPULSE RESPONSE

In Section 3.5 we studied the problem of choosing the values of the adjustable parameters of a system in such a way as to obtain the best possible response. It was assumed that the configuration of the system was specified in advance, or that the form of the transfer function was prescribed, with only certain coefficients of the transfer function being adjustable. Now let us suppose that we are completely free to specify whatever form of transfer function we wish, and let us study the problem of finding the system which responds in the best possible way in a given situation. The one restriction we shall impose is that the system must be physically realizable, in the sense that it cannot respond to an input before that input is applied to it. Mathematically speaking, the impulse response $w(t)$ of a physically realizable system is zero for all values of time t less than zero.

It should, of course, be understood that a system may be physically realizable in the mathematical sense as defined in the previous paragraph, and yet be very difficult or impossible to synthesize using practical components. However, even if we cannot synthesize the optimum system in practice, the finding of the theoretical optimum is still useful in that it tells us how close our practical system is to that optimum. This is, indeed, one of the major contributions of the theory of optimal control in general; it tells us how far our practical systems fall short of what is theoretically achievable.

Let us consider the problem of finding the optimum impulse response of the linear system shown in Fig. 3.3. The optimum impulse response will be that of the system which, when subjected to an input $x(t)$ with specified properties, gives an output $y(t)$ which is as close as possible to a specified function $d(t)$ in the sense that the mean square error $\overline{e^2(t)}$ between y and d is minimized.

This problem is different from any of those which we have considered in the earlier parts of this book. Up to now we have considered the maximization or minimization of a function of one or more independent variables; now we have the problem of choosing a function, the impulse response of the system, which causes a specified quantity to be optimized. This problem of finding a function which optimizes a specified quality is typical of the problems encountered in the calculus of variations, and we shall study such problems in more detail in Chapter 5 and subsequent chapters. In this section we shall study the specific problem of finding the optimum impulse response of the system shown in Fig. 3.3.

Let us assume that the optimum physically realizable impulse response is $w_0(t)$. This means that, if the input $x(t)$ is applied to a linear system with impulse response $w_0(t)$, the mean squared error between the output $y(t)$ and the desired output $d(t)$ is less than would be the case if the same input $x(t)$ were applied to a linear system with any other impulse response.

Let us consider an arbitrary linear system with a physically realizable impulse response $\eta(t)$. If we consider this system in combination with the

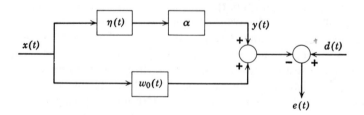

Fig. 3.8. Combination of optimal system with arbitrary system.

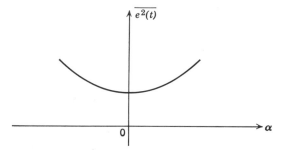

Fig. 3.9. Sketch of $\overline{e^2(t)}$ vs. α, for a particular $\eta(t)$.

optimal system, as shown in Fig. 3.8, we see that the combination acts like a single linear system with an impulse response $w(t)$ given by the expression

$$w(t) = w_0(t) + \alpha\eta(t) \tag{3.57}$$

where α is a gain constant. If we suppose that α can be varied continuously over a range of positive and negative values, we would expect to find a relationship between the mean squared error $\overline{e^2(t)}$ and the value of α, as shown in Fig. 3.9. That is, no matter what may be the form of $\eta(t)$, provided that it is physically realizable (and not identically zero), we would expect $\overline{e^2(t)}$ to reach a minimum at $\alpha = 0$ because under that condition $w(t) = w_0(t)$, the best achievable impulse response.

Let us define the change in mean squared error, as a function of α, by the expression

$$\Delta(\alpha) = \overline{e^2(t)} - \overline{e_0{}^2(t)} \tag{3.58}$$

where $e(t)$ corresponds to $w(t)$, and $e_0(t)$ to $w_0(t)$. It is assumed that a specific $\eta(t)$ is being considered, so that Δ is a function of α only.

Using the expression for the mean squared error given in Equation 3.17 we can express the change $\Delta(\alpha)$ by the expression

$$\Delta(\alpha) = \int_{-\infty}^{\infty}\int_{-\infty}^{\infty} \phi_{xx}(u - v)[w_0(u) + \alpha\eta(u)][w_0(v) + \alpha\eta(v)]\,du\,dv$$

$$- \int_{-\infty}^{\infty}\int_{-\infty}^{\infty} \phi_{xx}(u - v)w_0(u)w_0(v)\,du\,dv$$

$$- 2\int_{-\infty}^{\infty} \phi_{xd}(u)[w_0(u) + \alpha\eta(u)]\,du + 2\int_{-\infty}^{\infty} \phi_{xd}(u)w_0(u)\,du \tag{3.59}$$

where the terms in $\phi_{dd}(0)$ disappeared by cancellation. Expanding the separate terms, we obtain

$$\Delta(\alpha) = \int_{-\infty}^{\infty} \int_{-\infty}^{\infty} \phi_{xx}(u - v)w_0(u)w_0(v) \, du \, dv$$

$$+ \alpha \int_{-\infty}^{\infty} \int_{-\infty}^{\infty} \phi_{xx}(u - v)w_0(u)\eta(v) \, du \, dv$$

$$+ \alpha \int_{-\infty}^{\infty} \int_{-\infty}^{\infty} \phi_{xx}(u - v)\eta(u)w_0(v) \, du \, dv$$

$$+ \alpha^2 \int_{-\infty}^{\infty} \int_{-\infty}^{\infty} \phi_{xx}(u - v)\eta(u)\eta(v) \, du \, dv$$

$$- \int_{-\infty}^{\infty} \int_{-\infty}^{\infty} \phi_{xx}(u - v)w_0(u)w_0(v) \, du \, dv$$

$$- 2\int_{-\infty}^{\infty} \phi_{xd}(u)w_0(u) \, du - 2\alpha \int_{-\infty}^{\infty} \phi_{xd}(u)\eta(u) \, du$$

$$+ 2\int_{-\infty}^{\infty} \phi_{xd}(u)w_0(u) \, du \qquad (3.60)$$

Cancelling and collecting terms where possible (noting that the two double integrals with coefficient α are equal), we obtain

$$\Delta(\alpha) = 2\alpha \int_{-\infty}^{\infty} \int_{-\infty}^{\infty} \phi_{xx}(u - v)w_0(v)\eta(u) \, du \, dv$$

$$- 2\alpha \int_{-\infty}^{\infty} \phi_{xd}(u)\eta(u) \, du$$

$$+ \alpha^2 \int_{-\infty}^{\infty} \int_{-\infty}^{\infty} \phi_{xx}(u - v)\eta(u)\eta(v) \, du \, dv \qquad (3.61)$$

If we now differentiate $\Delta(\alpha)$ with respect to α, we obtain

$$\frac{d\Delta}{d\alpha} = 2\left[\int_{-\infty}^{\infty} \int_{-\infty}^{\infty} \phi_{xx}(u - v)w_0(v)\eta(u) \, du \, dv - \int_{-\infty}^{\infty} \phi_{xd}(u)\eta(u) \, du \right]$$

$$+ 2\alpha \int_{-\infty}^{\infty} \int_{-\infty}^{\infty} \phi_{xx}(u - v)\eta(u)\eta(v) \, du \, dv \qquad (3.62)$$

Now, if $w_0(t)$ is in fact the optimum physically realizable impulse response, we must have, by elementary calculus

$$\frac{d\Delta}{d\alpha} = 0 \qquad \text{for } \alpha = 0 \qquad (3.63)$$

This is obvious by observation of Fig. 3.9. Expression 3.62 shows that this requirement will be satisfied if and only if

$$\int_{-\infty}^{\infty} \int_{-\infty}^{\infty} \phi_{xx}(u - v)w_0(v)\eta(u) \, du \, dv - \int_{-\infty}^{\infty} \phi_{xd}(u)\eta(u) \, du = 0 \quad (3.64)$$

This expression can be written in the form

$$\int_{-\infty}^{\infty} \left[\int_{-\infty}^{\infty} \phi_{xx}(u - v)w_0(v) \, dv - \phi_{xd}(u) \right] \eta(u) \, du = 0 \quad (3.65)$$

Because $\eta(u)$ is an arbitrary physically realizable impulse response, expression 3.65 can only be zero if the quantity in square brackets is zero for all u greater than or equal to zero.[7] The impulse response $w_0(t)$ must satisfy the equation

$$\int_{-\infty}^{\infty} \phi_{xx}(u - v)w_0(v) \, dv = \phi_{xd}(u) \qquad \text{for all } u \geqslant 0 \quad (3.66)$$

Furthermore, since $w_0(v) = 0$ for $v < 0$, we can change the lower limit of integration to zero and write Equation 3.66 in the form

$$\int_{0}^{\infty} \phi_{xx}(u - v)w_0(v) \, dv = \phi_{xd}(u) \qquad \text{for all } u \geqslant 0 \quad (3.67)$$

Equation 3.67 is an integral equation, as the unknown function $w_0(t)$ appears under an integral sign. Some methods of solution of integral equations are described by Pipes [14]. This particular integral equation is known as the Wiener-Hopf equation. We shall now show that, for the impulse response $w_0(t)$ which satisfies the Wiener-Hopf Equation 3.67, the sign of the second derivative $d^2\Delta/d\alpha^2$ is positive at $\alpha = 0$, thus showing that the system with such an impulse response causes the mean squared error to be a minimum. From Equation 3.62 we can easily see that the second derivative is given by the expression

$$\frac{d^2\Delta}{d\alpha^2} = 2 \int_{-\infty}^{\infty} \int_{-\infty}^{\infty} \phi_{xx}(u - v)\eta(u)\eta(v) \, du \, dv \quad (3.68)$$

An interpretation of the right side of Equation 3.68 can very easily be obtained by considering the system with impulse response $\eta(t)$ with the input $x(t)$ applied to it, as shown in Fig. 3.10. The expression for the mean squared value of the output is very easy to find, from the foregoing development.

---

[7] This assumes the truth of the fundamental lemma of the calculus of variations. An approximate statement of this lemma is as follows: "If a function $g(x)$ is continuous throughout an interval $x_0 \leqslant x \leqslant x_1$, and if the integral $\int_{x_0}^{x_1} g(x)\eta(x) \, dx$ is equal to zero for every function $\eta(x)$, the function $g(x)$ is identically zero throughout the interval." A more precise statement of the lemma, and a proof, can be found in reference [7]. See also Chapter 5.

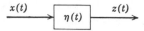

$$x(t) \longrightarrow \boxed{\eta(t)} \xrightarrow{\ z(t)\ }$$

Fig. 3.10. System with impulse response $\eta(t)$.

It is a special case of the expression for the mean squared error (Equation 3.17), with the desired output $d(t)$ taken to be identically zero and the impulse response taken to be $\eta(t)$. We see that expression 3.68 is simply double the mean squared value of $z(t)$, and that it must therefore be a positive quantity. This means that the second derivative is positive, and hence that the condition represented by the Wiener-Hopf Equation 3.67 gives a minimum of the mean squared error.

We have now shown that the impulse response $w_0(t)$ of the optimal system must satisfy the Wiener-Hopf Equation 3.67. A method of solving this equation is given in the next section.

3.8 SOLUTION OF THE WIENER-HOPF EQUATION

In order to solve the Wiener-Hopf equation, we shall make use of the frequency-domain representation of random signals and the properties of the Laplace transform. It is pointed out in Appendix B that, in dealing with inverse Laplace transformations evaluated along the imaginary axis of the s plane, poles in the left half of the plane correspond to time functions existing in positive time, while poles in the right-half plane correspond to time functions existing in negative time. Similar considerations apply to the power-density spectra which are the Fourier transforms of the autocorrelation functions. The fact that the Wiener-Hopf Equation 3.67 is valid for all positive u will be interpreted in terms of the poles of the corresponding frequency-domain functions, and thus we shall be able to obtain the solution of the Wiener-Hopf equation. This procedure will now be described.

Let us rewrite the Wiener-Hopf Equation 3.67 by defining the quantity $q(u)$ as

$$q(u) \triangleq \int_0^\infty \phi_{xx}(u - v)w_0(v)\,dv - \phi_{xd}(u) \tag{3.69}$$

where the Wiener-Hopf equation requires that

$$q(u) = 0 \qquad \text{for all } u \geqslant 0 \tag{3.70}$$

If we form the corresponding frequency-domain function $Q(s)$, defined by

$$Q(s) \triangleq \int_{-\infty}^\infty q(u)\mathrm{e}^{-su}\,du \tag{3.71}$$

Equation 3.70 requires that $Q(s)$ have no poles in the left half of the s plane. Furthermore, we know that, because the optimal system is to be physically realizable, $w_0(t) = 0$ for $t < 0$, and therefore $W_0(s)$ must have no poles in the right-half plane. If we take the Laplace transform of Equation 3.69, we obtain (noting that the first term on the right of Equation 3.69 is the convolution integral):

$$Q(s) = \Phi_{xx}(s)W_0(s) - \Phi_{xd}(s) \tag{3.72}$$

The basis of the solution is therefore as follows. We must choose $W_0(s)$, with no poles in the right-half plane, in such a way that $Q(s)$ as given by Equation 3.72 has no poles in the left-half plane. This can be done using spectrum factorization, which we shall now describe.

SPECTRUM FACTORIZATION

We shall restrict ourselves to the case where $\Phi_{xx}(s)$ is a rational function of s^2, as is usually the case. In this case, $\Phi_{xx}(s)$ can be written in the form

$$\Phi_{xx}(s) = \frac{K \prod_{i=0}^{m} (b_i + s) \prod_{i=0}^{m} (b_i - s)}{\prod_{i=0}^{n} (a_i + s) \prod_{i=0}^{n} (a_i - s)} \tag{3.73}$$

where $Re[b_i] > 0$, $Re[a_i] > 0$, for all i, and K is a positive real constant. The constant K is known to be positive because the value of $\Phi_{xx}(s)$ must be nonnegative at $s = 0$ [the power-density spectrum $\Phi_{xx}(j\omega)$ must be nonnegative for a real signal $x(t)$, and this includes the case $\omega = 0$]; the quantities $\prod_{i=0}^{m} b_i$ and $\prod_{i=0}^{n} a_i$ must both be positive because the a_i and b_i either are positive real or occur in conjugate complex pairs so that the product is positive and hence K is positive.

Equation 3.73 shows that $\Phi_{xx}(s)$ can be factored into two components, one with all its poles and zeros in the left half of the complex s plane, and one with all its poles and zeros in the right-half plane. We shall define the quantity

$$\Phi_{xx}^+(s) \triangleq \frac{\sqrt{K} \prod_{i=0}^{m} (b_i + s)}{\prod_{i=0}^{n} (a_i + s)} \tag{3.74}$$

The poles and zeros of the expression on the right of Equation 3.74 are $-a_i$ and $-b_i$, respectively, which are all in the left-half plane. The superscript $+$ on the left side of Equation 3.74 indicates that this is a frequency-domain function whose corresponding time-domain function exists only in positive time. Similarly we define

$$\Phi_{xx}^{-}(s) \triangleq \frac{\sqrt{K} \prod_{i=0}^{m} (b_i - s)}{\prod_{i=0}^{n} (a_i - s)} \tag{3.75}$$

where in this case all the poles are in the right-half plane and where the superscript − indicates the transform of a function which exists only in negative time.

We can now write Equation 3.72 in the form

$$Q(s) = \Phi_{xx}^{+}(s)\Phi_{xx}^{-}(s)W_0(s) - \Phi_{xd}(s) \tag{3.76}$$

which can be written as

$$Q(s) = \Phi_{xx}^{-}(s)\left[W_0(s)\Phi_{xx}^{+}(s) - \frac{\Phi_{xd}(s)}{\Phi_{xx}^{-}(s)}\right] \tag{3.77}$$

It is required that $Q(s)$ have all its poles in the right-half plane. Since we know that $\Phi_{xx}^{-}(s)$ has all its poles in the right-half plane, this requirement will be satisfied if the quantity in square brackets in Equation 3.77 has all its poles in the right-half plane. In order to arrange for this condition to be satisfied, we must perform one more decomposition, expressing the second term inside the square brackets of Equation 3.77 as the sum of two terms as follows:

$$\frac{\Phi_{xd}(s)}{\Phi_{xx}^{-}(s)} = \left[\frac{\Phi_{xd}(s)}{\Phi_{xx}^{-}(s)}\right]_+ + \left[\frac{\Phi_{xd}(s)}{\Phi_{xx}^{-}(s)}\right]_- \tag{3.78}$$

where [ ]$_+$ has all its poles in the left-half plane and [ ]$_-$ has all its poles in the right-half plane. This decomposition can be done by partial fractions if the left side of Equation 3.78 is a rational fraction. The term [ ]$_+$ in Equation 3.78 corresponds to a time function which exists only in positive time, and [ ]$_-$ to one which exists only in negative time. It is now possible to write Equation 3.77 in the form

$$Q(s) = \Phi_{xx}^{-}(s)\left\{W_0(s)\Phi_{xx}^{+}(s) - \left[\frac{\Phi_{xd}(s)}{\Phi_{xx}^{-}(s)}\right]_+ - \left[\frac{\Phi_{xd}(s)}{\Phi_{xx}^{-}(s)}\right]_-\right\} \tag{3.79}$$

If $Q(s)$ is to satisfy the requirement of having all its poles in the right-half plane, this can only occur if the quantity in braces in Equation 3.79 has its poles in the right-half plane. This means that the first two terms in the braces, which both have all their poles in the left-half plane, must add to zero. Therefore, we have

$$W_0(s)\Phi_{xx}^{+}(s) - \left[\frac{\Phi_{xd}(s)}{\Phi_{xx}^{-}(s)}\right]_+ = 0 \tag{3.80}$$

which immediately provides the expression for $W_0(s)$

$$W_0(s) = \frac{1}{\Phi_{xx}^+(s)} \left[\frac{\Phi_{xd}(s)}{\Phi_{xx}^-(s)}\right]_+ \qquad (3.81)$$

Recalling that $\Phi_{xx}^+(s)$ has all its poles and zeros in the left-half plane, the inverse $1/\Phi_{xx}^+(s)$ must also have all its poles and zeros in the left-half plane. Hence $W_0(s)$ has all its poles in the left-half plane, and is therefore physically realizable as required.

TIME-DOMAIN INTERPRETATION OF SPECTRAL FACTORIZATION

In order to help in the understanding of the procedure described in the last section, an interesting time-domain interpretation of this spectral factorization, due to Bode and Shannon [8], will now be presented. To take a specific example, we shall consider the case of pure prediction, where the value of the desired signal at a given instant is the value of the random signal $x(t)$ at some instant in the future. That is,

$$d(t) = x(t + a) \qquad (3.82)$$

We wish to determine the physically realizable filter which, when the input $x(t)$ is applied to it, will give an output $y(t)$ which is as close as possible (in the sense of minimum mean squared error) to the desired output $d(t)$ or $x(t + a)$. We know from the foregoing work that the filter which is optimum for $x(t)$ will also be optimum for all signals which have the same auto-correlation function and power-density spectrum as $x(t)$. Let us consider the frequency-domain function $\Phi_{xx}(s)$. It can be decomposed into the two factors $\Phi_{xx}^+(s)$ and $\Phi_{xx}^-(s)$ as shown below.

$$\Phi_{xx}(s) = \Phi_{xx}^+(s)\Phi_{xx}^-(s) \qquad (3.83)$$

By virtue of the relationship (Equation 3.36) which gives the power-density spectrum of the output of a linear system in terms of the transfer function of the system and the power-density spectrum of the input, we can suppose that the signal $x(t)$ has been obtained by the application of a "purely random signal" $r(t)$ to the input of a linear system with transfer function $\Phi_{xx}^+(s)$. By a "purely random signal" we mean one whose power-density spectrum $\Phi_{rr}(s)$ is identically unity, which corresponds to an autocorrelation function $\phi_{rr}(\tau)$ which is an impulse or delta function at $\tau = 0$. This implies that the value of $r(t)$ at any instant of time is completely uncorrelated with the value at all other instants, and that the average value of $r(t)$ is zero; we may think of $r(t)$ as a function made up of randomly occurring pulses as shown in Fig. 3.11. The function $x(t)$, as represented graphically by the right side of Fig. 3.11, is the superposition of the responses to the separate pulses appearing at the

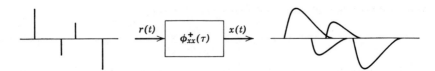

Fig. 3.11. Linear system whose output is $x(t)$.

input. As the transfer function $\Phi_{xx}^+(s)$ corresponding to the impulse response $\phi_{xx}^+(\tau)$ has all its poles and zeros in the left-half plane, the filter with transfer function $1/\Phi_{xx}^+(s)$ is physically realizable. If the function $x(t)$ is applied as the input to such a filter, the output of the filter will be the same as the original "purely random signal" or set of pulses $r(t)$.

Having represented $x(t)$ as the output of the filter shown in Fig. 3.11, we can now consider the prediction of the future values of $x(t)$. If we consider the value of the function $x(t)$ at a seconds after a particular instant $t = t_0$, we can see that the value of the function at $t = t_0 + a$ is made up of two components: (1) a component due to the "tails" of the responses to impulses which occurred before $t = t_0$; (2) a component produced by the impulses which occur between $t = t_0$ and $t = t_0 + a$.

If we know $r(t)$ up to $t = t_0$, component (1) is completely known. Suppose the impulse response of the filter which produces $x(t)$ from $r(t)$ is as shown in Fig. 3.12a, then it will readily be appreciated that, if $r(t)$ is applied to the input of a filter whose impulse response is $g(t)$ as shown in Fig. 3.12b (which is obtained by advancing the impulse response of Fig. 3.12a, a seconds in time, and setting the portion prior to $t = 0$ to zero) the output of this filter at $t = t_0$ will be component (1) of the predicted value of $x(t_0 + a)$.

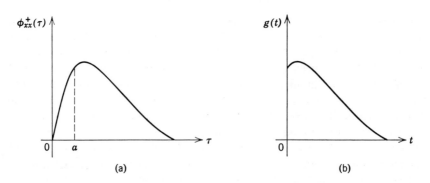

Fig. 3.12. (a) Impulse response of filter shown in Fig. 3.11. (b) Impulse response of filter which predicts component (1) of the predicted function.

Fig. 3.13. The optimum filter.

Component (2) of $x(t_0 + a)$ is completely unpredictable, because the input $r(t)$ is completely random. Because the time-average value of $r(t)$ is zero, it turns out that the best prediction is obtained by predicting zero as the value of this component.

We see, therefore, that the optimum predictor is obtained by applying the signal $x(t)$ to the input of the system shown in Fig. 3.13, where $G(s)$ is the transfer function corresponding to the impulse response $g(t)$ of Fig. 3.12b.

Let us now compare this to the optimum transfer function obtained by spectral factorization in the frequency domain, given in Equation 3.81. To begin with, the $1/\Phi_{xx}^+(s)$ transfer function appears in both. In order to compare the two results further, for the particular case of prediction, let us consider the autocorrelation function $\phi_{xd}(\tau)$. In this case, because $d(t) = x(t + a)$, we find that

$$\phi_{xd}(\tau) = \overline{x(t)\,d(t + \tau)} = \overline{x(t)x(t + a + \tau)} = \phi_{xx}(a + \tau) \quad (3.84)$$

In terms of frequency-domain functions, this means that

$$\Phi_{xd}(s) = e^{as}\Phi_{xx}(s) \quad (3.85)$$

The bracketed quantity of Equation 3.81 therefore becomes

$$\left[\frac{e^{as}\Phi_{xx}(s)}{\Phi_{xx}^-(s)}\right]_+ = [e^{as}\Phi_{xx}^+(s)]_+ \quad (3.86)$$

The interpretation of the right side of Equation 3.86 is quite simple. The time function corresponding to $e^{as}\Phi_{xx}^+(s)$ is merely the impulse response of Fig. 3.12a advanced in time by a seconds; the time function corresponding to $[e^{as}\Phi_{xx}^+(s)]_+$ is merely the same function, taking only the portion which exists in positive time, and this is clearly the same as the impulse response $g(t)$ of Fig. 3.12b. We see, therefore, that the two methods of obtaining the optimum filter provide the same result.

3.9 A SIMPLE EXAMPLE OF OPTIMAL FILTERING

In order to illustrate the methods of solution described in the previous section, let us consider once again the filtering problem studied in Section 3.5.

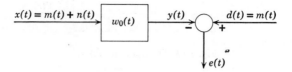

Fig. 3.14. Filter to separate signal and noise.

We shall assume, as before, that the input $x(t)$ is given by Equation 3.31 and that the filter is desired to eliminate the noise and leave the message. Let us find the optimum physically realizable filter, meaning the filter which achieves the minimum mean squared error.

The diagram in Fig. 3.14 illustrates the function the filter is to perform. We wish to find the impulse response or the transfer function of the filter which will give the smallest possible value of the mean squared error $\overline{e^2(t)}$.

We shall assume as before that the message and noise are uncorrelated. This being the case, it is shown in Appendix C that the autocorrelation function $\phi_{xx}(\tau)$ is given by

$$\phi_{xx}(\tau) = \phi_{mm}(\tau) + \phi_{nn}(\tau) \tag{3.87}$$

Another correlation function we shall need in this problem is $\phi_{xd}(\tau)$, which in this case may be written as

$$\phi_{xd}(\tau) = \phi_{xm}(\tau) = \overline{x(t)m(t + \tau)} = \overline{[m(t) + n(t)]m(t + \tau)}$$
$$= \phi_{mm}(\tau) + \phi_{nm}(\tau) \tag{3.88}$$

Because m and n are uncorrelated, we can say that

$$\phi_{xd}(\tau) = \phi_{mm}(\tau) \tag{3.89}$$

To correspond with the problem studied in Section 3.5, let us take the power-density spectra $\Phi_{mm}(s)$ and $\Phi_{nn}(s)$ to be the same as those defined by Equations 3.32 and 3.33. Because the two components of $x(t)$ are assumed to be uncorrelated, the power-density spectrum of $x(t)$ is given by

$$\Phi_{xx}(s) = \frac{3}{1 - s^2} + 1 = \frac{4 - s^2}{1 - s^2} \tag{3.90}$$

We can now proceed with the spectrum factorization by writing $\Phi_{xx}(s)$ in the form

$$\Phi_{xx}(s) = \left(\frac{2 + s}{1 + s}\right)\left(\frac{2 - s}{1 - s}\right) \tag{3.91}$$

from which we obtain

$$\Phi_{xx}^+(s) = \frac{2 + s}{1 + s} \tag{3.92}$$

and

$$\Phi_{xx}^-(s) = \frac{2 - s}{1 - s} \tag{3.93}$$

We also have

$$\Phi_{xd}(s) = \Phi_{mm}(s) = \frac{3}{1 - s^2} \tag{3.94}$$

Hence we have

$$\frac{\Phi_{xd}(s)}{\Phi_{xx}^-(s)} = \frac{3}{(1 - s^2)} \frac{(1 - s)}{(2 - s)} = \frac{3}{(1 + s)(2 - s)} \tag{3.95}$$

The expression at the right side of Equation 3.95 can be expanded in partial fractions in the form

$$\frac{\Phi_{xd}(s)}{\Phi_{xx}^-(s)} = \frac{1}{1 + s} + \frac{1}{2 - s} \tag{3.96}$$

Taking only the portion with the pole in the left-half plane, we have

$$\left[\frac{\Phi_{xd}(s)}{\Phi_{xx}^-(s)} \right]_+ = \frac{1}{1 + s} \tag{3.97}$$

Therefore, the optimal transfer function, given by Equation 3.81, may be written as

$$W_0(s) = \left(\frac{1 + s}{2 + s} \right) \left(\frac{1}{1 + s} \right) = \frac{1}{2 + s} \tag{3.98}$$

If we compare the transfer function (Equation 3.98) with the optimum transfer function derived in Section 3.5 (the optimum parameter values being given by Equation 3.45), we see that the transfer function we had already found in Section 3.5 was in fact that of the best possible physically realizable linear system.

3.10   OPTIMAL FILTERING OF NONSTATIONARY PROCESSES

If the statistics of our random process, or ensemble of signals, vary with time, the foregoing material is no longer applicable. Instead of considering the autocorrelation function to be the average over all time of a certain product, we must instead take the average over the ensemble of functions.

To be specific, we can define the autocorrelation function of a nonstationary random process by the equation

$$\phi_{xx}(t_1, t_2) = \overset{\wedge\wedge\wedge\wedge}{\overline{x(t_1)x(t_2)}} \tag{3.99}$$

where the wavy line indicates the ensemble average, as distinct from the straight line in the earlier sections of this chapter to represent a time average. Cross-correlation functions are defined in a similar manner as follows:

$$\phi_{xy}(t_1, t_2) = \overset{\wedge\wedge\wedge\wedge}{\overline{x(t_1)y(t_2)}} \tag{3.100}$$

Because the statistics of a nonstationary process vary with time, the optimum filter will also vary with time. The study of nonstationary processes is therefore very closely linked with the study of time-varying systems. For the present, we may consider the input-output relationship of a time-varying linear system or filter to be specified by its impulse response $w(t, \tau)$. The notation $w(t, \tau)$ means that the output of a system at time t, due to a unit impulse applied at time τ, is $w(t, \tau)$. The response $y(t)$ to an input $x(t)$ is given by the superposition integral, which is closely related to the convolution integral of time-invariant linear systems, and which has the form

$$y(t) = \int_{t_0}^{t} w(t, \tau)x(\tau)\, d\tau \tag{3.101}$$

where t_0 is the instant at which the input $x(t)$ began to be applied.

We can derive a Wiener-Hopf equation of somewhat similar form to that obtained for the stationary case. Consider the system shown in Fig. 3.15 below, which is similar to Fig. 3.3 but with a time-varying system. By methods which are very similar to those used for the time-invariant stationary case, we can derive the necessary equation for the mean squared error $\overset{\wedge\wedge\wedge}{\overline{e^2(t)}}$ to be minimum, as follows:

$$\int_{t_0}^{t} w_0(t, \tau)\phi_{xx}(\sigma, \tau)\, d\tau = \phi_{dx}(t, \sigma) \qquad (t_0 \leqslant \sigma \leqslant t) \tag{3.102}$$

where $w_0(t, \tau)$ is the impulse response of the optimum physically realizable linear system. The derivation of this equation, which may be considered as a generalization of the Wiener-Hopf Equation 3.67, is given by Peterson [9].

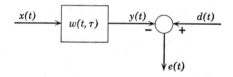

Fig. 3.15. A time-varying system.

VECTOR INTERPRETATION OF MINIMIZATION OF $\overline{e^2(t)}$

It is interesting to study the interpretation of the minimization of $\overline{e^2(t)}$ in terms of the orthogonality of vectors; this interpretation has been pointed out by Kalman [10, 11] and Yaglom [12]. In order to study this interpretation in its simplest possible terms, let us suppose we have an ensemble of three functions $x_1(t)$, $x_2(t)$, and $x_3(t)$. We can imagine the values of these three functions at any instant t as being represented by the coordinates of a vector **x** in a three-dimensional space. By the same token, we can represent the three outputs $y_1(t)$, $y_2(t)$, and $y_3(t)$, of three identical systems with inputs x_1, x_2, and x_3, respectively, as the coordinates of a vector **y** in a three-dimensional space. The three desired outputs $d_1(t)$, $d_2(t)$, and $d_3(t)$ (which have the same value for all three systems) can also be so represented. Let us suppose that the quantities **y** and **d** are as shown in Fig. 3.16. The vector $e(t)$ shown in Fig. 3.16 represents the three values of error $e_1(t)$, $e_2(t)$, and $e_3(t)$. The sum of the squares of the three errors is therefore equal to the square of the magnitude of the vector $e(t)$. The mean squared error is obviously minimum if the length of the vector **e** is minimum. Since it is obviously possible to connect a fixed-gain element, with gain different from unity, in cascade with the system shown in Fig. 3.15, it is possible to increase or decrease the length of the vector $y(t)$ of Fig. 3.16 at will. Inspection of Fig. 3.16 shows that a necessary condition for $y(t)$ to be closest to $d(t)$ in the mean squared error sense is that the vectors $e(t)$ and $y(t)$ are orthogonal, for if they are not it is possible to reduce the mean squared error [which is equivalent to reducing the length of the vector $e(t)$] by increasing or decreasing the length of the vector $y(t)$. If we now allow the number of signals in the ensemble to increase,

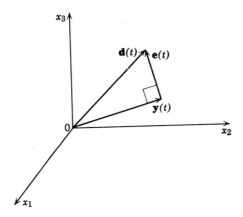

Fig. 3.16. Graphical representation of vectors $y(t)$ and $d(t)$.

the orthogonality property is retained. In terms of ensemble averages, this condition can be written in the form

$$\phi_{ey}(t, t) = 0 \qquad (3.103)$$

We can extend this idea to obtain a simple derivation of the Wiener-Hopf equation itself; this has been described by Yaglom [12]. If we consider the integral in Equation 3.101 to represent the output $y(t)$ as a linear combination of all the past inputs of the system (back to time t_0), the problem is to find which linear combination of the past inputs makes $\overline{e^2(t)}$ a minimum. If we consider again the ensemble of three functions x_1, x_2, and x_3, we can consider the set of all possible linear combinations of the past of the vector $\mathbf{x}$ to be represented by a plane as shown in Fig. 3.17. As before, the vector $\mathbf{d}(t)$ represents the desired output, and the vector $\mathbf{e}(t)$ the error. It is obvious that the condition for the optimal solution is that the error vector $\mathbf{e}(t)$ is orthogonal to the plane representing all possible linear combinations of the past of the input vector $\mathbf{x}$. If this is the case, then the error vector $\mathbf{e}(t)$ must be orthogonal to all possible past values of the vector $\mathbf{x}$ itself (back to time t_0). Expressing this in terms of scalar products of vectors, we have

$$\mathbf{e}(t) \cdot \mathbf{x}(\sigma) = 0 \qquad (3.104)$$

for all σ such that $t_0 \leqslant \sigma \leqslant t$. Hence we have

$$[\mathbf{d}(t) - \mathbf{y}(t)] \cdot \mathbf{x}(\sigma) = 0 \qquad (3.105)$$

From this we obtain

$$\mathbf{d}(t) \cdot \mathbf{x}(\sigma) = \left[\int_{t_0}^{t} w(t, \tau)\mathbf{x}(\tau)\, d\tau \right] \cdot \mathbf{x}(\sigma) \qquad (3.106)$$

$$= \int_{t_0}^{t} w(t, \tau)\mathbf{x}(\tau) \cdot \mathbf{x}(\sigma)\, d\tau \qquad (3.107)$$

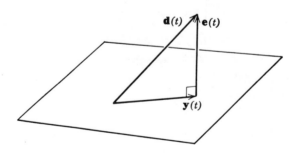

Fig. 3.17

Expressing Equation 3.107 in terms of ensemble averages, we obtain

$$\phi_{dx}(t, \sigma) = \int_{t_0}^{t} w(t, \tau)\phi_{xx}(\tau, \sigma)\, d\tau \qquad (3.108)$$

for all σ such that $t_0 \leqslant \sigma \leqslant t$. Equation 3.108 is the same as the Wiener-Hopf Equation 3.102.

The above is a rather simplified explanation of the ideas of orthogonal projection as applied to minimization problems of this kind; we shall use the results derived here to help in our development of the Kalman filter in the next section. For a fuller and more rigorous discussion of these ideas, the book by Yaglom [12] is recommended.

3.11 THE KALMAN FILTER

A new method of filtering nonstationary random processes has been described by Kalman and Bucy [10, 11]. This method is particularly suitable for the estimation of the variables of a system, when the measurements of these variables are contaminated by noise. This section is devoted to a simplified explanation of the method, the main simplification being a treatment of scalar or single-variable processes instead of the filtering of vector processes as described in the original papers. After reading this section and Chapter 4 which deals with the state representation of systems, the reader may wish to read the original papers to gain a fuller understanding of the subject.

The notation of this section is, to a large extent, analogous to that of reference [11] but appropriate to scalar variables instead of vectors.

Let us suppose that the message process can be assumed to be generated by a time-varying linear system which behaves in accordance with the differential equation

$$\frac{dx}{dt} = f(t)x(t) + u(t) \qquad (3.109)$$

where $x(t)$ is a dependent variable of the system, $u(t)$ is the input, and $f(t)$ is a time-varying parameter of the system. Suppose that the observed output of the system is $z(t)$, which is the dependent variable contaminated by noise $v(t)$ as given by the equation

$$z(t) = x(t) + v(t) \qquad (3.110)$$

Let us suppose that $u(t)$ and $v(t)$ are nonstationary white-noise signals whose autocorrelation and cross-correlation functions are given by

$$\phi_{uu}(t, \tau) = \overline{u(t)u(\tau)} = q(t)\delta(t - \tau)$$
$$\phi_{vv}(t, \tau) = \overline{v(t)v(\tau)} = r(t)\delta(t - \tau) \qquad (3.111)$$
$$\phi_{uv}(t, \tau) = \overline{u(t)v(\tau)} = 0$$

for all t and τ, where $\delta(t)$ is the Dirac delta function. The functions $q(t)$ and $r(t)$ are assumed to be continuously differentiable; $q(t)$ is assumed to be nonnegative definite (nonnegative for all values of t) and $r(t)$ to be positive definite (positive for all values of t). The fact that $r(t)$ is positive definite means that observations are at all times corrupted by additive noise.

The system described by Equations 3.109 and 3.110 can be represented in block-diagram form as in Fig. 3.18.

The problem may now be stated as follows: Find the optimum physically realizable time-varying filter such that, with input $z(t)$ for all $t \geqslant t_0$, the output is the best possible estimate, in the mean-squared-error sense, of the instantaneous value of $x(t)$. It is assumed that $f(t)$, $q(t)$, and $r(t)$ are known, but that the only system variable which is directly observable is $z(t)$.

Let $x_0(t)$ be the optimal estimate of $x(t)$, and let the impulse response of the optimum filter be $a(t, \tau)$, which is assumed to be continuously differentiable with respect to both arguments. The optimal estimate $x_0(t)$ is given by

$$x_0(t) = \int_{t_0}^{t} a(t, \tau)z(\tau)\, d\tau \qquad (3.112)$$

The Wiener-Hopf equation may be written, by transcribing Equation 3.102 and altering the notation to suit, in the form

$$\int_{t_0}^{t} a(t, \tau)\phi_{zz}(\sigma, \tau)\, d\tau = \phi_{xz}(t, \sigma) \qquad (3.113)$$

for all σ such that $t_0 \leqslant \sigma < t$. The right-hand inequality is a strict inequality

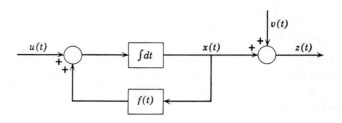

Fig. 3.18. Block-diagram representation of message process.

in this case, because $a(t, \tau)$ is continuously differentiable with respect to both arguments.[8]

In this case the solution of the Wiener-Hopf equation is carried out in the time domain, and proceeds by differentiating both sides of Equation 3.113 with respect to t, assuming τ and σ to be constant. Differentiating the left side of Equation 3.113 with respect to t, we obtain

$$\int_{t_0}^{t} \frac{\partial}{\partial t}\, [a(t, \tau)\phi_{zz}(\sigma, \tau)]\, d\tau + a(t, t)\phi_{zz}(\sigma, t) \qquad (3.114)$$

The quantity $\phi_{zz}(\sigma, t)$ in Equation 3.114 can be expressed in the form

$$\phi_{zz}(\sigma, t) = \overline{[x(\sigma) + v(\sigma)][x(t) + v(t)]} \qquad (3.115)$$

Because v and x are uncorrelated, and because $v(\sigma)$ and $v(t)$ are uncorrelated for all $\sigma < t$, expression 3.115 can be written in the form

$$\phi_{zz}(\sigma, t) = \phi_{xx}(\sigma, t) = \phi_{zx}(\sigma, t) \qquad (3.116)$$

The derivative of the right side of Equation 3.113 with respect to time can be written in the form

$$\frac{d}{dt}\, [\overline{x(t)z(\sigma)}] = f(t)\overline{x(t)z(\sigma)} + \overline{u(t)z(\sigma)}$$

$$= f(t)\phi_{xz}(t, \sigma) + \phi_{uz}(t, \sigma) \qquad (3.117)$$

Because $z(\sigma)$ cannot be correlated with the later input $u(t)$, the last term on the right of Equation 3.117 is zero for all $\sigma < t$. Therefore, equating expressions 3.114 and 3.117, and taking Equation 3.116 into account, we have

$$\int_{t_0}^{t} \frac{\partial}{\partial t}\, [a(t, \tau)]\phi_{zz}(\sigma, \tau)\, d\tau + a(t, t)\phi_{xz}(t, \sigma) = f(t)\phi_{xz}(t, \sigma) \qquad (3.118)$$

for all σ such that $t_0 \leqslant \sigma < t$.

Substituting Equation 3.113 in Equation 3.118, and rearranging, we obtain

$$\int_{t_0}^{t} \left\{ f(t)a(t, \tau) - a(t, t)a(t, \tau) - \frac{\partial}{\partial t}\, [a(t, \tau)] \right\} \phi_{zz}(\sigma, \tau)\, d\tau = 0 \qquad (3.119)$$

$$(t_0 \leqslant \sigma < t)$$

If the quantity in the braces in Equation 3.119 is represented by the notation $b(t, \tau)$, then Equation 3.119 will certainly be satisfied if $b(t, \tau) = 0$ for all τ such that $t_0 \leqslant \tau \leqslant t$. It is also *necessary* that $b(t, \tau)$ be zero in this interval; if we compare Equations 3.119 and 3.113, we see that if $a(t, \tau)$ satisfies the

---

[8] The significance of $a(t, \tau)$ being continuously differentiable with respect to both arguments is that the filter output depends only on the past values of the input and not on its present value.

Wiener-Hopf equation, then so does $[a(t, \tau) + b(t, \tau)]$. As is shown by Kalman and Bucy [11], and by Stear [16], this means that $b(t, \tau)$ must be zero. In other words, we have from Equation 3.119:

$$\frac{\partial}{\partial t}\,[a(t, \tau)] = f(t)a(t, \tau) - a(t, t)a(t, \tau) \qquad (3.120)$$

Now let us differentiate Equation 3.112 with respect to t, and we obtain

$$\frac{dx_0}{dt} = \int_{t_0}^{t} \frac{\partial}{\partial t}\,[a(t, \tau)]z(\tau)\,d\tau + a(t, t)z(t) \qquad (3.121)$$

Substituting Equation 3.120 in Equation 3.121, we obtain

$$\frac{dx_0}{dt} = \int_{t_0}^{t} [f(t)a(t, \tau) - a(t, t)a(t, \tau)]z(\tau)\,d\tau + a(t, t)z(t) \qquad (3.122)$$

Defining a time-varying gain $k(t)$ to be

$$k(t) \triangleq a(t, t) \qquad (3.123)$$

and substituting Equation 3.112 in Equation 3.122, we obtain

$$\frac{dx_0}{dt} = f(t)x_0(t) - k(t)x_0(t) + k(t)z(t) \qquad (3.124)$$

Equation 3.124 is the differential equation of a system with output variable $x_0(t)$ and input $z(t)$; in other words, it is the differential equation of the optimum filter and can be represented by the block diagram shown in Fig. 3.19.

On comparing Fig. 3.19 with Fig. 3.18, we see that the dotted rectangle of Fig. 3.19 encloses a model of the message process. The only unknown quantity in Fig. 3.19 is the time-varying gain $k(t)$. Let us now proceed to find this quantity.

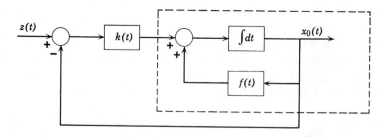

Fig. 3.19. Block diagram of the optimum filter.

METHOD OF FINDING $k(t)$

Substituting Equation 3.110 in Equation 3.124 and rearranging, we obtain

$$\frac{dx_0}{dt} = f(t)x_0(t) + k(t)[x(t) - x_0(t)] + k(t)v(t) \qquad (3.125)$$

Let us define a quantity $e_0(t)$ to represent the optimal error, as follows

$$e_0(t) \overset{\Delta}{=} x(t) - x_0(t) \qquad (3.126)$$

We obtain from Equation 3.125 and Equation 3.109 the following differential equation for the optimal error e_0:

$$\frac{de_0}{dt} = [f(t) - k(t)]e_0(t) + u(t) - k(t)v(t) \qquad (3.127)$$

The solution of Equation 3.127 can be written in the form

$$e_0(t) = \int_{t_0}^{t} \psi(t, \tau)[u(\tau) - k(\tau)v(\tau)] \, d\tau + \psi(t, t_0)e_0(t_0) \qquad (3.128)$$

where $\psi(t, \tau)$ is the solution of the equation

$$\frac{d\psi(t, \tau)}{dt} = [f(t) - k(t)]\psi(t, \tau) \qquad (3.129)$$

with initial condition $\psi(\tau, \tau) = 1$. See Chapter 4 for more details of solutions of this type.

The time derivative of the square of the optimal error can be written as

$$\frac{de_0^2}{dt} = 2e_0 \frac{de_0}{dt} \qquad (3.130)$$

Expressing Equation 3.130 in terms of Equation 3.127, we obtain

$$\frac{de_0^2(t)}{dt} = 2[f(t) - k(t)]e_0^2(t) + 2u(t)e_0(t) - 2k(t)v(t)e_0(t) \qquad (3.131)$$

Taking ensemble averages of Equation 3.131, and defining the quantity p as follows

$$p(t) \overset{\Delta}{=} \overline{e_0^2(t)} \qquad (3.132)$$

we obtain

$$\frac{dp(t)}{dt} = 2[f(t) - k(t)]p(t) + 2\overline{u(t)e_0(t)} - 2k(t)\overline{v(t)e_0(t)} \qquad (3.133)$$

The ensemble averages $\overline{u(t)e_0(t)}$ and $\overline{v(t)e_0(t)}$ can be found from Equation 3.128 as follows:

$$\overline{u(t)e_0(t)} = \int_{t_0}^{t} \psi(t, \tau)[\overline{u(t)u(\tau)} - k(\tau)\overline{u(t)v(\tau)}] \, d\tau + \psi(t, t_0)\overline{u(t)e_0(t_0)} \qquad (3.134)$$

Because u and v are uncorrelated, the second term in the integrand of Equation 3.134 is zero; the last term on the right side of Equation 3.134 is also zero because the white noise input $u(t)$ is uncorrelated with the initial error $e_0(t_0)$. In view of the autocorrelation function of u, as given by Equation 3.111, Equation 3.134 can be expressed in the form

$$\overline{u(t)e_0(t)} = \tfrac{1}{2}q(t) \tag{3.135}$$

where the $\tfrac{1}{2}$ arises because of the symmetry of the delta function in Equation 3.111. Similarly we can show that

$$\overline{v(t)e_0(t)} = -\tfrac{1}{2}k(t)r(t) \tag{3.136}$$

The differential equation for $p(t)$ (Equation 3.133), can now be written in the form

$$\frac{dp}{dt} = 2[f(t) - k(t)]p(t) + q(t) + k^2(t)r(t) \tag{3.137}$$

As is shown in the previous section (Equations 3.103 and 3.104), the Wiener-Hopf equation is equivalent to the conditions

$$\phi_{e_0x_0}(t, t) = 0 \tag{3.138}$$

and

$$\overline{e_0(t)z(\sigma)} = \phi_{e_0z}(t, \sigma) = 0 \qquad (t_0 \leqslant \sigma < t) \tag{3.139}$$

where the right-hand inequality is again a strict inequality as pointed out above.

Expressing Equation 3.139 in the form

$$\overline{[x(t) - x_0(t)][x(\sigma) + v(\sigma)]} = 0 \tag{3.140}$$

we can derive the relationship

$$\overline{x(t)x(\sigma)} - \int_{t_0}^{t} a(t, \tau)\overline{[x(\tau) + v(\tau)][x(\sigma) + v(\sigma)]}\, d\tau = 0 \tag{3.141}$$

Because x and v are uncorrelated, we can write Equation 3.141 in the form

$$\phi_{xx}(t, \sigma) - \int_{t_0}^{t} a(t, \tau)[\overline{x(\tau)x(\sigma)} + \overline{v(\tau)v(\sigma)}]\, d\tau = 0 \tag{3.142}$$

Using the relationships in Equations 3.111, we can write Equation 3.142 in the form

$$\phi_{xx}(t, \sigma) - \int_{t_0}^{t} a(t, \tau)\phi_{xx}(\tau, \sigma)\, d\tau = a(t, \sigma)r(\sigma) \qquad (t_0 \leqslant \sigma < t) \tag{3.143}$$

Because both sides of Equation 3.143 are continuous functions of σ, Equation 3.143 will hold at $\sigma = t$. Hence we have

$$\phi_{xx}(t, t) - \int_{t_0}^{t} a(t, \tau)\phi_{xx}(\tau, t)\, d\tau = k(t)r(t) \tag{3.144}$$

Noting that $\phi_{xx}(\tau, t) = \phi_{zx}(\tau, t)$, Equation 3.144 can be written in the form

$$\overbrace{x(t)x(t)} - \overbrace{x_0(t)x(t)} = k(t)r(t) \tag{3.145}$$

Equation 3.145 can be written in the form

$$\overbrace{e_0(t)[e_0(t) + x_0(t)]} = k(t)r(t) \tag{3.146}$$

Taking Equation 3.138 into account, Equation 3.146 gives

$$k(t) = \frac{p(t)}{r(t)} \tag{3.147}$$

Equation 3.147 allows $k(t)$ to be found in terms of $p(t)$ and $r(t)$. Substituting Equation 3.147 in the differential Equation 3.137 for p, we obtain

$$\frac{dp}{dt} = 2f(t)p(t) - \frac{p^2(t)}{r(t)} + q(t) \tag{3.148}$$

This is a form of differential equation known as the Riccati equation [13]. It arises in many problems involving the optimization of linear systems with quadratic performance criteria, and will be met again in Chapter 7. The Riccati equation in this case allows us to find the solution for $p(t)$ if the initial value $p(t_0)$ is known.

Let us assume that the output of the filter is zero initially; that is, $x_0(t_0) = 0$. In this case, the mean squared value of e_0 at time t_0 is equal to the mean squared value of x at time t_0, and this is given by $\phi_{xx}(t_0, t_0)$. Therefore, the initial value $p(t_0)$ is given by

$$p(t_0) = \phi_{xx}(t_0, t_0) \tag{3.149}$$

We can now solve Equation 3.148 for $p(t)$, and substitute in Equation 3.147 to find $k(t)$; thus the parameters of the optimum filter of Fig. 3.19 are completely specified.

A SIMPLE EXAMPLE

Let us use the Kalman method to derive the optimum filter in a simple case. To be specific, let us consider the example already studied in Section 3.9, where we wished to obtain the best estimate of a message contaminated by noise. The spectra of the message and noise are given by Equations 3.32 and 3.33, respectively. As the random processes are stationary in this case, the

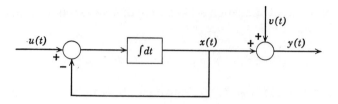

Fig. 3.20. A linear system.

systems we deal with are all time-invariant. It is easy to see from previous work that the message signal with spectrum given by Equation 3.32 can be considered to be the quantity $x(t)$ in the linear system shown in Fig. 3.20, with a white noise input with autocorrelation function $3\delta(\tau)$.

The diagram of Fig. 3.20 has been labelled to suit the notation of the present section. It is easy to see that the pertinent parameters have the following values in this case:

$$
\begin{aligned}
f &= -1 \\
q &= 3 \\
r &= 1
\end{aligned}
\tag{3.150}
$$

The optimal filter is therefore as shown in the block diagram of Fig. 3.21. The Riccati differential Equation 3.148 may be written as follows for this case:

$$\frac{dp}{dt} = -2p - p^2 + 3 \tag{3.151}$$

In the stationary case, the mean squared error must be constant, so that dp/dt is zero. Solving Equation 3.151 for p, we obtain the result

$$p = 1 \tag{3.152}$$

where we have discarded the negative solution of the quadratic equation, because p is the mean squared error and cannot be negative. Substituting the known quantities in Equation 3.147 we obtain

$$k = 1 \tag{3.153}$$

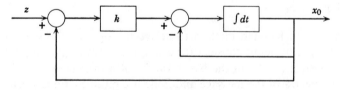

Fig. 3.21. Block diagram of optimal filter.

In view of this value of k, the transfer function of the filter of Fig. 3.21 is shown to be

$$W_0(s) = \frac{1}{2 + s} \tag{3.154}$$

which is the same as that found by the original method (Equation 3.98).

SUMMARY

This chapter has introduced the theory underlying the statistical optimization of linear systems with random inputs. For a more thorough treatment of statistical optimization, the reader is recommended to study the books by Newton, Gould, and Kaiser [4] and Laning and Battin [6].

The chapter concludes with a simplified description of the Kalman filter. After studying this chapter and Chapter 4 on the state representation of systems, the reader may be able to understand some of the published papers on this subject [10, 11, 15, 16].

REFERENCES

[1] Wiener, N., *Extrapolation, Interpolation, and Smoothing of Stationary Time Series*, published jointly by the Technology Press of M.I.T. and Wiley, New York, 1949.
[2] Schwarz, R. J., and B. Friedland, *Linear Systems*, McGraw-Hill, New York, 1965.
[3] Cooper, G. R., and C. D. McGillem, *Methods of Signal and System Analysis*, Holt, Rinehart, and Winston, New York, 1967.
[4] Newton, G. C., L. A. Gould, and J. F. Kaiser, *Analytical Design of Linear Feedback Controls*, Wiley, New York, 1957.
[5] Etkin, B., "A Simple Method for the Analogue Computation of the Mean-Square Response of Airplanes to Atmospheric Turbulence." UTIA Technical Note No. 32, Institute of Aerophysics, University of Toronto, January, 1960.
[6] Laning, J. H., and R. H. Battin, *Random Processes in Automatic Control*, McGraw-Hill, New York, 1956.
[7] Elsgolc, L. E., *Calculus of Variations*, Pergamon Press, London, England, and Addison-Wesley, Reading, Mass., 1962.
[8] Bode, H. W., and C. E. Shannon, "A Simplified Derivation of Linear Least Square Smoothing and Prediction Theory," *Proc. I.R.E.*, **38**, 417–425 (1950).
[9] Peterson, E. L., *Statistical Analysis and Optimization of Systems*, Wiley, New York, 1961.
[10] Kalman, R. E., "A New Approach to Linear Filtering and Prediction Problems," *ASME Trans.*, Series D (*J. Basic Eng.*), **82**, 35–45 (1960).
[11] Kalman, R. E., and R. S. Bucy, "New Results in Linear Filtering and Prediction Theory," *ASME Trans.*, Series D (*J. Basic Eng.*), **83**, 95–108 (1961).
[12] Yaglom, A. M., *An Introduction to the Theory of Stationary Random Functions*, Prentice-Hall, Englewood Cliffs, N.J., 1962.

[13] Piaggio, H. T. H., *Differential Equations*, G. Bell & Sons, Ltd., London, 1952.

[14] Pipes, L. A., *Applied Mathematics for Engineers and Physicists*, 2nd ed., McGraw-Hill, New York, 1958.

[15] Sorenson, H. W., "Kalman Filtering Techniques," in *Advances in Control Systems*, Vol. 3, C. T. Leondes, ed., Academic Press, New York and London, 1966, pp. 219–292.

[16] Stear, E. B., "Shaping Filters for Stochastic Processes," in *Modern Control Systems Theory*, C. T. Leondes, ed., McGraw-Hill, New York, 1965, Chap. 4.

PROBLEMS

1. For the system shown in Fig. 3.22 with a steady sinusoidal input, the output $y(t)$ is given by

$$y(t) = A \sin(\omega t + \theta) \tag{3.155}$$

where θ is an arbitrary phase angle.
(a) Find the autocorrelation function $\phi_{xx}(\tau)$.
(b) Find the cross-correlation function $\phi_{xy}(\tau)$.

2. It is desired to design a simple linear predictor which, with an input $x(t)$, gives an output $y(t)$ defined by

$$y(t) = px(t - u) + qx(t) \tag{3.156}$$

The problem is to choose the constants p and q in Equation 3.156 in such a way that $y(t)$ is a good approximation of $x(t + v)$, where both u and v are positive. The prediction error is defined by

$$e(t) = x(t + v) - y(t) \tag{3.157}$$

(a) For an arbitrary autocorrelation function $\phi_{xx}(\tau)$, find the mean squared error in terms of $\phi_{xx}(\tau)$.
(b) For the random square wave described in Section 3.1 and for the values $u = v = T/2$, find the values of p and q for minimum mean squared error.

3. A signal $x(t)$ is a member of a stationary random process, with spectrum $\Phi_{xx}(s) = 1/(1 - s^2)$. Find the transfer function of the optimum physically realizable predictor to estimate the value of $x(t + T)$.

4. A message with spectrum $\Phi_{mm}(s) = 1/(1 - s^2)$ is contaminated by additive noise with spectrum $\Phi_{nn}(s) = s^2/(s^2 - 1)$.
(a) Assuming a filter of the form $1/(1 + Ts)$ is used, find the value of T such that the filter output is the best possible approximation of the message, in

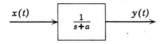

Fig. 3.22

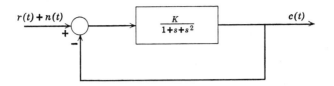

Fig. 3.23

the mean-squared-error sense. Find the value of the mean squared error.

(b) Find the best physically realizable filter for this situation, and find the value of the mean squared error.

5. In the feedback system of Fig. 3.23, the reference input signal $r(t)$ is contaminated by white noise $n(t)$, $r(t)$ and $n(t)$ being uncorrelated. The spectra of the signal and noise are given by

$$\Phi_{rr}(s) = \frac{12}{1 - s^2} \qquad \Phi_{nn}(s) = 1 \qquad (3.158)$$

Find the value of K such that the error $r(t) - c(t)$ has minimum mean squared value.

6. Figure 3.24 shows a linear filter with a white noise input $n_1(t)$, whose output $m(t)$ is contaminated by white noise $n_2(t)$. The noise inputs $n_1(t)$ and $n_2(t)$ are uncorrelated, and each has a power-density spectrum of unity. Find the transfer function of the linear filter, with input $x(t)$, whose output is the best possible approximation, in the mean-squared-error sense, to the message $m(t)$.

Fig. 3.24

4

State Representation of Systems

The behavior of many dynamic systems can be expressed in the form of ordinary differential equations. For example, a typical linear system might be characterized by the differential equation

$$a_n \frac{d^n x}{dt^n} + \cdots + a_1 \frac{dx}{dt} + a_0 x = u \qquad (4.1)$$

where $x(t)$ is the system output, and $u(t)$ is the input or forcing function. The coefficients a_i may be constant, or may vary with time.

It is often more convenient, for the purpose of optimal control studies, to characterize the behavior of the system by n first-order differential equations instead of one nth-order equation. The n first-order equations can then be represented as a single first-order equation in a vector variable. Such a representation has advantages in the numerical solution of differential equations, because most numerical methods available are valid only for equations expressed as first-order differential or difference equations. The representation of a system in this way has the added advantage that it allows a convenient and consistent notation to be adopted. The purpose of this chapter is to introduce the method of representing a system by a first-order differential equation in terms of the state variables of the system.

4.1 REPRESENTATION OF SYSTEM BY STATE EQUATIONS

To take a simple example, let us consider the linear control system shown in Fig. 4.1. Suppose the transfer function from the input U to the output X is given by

$$\frac{X(s)}{U(s)} = W(s) = \frac{\omega_n^2}{s^2 + 2\zeta\omega_n s + \omega_n^2} \qquad (4.2)$$

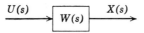

$U(s)$ $\longrightarrow$ $W(s)$ $\longrightarrow$ $X(s)$

Fig. 4.1. A linear control system.

The significance of the transfer function is that, *if the initial conditions of the system are such that the energy stored in the system is zero*, the Laplace transform of the output may be obtained by multiplying the Laplace transform of the input by the transfer function $W(s)$. The differential equation relating the input and output of this system may be written as

$$\frac{d^2x}{dt^2} + 2\zeta\omega_n \frac{dx}{dt} + \omega_n{}^2x = \omega_n{}^2u \qquad (4.3)$$

If a known signal $u(t)$ is applied to the input of the system, starting at some particular instant such as $t = 0$, it is not possible without further information to find the response of the system after that instant. It is possible to determine the response for all time, however, if we know $u(t)$ for all time and if we also know the values of x and its time derivative at $t = 0$. We take the pair of values, of x and of its time derivative, to represent the *state* of the system. In more general terms, the state of a system may be defined as the minimum amount of information required to describe the condition of the system at any given time in such a way that, if the system input is known from that time on (and if the differential equation governing the behavior of the system is also known), the condition of the system at any future time is completely determined.

In the second-order system described by Equation 4.3, two quantities were necessary to describe the state of the system. More generally, if we had an nth-order differential equation, we would need n quantities, for example the values of the output variable and its first $n - 1$ derivatives, to specify the state of the system. The values of these quantities may be thought of as the coordinates of a point in an n-dimensional Euclidean space, which is usually called the state space or the phase space[1] of the system. In the particular case of a second-order system, such as that considered in the example above, the two-dimensional space on which x and its time derivative are plotted is usually called the phase plane.

It should be pointed out that there is not necessarily a unique set of n variables which specifies the state of a system. If we are given one such set,

---

[1] Some authors (for example Kalman [1]) use the term *phase* to include the *state* variables and the time t. However, as the term *phase plane* seems to be firmly established as the name of the two-dimensional state space, it is assumed in this book that the terms "state" and "phase" are synonymous.

and if there is another set of n variables such that there is a unique relationship between the two sets, the second set may equally well be used to represent the state of the system. However, it is usual to choose a particular set of n variables, and to refer to the vector space of these variables as the phase space of the system.

We can replace the second-order differential Equation 4.3 by two first-order differential equations in terms of the state variables. This can most easily be done by designating two quantities x_1 and x_2 as the state variables, defined as follows

$$x_1 \triangleq x$$
$$x_2 \triangleq \frac{dx}{dt} \tag{4.4}$$

Having defined these quantities, we can write the second-order differential Equation 4.3 as the following two first-order equations

$$\frac{dx_1}{dt} = x_2$$
$$\frac{dx_2}{dt} = -\omega_n^2 x_1 - 2\zeta\omega_n x_2 + \omega_n^2 u \tag{4.5}$$

Equations 4.5 may be written in the vector-matrix form as follows

$$\frac{d}{dt} \begin{bmatrix} x_1 \\ x_2 \end{bmatrix} = \begin{bmatrix} 0 & 1 \\ -\omega_n^2 & -2\zeta\omega_n \end{bmatrix} \begin{bmatrix} x_1 \\ x_2 \end{bmatrix} + \begin{bmatrix} 0 \\ \omega_n^2 \end{bmatrix} u \tag{4.6}$$

More generally, an nth-order linear differential equation with constant coefficients can be written as n first-order linear differential equations in terms of the state variables of the system. Consider, for example, the equation

$$\frac{d^n x}{dt^n} + a_{n-1} \frac{d^{n-1} x}{dt^{n-1}} + \cdots + a_0 x = u \tag{4.7}$$

where we have assumed, without loss of generality, that the coefficient of $d^n x/dt^n$ is unity. It is assumed that the coefficients $a_0, \ldots, a_{n-1}$ are constant. If we make the following definitions

$$x_1 \triangleq x$$
$$x_2 \triangleq \frac{dx}{dt}$$
$$\vdots$$
$$x_n \triangleq \frac{d^{n-1} x}{dt^{n-1}} \tag{4.8}$$

we can replace the nth-order Equation 4.7 by the following n first-order equations in terms of the state variables

$$\frac{dx_1}{dt} = x_2$$

$$\vdots$$

$$\frac{dx_{n-1}}{dt} = x_n \tag{4.9}$$

$$\frac{dx_n}{dt} = -a_0 x_1 - \cdots - a_{n-1} x_n + u$$

Equation 4.9 may be written in vector-matrix form as follows

$$\frac{d}{dt}\begin{bmatrix} x_1 \\ x_2 \\ \vdots \\ x_{n-1} \\ x_n \end{bmatrix} = \begin{bmatrix} 0 & 1 & 0 & \cdots & & 0 \\ 0 & 0 & 1 & 0 & \cdots & 0 \\ & & \cdot & \cdot & \cdot & \cdot \\ 0 & & \cdots & & 0 & 1 \\ -a_0 & & \cdots & & & -a_{n-1} \end{bmatrix} \begin{bmatrix} x_1 \\ x_2 \\ \vdots \\ x_{n-1} \\ x_n \end{bmatrix} + \begin{bmatrix} 0 \\ 0 \\ \vdots \\ 0 \\ 1 \end{bmatrix} u \tag{4.10}$$

Using matrix notation, and considering the more general case where there are r inputs $u_1, u_2, \ldots, u_r$ instead of only one input, we can write the equations of an nth-order system in the form

$$\dot{x} = Ax + Bu \tag{4.11}$$

where **x** is an $n \times 1$ column vector
   A is an $n \times n$ matrix
   u is an $r \times 1$ column vector
   B is an $n \times r$ matrix

and the superscript dot represents differentiation with respect to time t.

The state variables themselves may in some cases be considered to be the system outputs. In other cases, we may not be able to observe the state variables directly, but may be able to observe instead a set of outputs y_i ($i = 1, \ldots, p$), or a p-vector **y** defined by the equation

$$y = Cx + Du \tag{4.12}$$

where **C** is a $p \times n$ matrix, and **D** is a $p \times r$ matrix. The entries of the **A**, **B**, **C**, and **D** matrices are all constant for a time-invariant system. We shall assume throughout this chapter that all the entries of the **A**, **B**, **C**, and **D** matrices are real, and that they are constant unless otherwise stated.

4.2 SYSTEMS WITH TRANSFER-FUNCTION ZEROS

If the system transfer function has one or more zeros, the direct method of representing the state by one variable and its derivatives of various orders may fail to give a set of state equations in the form of Equation 4.11. For example, consider the system characterized by the differential equation

$$\frac{d^2y}{dt^2} + a_1 \frac{dy}{dt} + a_0 y = b_0 u + b_1 \frac{du}{dt} \tag{4.13}$$

An attempt to apply the foregoing method directly will result in terms involving the derivative of u, and terms of this kind should not appear in the normal form of the state equations because sudden changes in the control input u would then cause instantaneous jumps in the values of one or more state variables. In the normal form of the state Equations 4.11, state variables cannot change by finite amounts instantaneously unless the control input contains impulses. Two possible methods of dealing with this case will now be considered with reference to the simple example quoted (Equation 4.13).

Method 1. Define the state variables in the following way

$$x_1 \overset{\Delta}{=} y$$

$$x_2 \overset{\Delta}{=} \frac{dy}{dt} - b_1 u \tag{4.14}$$

The derivatives of the state variables can therefore be written in the form

$$\frac{dx_1}{dt} = x_2 + b_1 u$$

$$\frac{dx_2}{dt} = -a_0 x_1 - a_1(x_2 + b_1 u) + b_0 u \tag{4.15}$$

Equations 4.15 can be written in vector-matrix form as follows

$$\frac{d}{dt} \begin{bmatrix} x_1 \\ x_2 \end{bmatrix} = \begin{bmatrix} 0 & 1 \\ -a_0 & -a_1 \end{bmatrix} \begin{bmatrix} x_1 \\ x_2 \end{bmatrix} + \begin{bmatrix} b_1 \\ b_0 - a_1 b_1 \end{bmatrix} u \tag{4.16}$$

This form corresponds to Equation 4.11 and does not involve derivatives of the control input u.

Method 2. The block diagram of the system can be represented in the form shown in Fig. 4.2, in which the numerator and denominator of the transfer function are shown separately. Suppose we consider the variable $z(t)$ at the output of the left-hand portion of the system, and take z and its first

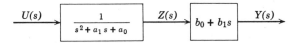

Fig. 4.2. Block-diagram representation of system.

derivative to be the state variables. In other words, let the state variables be defined by the equations

$$z_1 \triangleq z$$

$$z_2 \triangleq \frac{dz}{dt} \tag{4.17}$$

We can express the state differential equation in terms of these variables, as follows.

$$\frac{dz_1}{dt} = z_2$$

$$\frac{dz_2}{dt} = -a_0 z_1 - a_1 z_2 + u \tag{4.18}$$

The system may therefore be represented by the following two vector-matrix equations

$$\frac{d}{dt}\begin{bmatrix} z_1 \\ z_2 \end{bmatrix} = \begin{bmatrix} 0 & 1 \\ -a_0 & -a_1 \end{bmatrix}\begin{bmatrix} z_1 \\ z_2 \end{bmatrix} + \begin{bmatrix} 0 \\ 1 \end{bmatrix} u \tag{4.19}$$

$$y = [b_0 \quad b_1]\begin{bmatrix} z_1 \\ z_2 \end{bmatrix} \tag{4.20}$$

Equations 4.19 and 4.20 correspond to Equations 4.11 and 4.12, respectively, and do not involve derivatives of u.

The problems of transfer-function zeros are discussed in more detail by Fuller [7] and in the various books on state representation which are referred to at the end of this chapter.

4.3 EIGENVALUES AND EIGENVECTORS OF A MATRIX

We shall now proceed to study some of the theory of the state representation of systems, assuming for the present that the state variables x_i are directly observable as outputs. We shall use a second-order linear system extensively as an example, in order to be able to represent certain features of the theory by graphical constructions in the phase plane or state plane. It is hoped that the use of this simple representation will help the reader to understand the behavior of systems whose state spaces are of higher dimension, where it is not possible to use such simple graphical representations.

If the differential equations of a linear system are written in a vector-matrix form as in Equation 4.11, the response of the system may be represented in terms of the *eigenvalues* and *eigenvectors* of the **A** matrix. In order to proceed to this method of representation, we shall now make a very brief study of eigenvalues and eigenvectors.

Let us consider the matrix equation

$$\mathbf{y} = \mathbf{A}\mathbf{x} \tag{4.21}$$

which represents, in the two-dimensional case, a relationship of the form

$$\begin{bmatrix} y_1 \\ y_2 \end{bmatrix} = \begin{bmatrix} a_{11} & a_{12} \\ a_{21} & a_{22} \end{bmatrix} \begin{bmatrix} x_1 \\ x_2 \end{bmatrix} \tag{4.22}$$

The matrix **A** operates on a vector **x** to give a new vector **y**, which is in general different in magnitude and direction from **x**. For example, consider the vector $\mathbf{x}^1$ whose components are 1 and 0. In this case the transformed vector $\mathbf{y}^1$ is given by

$$\mathbf{y}^1 = \begin{bmatrix} a_{11} & a_{12} \\ a_{21} & a_{22} \end{bmatrix} \begin{bmatrix} 1 \\ 0 \end{bmatrix} = \begin{bmatrix} a_{11} \\ a_{21} \end{bmatrix} \tag{4.23}$$

Similarly, the vector $\mathbf{x}^2$ whose components are 0 and 1 is transformed into

$$\mathbf{y}^2 = \begin{bmatrix} a_{11} & a_{12} \\ a_{21} & a_{22} \end{bmatrix} \begin{bmatrix} 0 \\ 1 \end{bmatrix} = \begin{bmatrix} a_{12} \\ a_{22} \end{bmatrix} \tag{4.24}$$

We can represent the matrix transformation **A** by the vectors $\mathbf{y}^1$ and $\mathbf{y}^2$ into which the two unit vectors (1, 0) and (0, 1) are transformed. As any general vector **x** can be represented as a linear combination of $\mathbf{x}^1$ and $\mathbf{x}^2$, of the form

$$\mathbf{x} = a\mathbf{x}^1 + b\mathbf{x}^2 \tag{4.25}$$

(where a and b are scalars), the transform of **x**, or the vector **y** in Equation 4.21, can be expressed as

$$\mathbf{y} = a\mathbf{y}^1 + b\mathbf{y}^2 \tag{4.26}$$

Let us suppose that, in this particular case, the two vectors $\mathbf{y}^1$ and $\mathbf{y}^2$ are as shown in Fig. 4.3*b*, such that $\mathbf{y}^1$ is obtained from $\mathbf{x}^1$ by a rotation in the counterclockwise direction, and $\mathbf{y}^2$ from $\mathbf{x}^2$ by a rotation in the clockwise direction (with changes in magnitude in both cases, in general). Because the matrix transformation is linear, it is obvious that there is some vector **x**, in the first quadrant of the $x_1 x_2$ plane, such that the transform of **x**, given by Equation 4.21, is in the same direction in the $y_1 y_2$ plane as the **x** vector itself is in the $x_1 x_2$ plane. Such a vector is called an *eigenvector* of the matrix **A**.

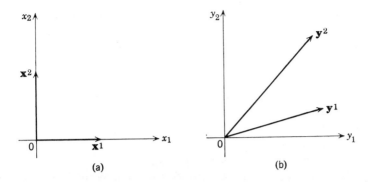

Fig. 4.3. (*a*) The vectors $\mathbf{x}^1$ and $\mathbf{x}^2$ in the x_1x_2 plane. (*b*) The vectors $\mathbf{y}^1$ and $\mathbf{y}^2$ in the y_1y_2 plane.

To express this relationship algebraically, a vector $\boldsymbol{\theta}$ is an eigenvector of the matrix $\mathbf{A}$ if

$$\mathbf{A}\boldsymbol{\theta} = \lambda\boldsymbol{\theta} \qquad (4.27)$$

where λ is a scalar constant, known as the *eigenvalue*[2] corresponding to the eigenvector $\boldsymbol{\theta}$. In general, the eigenvalue λ may be real or complex. If λ is complex, we cannot interpret the transformation in the simple geometrical terms of Fig. 4.3, but the algebraic relationship (Equation 4.27) is equally valid.

To find the eigenvalues and eigenvectors of a matrix

If we are given a matrix $\mathbf{A}$, the eigenvalues and eigenvectors of the matrix can be found as follows. Equation 4.27 is first written in the form

$$(\mathbf{A} - \lambda\mathbf{I})\boldsymbol{\theta} = \mathbf{0} \qquad (4.28)$$

where $\mathbf{I}$ is the unit matrix. For a nontrivial solution of Equation 4.28, that is, a solution other than $\boldsymbol{\theta} = \mathbf{0}$, we must have

$$\text{determinant}(\mathbf{A} - \lambda\mathbf{I}) = 0 \qquad (4.29)$$

This gives an equation which can be solved for λ. Let us find, for example, the eigenvalues of the 2×2 matrix which occurs in Equation 4.6. If this matrix is denoted by $\mathbf{A}$, the matrix $\mathbf{A} - \lambda\mathbf{I}$ may be written as

$$\begin{bmatrix} -\lambda & 1 \\ -\omega_n{}^2 & -2\zeta\omega_n - \lambda \end{bmatrix} \qquad (4.30)$$

---

[2] Various other names are used to denote this quantity. Some of these are: latent root, proper value, characteristic value, characteristic number, and characteristic root.

Setting the determinant of this matrix to zero, as in Equation 4.29, gives the *characteristic equation* of the matrix

$$\lambda^2 + 2\zeta\omega_n\lambda + \omega_n{}^2 = 0 \qquad (4.31)$$

If we compare Equation 4.31 with the differential equation of the system (Equation 4.3), we see that Equation 4.31 is the same as the characteristic equation of the system. Therefore, the eigenvalues are merely the roots of the characteristic equation of the system, which are the quantities that govern the transient response of the system; the eigenvalues are also the same as the poles of the system transfer function (Equation 4.2).

In the present example the eigenvalues are found by solving Equation 4.31 and may be written as

$$
\begin{aligned}
\lambda_1 &= -\zeta\omega_n + \omega_n\sqrt{\zeta^2 - 1} \\
\lambda_2 &= -\zeta\omega_n - \omega_n\sqrt{\zeta^2 - 1}
\end{aligned}
\qquad (4.32)
$$

In general, an $n \times n$ matrix has n eigenvalues. These may be real or complex, and they may all be distinct or have some values repeated. For a matrix whose entries are all real, which will always be the case if the matrix is obtained from a linear differential equation with real coefficients, the complex eigenvalues occur only in conjugate pairs. If the n eigenvalues are all distinct,[3] there are n distinct eigenvectors, each one corresponding to its own particular eigenvalue. The method of finding the eigenvectors will now be described.

Having found the eigenvalues, assumed to be distinct, the eigenvectors can be found by solving Equations 4.28 for each value of λ in turn. For example, consider the 2×2 matrix of Equation 4.6, for which the matrix $\mathbf{A} - \lambda\mathbf{I}$ is given by Equation 4.30. Using one value of λ, the matrix Equation 4.28 may be written as

$$-\lambda_1 x_1 + x_2 = 0 \qquad (4.33)$$

$$-\omega_n{}^2 x_1 - (2\zeta\omega_n + \lambda_1)x_2 = 0 \qquad (4.34)$$

where x_1 and x_2 are the components of the eigenvector corresponding to λ_1. Since λ_1 and λ_2 are as shown in Equation 4.32, Equation 4.34 may be written as

$$-\omega_n{}^2 x_1 + \lambda_2 x_2 = 0 \qquad (4.35)$$

Since λ_1 and λ_2 are the roots of Equation 4.31 we can say that

$$\lambda_1\lambda_2 = \omega_n{}^2 \qquad (4.36)$$

---

[3] For simplicity, we shall assume throughout this chapter that all eigenvalues are distinct.

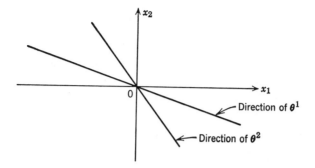

Fig. 4.4. Directions of the eigenvectors θ^1 and θ^2.

Substituting Equation 4.36 in Equation 4.35, we obtain

$$-\lambda_1 x_1 + x_2 = 0 \tag{4.37}$$

Equation 4.37 is the same as Equation 4.33, which shows that Equations 4.33 and 4.34 are not independent. However, there is really only one unknown here, the ratio of x_1 and x_2. In geometrical terms, it is the *direction* of the eigenvector which we wish to find; its *length* is not important. In general, if we have an $n \times n$ matrix with distinct eigenvalues, Equation 4.28 gives $n - 1$ independent equations for the n components of the eigenvector. This means that we can set any one component arbitrarily and then find all the others in terms of it. Let us suppose that in this case we take the x_1 component to be unity; we can then write the eigenvector corresponding to eigenvalue λ_1 as[4]

$$\theta^1 = \begin{bmatrix} 1 \\ \lambda_1 \end{bmatrix} = \begin{bmatrix} 1 \\ -\zeta\omega_n + \omega_n\sqrt{\zeta^2 - 1} \end{bmatrix} \tag{4.38}$$

Similarly we can write eigenvector θ^2, again taking the x_1 component to be unity, as

$$\theta^2 = \begin{bmatrix} 1 \\ \lambda_2 \end{bmatrix} = \begin{bmatrix} 1 \\ -\zeta\omega_n - \omega_n\sqrt{\zeta^2 - 1} \end{bmatrix} \tag{4.39}$$

If the eigenvalues are real, the eigenvectors have only real entries. If some eigenvalues are complex, some of the entries in the associated eigenvectors are also complex. For the 2×2 matrix we have considered, assuming that both ζ and ω_n are positive, the two eigenvectors corresponding to two real and distinct eigenvalues might be located as shown in Fig. 4.4.

---

[4] It should be noted that the form $(1, \lambda_1)$ is not a general result, but is true only for a matrix of the particular form used in this example.

4.4 RESPONSE OF A SYSTEM IN TERMS OF EIGENVALUES AND EIGENVECTORS

Let us now see how the eigenvalues and eigenvectors are related to the response of the linear system. Consider first the system with zero input, whose behavior is governed by the differential equation

$$\dot{\mathbf{x}} = \mathbf{A}\mathbf{x} \qquad (4.40)$$

Suppose that, at $t = 0$, the vector $\mathbf{x}$ happens to be a multiple of a certain eigenvector of the system matrix, which we shall call $\boldsymbol{\theta}$. That is, suppose

$$\mathbf{x}(0) = c\boldsymbol{\theta} \qquad (4.41)$$

where c is a scalar constant. It is easy to see that, at that instant, the time derivative of $\mathbf{x}$ is given by

$$\dot{\mathbf{x}}(0) = c\lambda\boldsymbol{\theta} = \lambda\mathbf{x}(0) \qquad (4.42)$$

where λ is the eigenvalue corresponding to the eigenvector $\boldsymbol{\theta}$. We shall assume that the solution of Equation 4.40, for the initial state given by Equation 4.41, is given by

$$\mathbf{x}(t) = \mathbf{x}(0)e^{\lambda t} \qquad (4.43)$$

The time derivative of expression 4.43 is

$$\dot{\mathbf{x}}(t) = \lambda\mathbf{x}(0)e^{\lambda t} \qquad (4.44)$$

Substituting Equations 4.43 and 4.44 in Equation 4.40, we obtain

$$\lambda\mathbf{x}(0)e^{\lambda t} = \mathbf{A}\mathbf{x}(0)e^{\lambda t} \qquad (4.45)$$

This equation is satisfied, provided that $\mathbf{x}(0)$ is as given by Equation 4.41. This verifies that Equation 4.43 is the correct response.

In geometrical terms, referring to Fig. 4.4, this means that, if the initial system state is represented by a point in state space anywhere along the direction of either one of the eigenvectors, and if the input is zero, the representative point (the point which represents the state of the system at any instant) moves towards the origin in a straight line along that eigenvector.

If the initial state is not one of the eigenvectors, it can be represented as a linear combination of the two eigenvectors if these are distinct. For example, consider the point P in Fig. 4.5. The coordinates of this point may be expressed in terms of the x_1 and x_2 coordinates, or the vector $\mathbf{x}^P$ may be expressed as

$$\mathbf{x}^P = c_1\boldsymbol{\theta}^1 + c_2\boldsymbol{\theta}^2 \qquad (4.46)$$

If we start at $t = 0$ with the initial state $\mathbf{x}^P$, with zero input, the response will be

$$\mathbf{x}(t) = c_1\boldsymbol{\theta}^1 e^{\lambda_1 t} + c_2\boldsymbol{\theta}^2 e^{\lambda_2 t} \qquad (4.47)$$

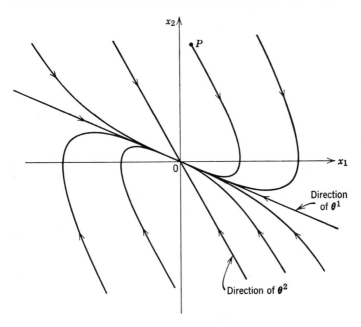

Fig. 4.5. Response of second-order system in terms of its eigenvectors.

As $|\lambda_2| > |\lambda_1|$ by Equation 4.32, the component in the direction of θ^2 will decay more quickly than that in the direction of θ^1. Hence, as time goes on, the representative point approaches the origin along a curve which approaches the θ^1 direction as shown in Fig. 4.5. Similarly, as we go backwards in time we move away from the origin and approach more closely the direction of θ^2. This explains the shapes of the various trajectories shown in Fig. 4.5, where the arrows on trajectories indicate the direction of motion of the representative point as the time t increases.

Let us now examine the natural response of the nth-order system in similar terms. Suppose that the eigenvalues of the **A** matrix of Equation 4.10 are all distinct, so that we can represent an arbitrary initial state by the expression

$$\mathbf{x}(0) = c_1\theta^1 + c_2\theta^2 + \cdots + c_n\theta^n \tag{4.48}$$

where the eigenvectors θ^i are assumed to have definitely specified lengths. The zero-input response of the system may therefore be written as

$$\mathbf{x}(t) = c_1\theta^1 e^{\lambda_1 t} + \cdots + c_n\theta^n e^{\lambda_n t} \tag{4.49}$$

If some of the eigenvalues occur in conjugate complex pairs, the values of the associated c_i and the entries of the associated eigenvectors have appropriate complex values, so as to make the entries of $\mathbf{x}(t)$ real at every instant of time. Equation 4.49 may be written as

$$\mathbf{x}(t) = [\boldsymbol{\theta}^1\, \boldsymbol{\theta}^2\, \cdots\, \boldsymbol{\theta}^n]\begin{bmatrix} c_1 e^{\lambda_1 t} \\ c_2 e^{\lambda_2 t} \\ \vdots \\ c_n e^{\lambda_n t} \end{bmatrix} \tag{4.50}$$

If each eigenvector is written in full, Equation 4.50 becomes

$$\mathbf{x}(t) = \begin{bmatrix} \theta_1{}^1 & \theta_1{}^2 & \cdots & \theta_1{}^n \\ \theta_2{}^1 & \theta_2{}^2 & \cdots & \theta_2{}^n \\ \vdots & \vdots & & \vdots \\ \theta_n{}^1 & \theta_n{}^2 & \cdots & \theta_n{}^n \end{bmatrix}\begin{bmatrix} c_1 e^{\lambda_1 t} \\ c_2 e^{\lambda_2 t} \\ \vdots \\ c_n e^{\lambda_n t} \end{bmatrix} \tag{4.51}$$

where each column represents an eigenvector, and $\theta_i{}^j$ is the ith component of the jth eigenvector. Here we see that the system state can be completely specified at any time t by the set of n numbers $c_i e^{\lambda_i t}$ instead of by the set of n numbers $x_i(t)$. These coordinates, or the coefficients of the separate eigenvectors, are known as *normal coordinates*, and we shall now discuss them in more detail.

Consider the matrix shown in Equation 4.51, which we shall denote by the symbol $\boldsymbol{\Theta}$. Because the columns $\boldsymbol{\Theta}$ are the several eigenvectors, the matrix $\mathbf{A}\boldsymbol{\Theta}$ is the same as $\boldsymbol{\Theta}$ but with all the entries in the ith column multiplied by λ_i, as shown in the equation

$$\mathbf{A}\boldsymbol{\Theta} = \begin{bmatrix} \lambda_1 \theta_1{}^1 & \lambda_2 \theta_1{}^2 & \cdots & \lambda_n \theta_1{}^n \\ \lambda_1 \theta_2{}^1 & \lambda_2 \theta_2{}^2 & \cdots & \lambda_n \theta_2{}^n \\ \vdots & \vdots & & \vdots \\ \lambda_1 \theta_n{}^1 & \lambda_2 \theta_n{}^2 & \cdots & \lambda_n \theta_n{}^n \end{bmatrix} \tag{4.52}$$

Now let us consider a new matrix $\boldsymbol{\Lambda}$, which is a diagonal matrix of the eigenvalues, as defined by the equation

$$\boldsymbol{\Lambda} \triangleq \begin{bmatrix} \lambda_1 & 0 & 0 & \cdots & 0 \\ 0 & \lambda_2 & 0 & \cdots & 0 \\ \cdot & \cdot & \cdot & \cdot & \cdot \\ \vdots & & & \ddots & 0 \\ 0 & & \cdots & 0 & \lambda_n \end{bmatrix} \tag{4.53}$$

We can now say that

$$\mathbf{A}\boldsymbol{\Theta} = \boldsymbol{\Theta}\boldsymbol{\Lambda} \tag{4.54}$$

As we have assumed that the eigenvalues λ_i are all distinct, it turns out that the eigenvectors $\boldsymbol{\theta}^i$ are linearly independent and the matrix $\boldsymbol{\Theta}$ is nonsingular [2]. If we premultiply both sides of Equation 4.54 by $\boldsymbol{\Theta}^{-1}$, we obtain

$$\boldsymbol{\Theta}^{-1}\mathbf{A}\boldsymbol{\Theta} = \boldsymbol{\Lambda} \tag{4.55}$$

We shall now consider the coordinate transformation required to express the system state in terms of the normal coordinates. Suppose we have a coordinate transformation represented by

$$\mathbf{x} = \boldsymbol{\Theta}\mathbf{g} \tag{4.56}$$

where $\mathbf{g}$ is in an $n \times 1$ column vector. We shall assume the system to be specified by a vector-matrix differential equation of the form

$$\dot{\mathbf{x}} = \mathbf{A}\mathbf{x} + \mathbf{B}\mathbf{u} \tag{4.57}$$

Substituting Equation 4.56 in Equation 4.57 we obtain

$$\boldsymbol{\Theta}\dot{\mathbf{g}} = \mathbf{A}\boldsymbol{\Theta}\mathbf{g} + \mathbf{B}\mathbf{u} \tag{4.58}$$

Premultiplying both sides of Equation 4.58 by $\boldsymbol{\Theta}^{-1}$ we obtain

$$\dot{\mathbf{g}} = \boldsymbol{\Lambda}\mathbf{g} + \boldsymbol{\Theta}^{-1}\mathbf{B}\mathbf{u} \tag{4.59}$$

which may be written as

$$\begin{aligned}
\dot{g}_1 &= \lambda_1 g_1 + \beta_1 \\
\vdots \quad & \quad \vdots \quad \vdots \\
\dot{g}_n &= \lambda_n g_n + \beta_n
\end{aligned} \tag{4.60}$$

where the β_i are the components of $\boldsymbol{\Theta}^{-1}\mathbf{B}\mathbf{u}$. The quantities g_i are equivalent to the quantities $c_i e^{\lambda_i t}$ of Equation 4.49.

For example, let us consider the second-order system with distinct eigenvalues, with the eigenvectors given by Equations 4.38 and 4.39. The matrix $\boldsymbol{\Theta}$ may be written as

$$\boldsymbol{\Theta} = \begin{bmatrix} 1 & 1 \\ \lambda_1 & \lambda_2 \end{bmatrix} \tag{4.61}$$

and its inverse turns out to be

$$\boldsymbol{\Theta}^{-1} = \frac{1}{\lambda_1 - \lambda_2} \begin{bmatrix} -\lambda_2 & 1 \\ \lambda_1 & -1 \end{bmatrix} \tag{4.62}$$

Hence we obtain as the normal coordinates

$$\begin{aligned}
g_1 &= \frac{1}{\lambda_1 - \lambda_2}(-\lambda_2 x_1 + x_2) \\
\\
g_2 &= \frac{1}{\lambda_1 - \lambda_2}(\lambda_1 x_1 - x_2)
\end{aligned} \tag{4.63}$$

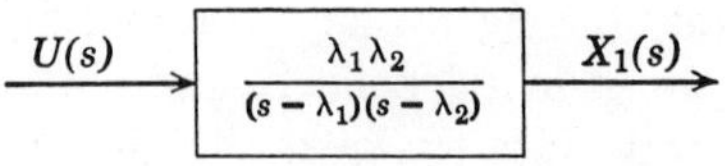

$$\frac{\lambda_1 \lambda_2}{(s - \lambda_1)(s - \lambda_2)}$$

U(s) $X_1(s)$

Fig. 4.6. Representation of the original transfer function in terms of λ_1 and λ_2.

In this case Equation 4.59 turns out to be

$$\dot{g}_1 = \lambda_1 g_1 + \frac{\lambda_1 \lambda_2}{\lambda_1 - \lambda_2} u$$

$$\dot{g}_2 = \lambda_2 g_2 - \frac{\lambda_1 \lambda_2}{\lambda_1 - \lambda_2} u$$

$$(4.64)$$

An interpretation of this may be found by imagining the transfer function of the system to be resolved into partial fractions. The original transfer function may be shown in block-diagram form as in Fig. 4.6. We can represent this transfer function as the sum of two first-order terms as follows:

$$\frac{\lambda_1 \lambda_2}{(s - \lambda_1)(s - \lambda_2)} = \frac{\lambda_1 \lambda_2 / (\lambda_1 - \lambda_2)}{(s - \lambda_1)} + \frac{\lambda_1 \lambda_2 / (\lambda_2 - \lambda_1)}{(s - \lambda_2)} \qquad (4.65)$$

and the transfer function can be represented as shown in Fig. 4.7. The outputs of the separate parallel branches of the system are g_1 and g_2 as shown. The values of x_1 and x_2 can be found by appropriate linear combinations of g_1 and g_2, as given by Equation 4.56 which becomes in this case

$$x_1 = g_1 + g_2$$
$$x_2 = \lambda_1 g_1 + \lambda_2 g_2$$

$$(4.66)$$

The relationships represented by Equations 4.66 are indicated in block-diagram form in Fig. 4.7.

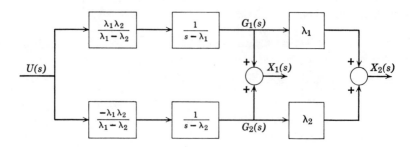

Fig. 4.7. Alternative representation of system transfer function.

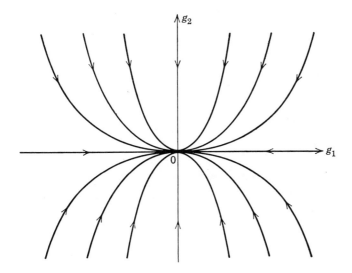

Fig. 4.8. Trajectories in the $g_1 g_2$ phase plane.

The coordinates g_1 and g_2 are independent or noninteracting, in the sense that changes in the initial value of g_1 do not affect the behavior of g_2, and vice versa. The $g_1 g_2$ plane, with a sample set of trajectories, is shown in Fig. 4.8. We see that the coordinate transformation merely causes the eigenvectors to be used as the coordinate axes of a Euclidean space. The quantities g_1 and g_2 may be called the normal coordinates of the system, or the system may be considered to be represented in terms of its normal modes of behavior. The matrix Θ may be called the modal matrix.

4.5   RESPONSE OF A SYSTEM IN TERMS OF FUNCTIONS OF A MATRIX

Suppose the system input is zero, so that the equations of the system may be written in the form

$$\dot{\mathbf{x}} = \mathbf{A}\mathbf{x} \tag{4.67}$$

Consider the matrix function $e^{\mathbf{A}t}$, defined as

$$e^{\mathbf{A}t} = \mathbf{I} + \frac{\mathbf{A}t}{1!} + \frac{\mathbf{A}^2 t^2}{2!} + \cdots \tag{4.68}$$

Differentiating this matrix with respect to time t, we obtain

$$\frac{d}{dt}[e^{\mathbf{A}t}] = \mathbf{A} + \frac{\mathbf{A}^2 t}{1!} + \frac{\mathbf{A}^3 t^2}{2!} \cdots \qquad (4.69)$$

which can be written as

$$\frac{d}{dt}[e^{\mathbf{A}t}] = \mathbf{A}e^{\mathbf{A}t} \qquad (4.70)$$

Also, it is clear that

$$e^{\mathbf{A}\cdot 0} = \mathbf{I} \qquad (4.71)$$

We shall assume that the solution of Equation 4.67 is the following

$$\mathbf{x}(t) = e^{\mathbf{A}t}\mathbf{x}(0) \qquad (4.72)$$

Taking the derivative of both sides we obtain

$$\dot{\mathbf{x}}(t) = \mathbf{A}e^{\mathbf{A}t}\mathbf{x}(0) = \mathbf{A}\mathbf{x}(t) \qquad (4.73)$$

This shows that Equation 4.72 satisfies the original differential Equation 4.67. It also satisfies the initial conditions, and is therefore a complete solution of Equation 4.67.

We have seen that the transient response of the system can be expressed in terms of functions of the form $\exp(\lambda_i t)$, where the λ_i are the solutions of the characteristic equation of the system, or the characteristic equation of the matrix $\mathbf{A}$. The expression $e^{\mathbf{A}t}$ occurring in Equation 4.72 may lead us to suspect that the matrix $\mathbf{A}$ itself has some property in common with its eigenvalues. The property in question is demonstrated by the Cayley-Hamilton theorem, which may be briefly stated as "a matrix satisfies its own characteristic equation." A proof of this theorem, valid for the case where the eigenvalues are distinct and the eigenvectors are consequently linearly independent, is as follows:

Equation 4.29 may, for the nth-order case, be written as

$$a_0 + a_1\lambda + \cdots + a_{n-1}\lambda^{n-1} + \lambda^n = 0 \qquad (4.74)$$

where the roots of the characteristic equation are the n eigenvalues λ_i. Now, if $\boldsymbol{\theta}^i$ is an eigenvector of the matrix $\mathbf{A}$, corresponding to the eigenvalue λ_i, we can say that the expression

$$[a_0\mathbf{I} + a_1\mathbf{A} + \cdots + a_{n-1}\mathbf{A}^{n-1} + \mathbf{A}^n]\boldsymbol{\theta}^i \qquad (4.75)$$

can be written as

$$[a_0 + a_1\lambda_i + \cdots + a_{n-1}\lambda_i^{n-1} + \lambda_i^n]\boldsymbol{\theta}^i \qquad (4.76)$$

But, because λ_i is a root of Equation 4.74, expression 4.76 is equal to zero. This means that the matrix expression

$$[a_0\mathbf{I} + a_1\mathbf{A} + \cdots + a_{n-1}\mathbf{A}^{n-1} + \mathbf{A}^n] \tag{4.77}$$

operating on any eigenvector (and hence on any linear combination of the eigenvectors) gives zero. As the eigenvectors are all linearly independent, any arbitrary vector $\mathbf{x}$ can be expressed as a linear combination of the eigenvectors, which means that matrix expression 4.77, operating on an arbitrary vector $\mathbf{x}$, gives zero. This can only happen if expression 4.77 is zero, which means that the matrix $\mathbf{A}$ must satisfy its own characteristic equation.

The matrix exp $(\mathbf{A}t)$, which appears in Equation 4.72, is called the *transition matrix* of the system. It is the matrix which, operating on the state vector of the system at $t = 0$, gives the state of the system at time t, assuming the input during that interval to be zero. Since the parameters of the system are time-invariant, the matrix exp $(\mathbf{A}t)$ specifies the transition which the system state undergoes in *any* t-second period, with zero input.

The transition matrix is a special case of what is called a *fundamental matrix* of the differential equation. We shall now discuss these matrices briefly.

4.6 FUNDAMENTAL MATRICES

A fundamental matrix, corresponding to the vector-matrix differential Equation 4.67, is any $n \times n$ matrix whose n columns are n linearly independent solutions of the differential equation. If such a matrix is denoted by $\mathbf{\Phi}(t)$, it satisfies the matrix differential equation

$$\dot{\mathbf{\Phi}} = \mathbf{A}\mathbf{\Phi} \tag{4.78}$$

Because the n columns of $\mathbf{\Phi}(t)$ are linearly independent, *any* solution of the differential Equation 4.67 can be expressed as a linear combination of the columns of $\mathbf{\Phi}(t)$. For example, a vector solution $\mathbf{\phi}$ can be expressed in the form

$$\mathbf{\phi}(t) = \sum_{i=1}^{n} g_i \mathbf{\phi}^i(t) \tag{4.79}$$

where the g_i are constants, not all zero, and $\mathbf{\phi}^i$ is the ith column of $\mathbf{\Phi}$. Equation 4.79 can be expressed in the form

$$\mathbf{\phi}(t) = \mathbf{\Phi}(t)\mathbf{g} \tag{4.80}$$

where $\mathbf{g}$ is a column vector with components $g_1, \ldots, g_n$.

If Φ is a fundamental matrix, and $\mathbf{G}$ is any constant nonsingular matrix, then $\Phi\mathbf{G}$ is also a fundamental matrix. It is obvious, therefore, that the fundamental matrix Φ is not uniquely defined by the matrix $\mathbf{A}$. However, if we postmultiply both sides of Equation 4.78 by Φ^{-1}, we have

$$\dot{\Phi}\Phi^{-1} = \mathbf{A} \tag{4.81}$$

showing that $\mathbf{A}$ is uniquely defined by $\Phi(t)$.

Let us now consider the matrix $\exp(\mathbf{A}t)$. The first column of this matrix may be written as

$$e^{\mathbf{A}t}\begin{bmatrix}1\\0\\\vdots\\0\end{bmatrix} \tag{4.82}$$

That is, the first column is the response of the system following an initial state specified by $x_1 = 1$, $x_i = 0$ for $i \neq 1$. Similarly the second column is the response following the initial state $x_2 = 1$, $x_i = 0$ for $i \neq 2$. The n columns of $\exp(\mathbf{A}t)$ are solutions of the differential Equation 4.67, and it can be shown that $\exp(\mathbf{A}t)$ is nonsingular for all $\mathbf{A}$ [3]. Hence $\exp(\mathbf{A}t)$ is a fundamental matrix of the differential Equation 4.67. We see that $\exp(\mathbf{A}t)$ is the solution of the matrix differential Equation 4.78 with the initial condition

$$\Phi(0) = \mathbf{I} \tag{4.83}$$

4.7 METHODS OF EVALUATING THE TRANSITION MATRIX

Let us now consider some of the possible methods by which the transition matrix $\exp(\mathbf{A}t)$ of a linear time-invariant system may be evaluated.

1. *By taking an inverse Laplace transformation.* Consider the vector-matrix differential Equation 4.67 for the system with zero input. Taking the unilateral Laplace transform of both sides of Equation 4.67, we obtain

$$s\mathbf{X}(s) - \mathbf{x}(0+) = \mathbf{A}\mathbf{X}(s) \tag{4.84}$$

where $\mathbf{X}(s)$ is the vector Laplace transform of $\mathbf{x}(t)$. From Equation 4.84 we obtain

$$(s\mathbf{I} - \mathbf{A})\mathbf{X}(s) = \mathbf{x}(0+) \tag{4.85}$$

Equation 4.85 can be written in the form

$$\mathbf{X}(s) = (s\mathbf{I} - \mathbf{A})^{-1}\mathbf{x}(0+) \tag{4.86}$$

Equation 4.86 represents, in the frequency domain, Equation 4.72 in the time domain. Because $\mathbf{x}(0+)$ is a vector of constants, we can say that

$(s\mathbf{I} - \mathbf{A})^{-1}$ is the Laplace transform of the transition matrix $\exp(\mathbf{A}t)$. The transition matrix $\exp(\mathbf{A}t)$ can therefore be found by evaluating the following inverse Laplace transform.

$$e^{\mathbf{A}t} = \mathscr{L}^{-1}[(s\mathbf{I} - \mathbf{A})^{-1}] \tag{4.87}$$

This relationship can also be justified in a non-rigorous way by noting that the Laplace transform of $\exp(\mathbf{A}t)$ may be written in the form

$$\mathscr{L}[e^{\mathbf{A}t}] = \frac{\mathbf{I}}{s} + \frac{\mathbf{A}}{s^2} + \frac{\mathbf{A}^2}{s^3} + \cdots \tag{4.88}$$

If both sides of Equation 4.88 are multiplied by $(s\mathbf{I} - \mathbf{A})$ the unit matrix is obtained [4].

As an example of the method, let us consider the second-order system whose $\mathbf{A}$ matrix is of the form

$$\mathbf{A} = \begin{bmatrix} 0 & 1 \\ -2 & -3 \end{bmatrix} \tag{4.89}$$

This is merely a special case of the matrix of Equation 4.6, where we have inserted numerical values for simplicity. The matrix $(s\mathbf{I} - \mathbf{A})$ is therefore given by

$$(s\mathbf{I} - \mathbf{A}) = \begin{bmatrix} s & -1 \\ 2 & s+3 \end{bmatrix} \tag{4.90}$$

whose inverse is given by

$$(s\mathbf{I} - \mathbf{A})^{-1} = \begin{bmatrix} \dfrac{s+3}{s^2+3s+2} & \dfrac{1}{s^2+3s+2} \\[2ex] \dfrac{-2}{s^2+3s+2} & \dfrac{s}{s^2+3s+2} \end{bmatrix} \tag{4.91}$$

The inverse Laplace transformation of each entry in the above matrix can be evaluated by the partial-fraction method, and the inverse Laplace transformation of the entire matrix is

$$e^{\mathbf{A}t} = \begin{bmatrix} 2e^{-t} - e^{-2t} & e^{-t} - e^{-2t} \\ -2e^{-t} + 2e^{-2t} & -e^{-t} + 2e^{-2t} \end{bmatrix} \tag{4.92}$$

Having found the transition matrix, it is a good idea to check it by making sure that it satisfies the differential Equation 4.78 and the initial condition $\boldsymbol{\Phi}(0) = \mathbf{I}$. These checks can easily be performed by the reader.

This method can also be used to find the matrix $\exp(-\mathbf{A}t)$, if this should be desired. The matrix $\exp(-\mathbf{A}t)$ can be evaluated using the expression

$$e^{-\mathbf{A}t} = \mathscr{L}^{-1}[(s\mathbf{I} + \mathbf{A})^{-1}] \tag{4.93}$$

There is an obvious analogy with the Laplace transforms of the time functions $\exp(at)$ and $\exp(-at)$.

2. *By using the block diagram.* As will be described in more detail in Section 4.11, we can represent the linear system by a block diagram, using only simple integrators and coefficient multipliers, in such a way that the state variables are represented by the integrator outputs. Inspection of the block diagram allows us to find the transition matrix in a very simple way [21]. The basis of the method will now be described.

Suppose that, at $t = 0$, the initial value of any one state variable x_i is unity, and the values of all other state variables are zero. If the system input is zero, the state at a later time t is given by the equation

$$\mathbf{x}(t) = e^{\mathbf{A}t} \begin{bmatrix} 0 \\ 0 \\ \vdots \\ 0 \\ 1 \\ 0 \\ \vdots \\ 0 \end{bmatrix} \tag{4.94}$$

where the 1 appears in the ith position of the column vector. Now, if $\phi_{ij}(t)$ is the entry in the ith row and the jth column of $\exp(\mathbf{A}t)$, we see that Equation 4.94 may be written as

$$\mathbf{x}(t) = \begin{bmatrix} \phi_{1i}(t) \\ \phi_{2i}(t) \\ \vdots \\ \phi_{ji}(t) \\ \vdots \\ \phi_{ni}(t) \end{bmatrix} \tag{4.95}$$

The column vector to the right of Equation 4.95 is the ith column of the transition matrix $\exp(\mathbf{A}t)$. In other words, $\phi_{ji}(t)$ is the value of x_j at time t, due to the variable x_i having an initial value of unity at time $t = 0$.

Let us consider once again, as a simple example, the system with matrix $\mathbf{A}$ given by Equation 4.89. We can represent this system, with zero input, by the block diagram shown in Fig. 4.9 (where we have inserted an auxiliary input $\delta(t)$ merely to establish desired initial conditions, as will be explained below). If we set the initial value of x_1 equal to unity, and the initial value of x_2 equal to zero, at $t = 0$, we can find the first column of the transition matrix $\exp(\mathbf{A}t)$ by finding $x_1(t)$ and $x_2(t)$ thereafter. It is easy to see that,

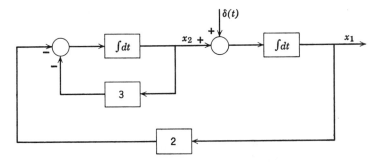

Fig. 4.9. Block-diagram representation of system.

if we apply an impulse input $\delta(t)$ as shown in Fig. 4.9, the initial conditions are set to the values desired, and the behavior of x_1 and x_2 thereafter can easily be found. By inspection of the block diagram Fig. 4.9, we see that $x_1(t)$, for $t > 0$, is given by

$$x_1(t) = \mathscr{L}^{-1}\left[\frac{\dfrac{1}{s}}{1 + \dfrac{2}{s(s + 3)}}\right] = \mathscr{L}^{-1}\left[\frac{s + 3}{s^2 + 3s + 2}\right] \qquad (4.96)$$

which we observe to be the same as the ϕ_{11} entry of $\exp{(\mathbf{A}t)}$ (see Equations 4.91 and 4.92). The value of $x_2(t)$ can be found using the equation

$$x_2(t) = \mathscr{L}^{-1}\left[\frac{-2}{s + 3}X_1(s)\right] = \mathscr{L}^{-1}\left[\frac{-2}{s^2 + 3s + 2}\right] \qquad (4.97)$$

which is the same as the ϕ_{21} entry found before. We can find the other two entries by considering a unit impulse to be applied to the input of the integrator whose output is x_2, instead of the one shown in Fig. 4.9.

3. *By using the* $\mathbf{\Lambda}$ *matrix.* Another method of finding the transition matrix is by using the $\mathbf{\Lambda}$ matrix which was defined in Equation 4.53. Using Equation 4.55 we obtain, after premultiplying both sides by $\mathbf{\Theta}$ and postmultiplying both sides by $\mathbf{\Theta}^{-1}$, the equation

$$\mathbf{A} = \mathbf{\Theta}\mathbf{\Lambda}\mathbf{\Theta}^{-1} \qquad (4.98)$$

From this we obtain, by squaring both sides, the equation

$$\mathbf{A}^2 = \mathbf{\Theta}\mathbf{\Lambda}\mathbf{\Theta}^{-1}\mathbf{\Theta}\mathbf{\Lambda}\mathbf{\Theta}^{-1} = \mathbf{\Theta}\mathbf{\Lambda}^2\mathbf{\Theta}^{-1} \qquad (4.99)$$

It is easy to see that this can be continued to give, for any positive integer m,

$$\mathbf{A}^m = \mathbf{\Theta}\mathbf{\Lambda}^m\mathbf{\Theta}^{-1} \qquad (4.100)$$

In view of Equation 4.100 it is easy to see that the transition matrix $\exp(\mathbf{A}t)$ can be expressed as

$$e^{\mathbf{A}t} = \mathbf{\Theta} e^{\mathbf{\Lambda}t} \mathbf{\Theta}^{-1} \tag{4.101}$$

The advantage of this representation is that the matrix $e^{\mathbf{\Lambda}t}$ is very easy to obtain because $\mathbf{\Lambda}$ is a diagonal matrix. The matrix $\mathbf{\Lambda}^m$ can easily be shown to be as given by the expression

$$\mathbf{\Lambda}^m = \begin{bmatrix} \lambda_1{}^m & 0 & 0 & 0 & \cdots & 0 \\ 0 & \lambda_2{}^m & 0 & 0 & \cdots & 0 \\ \cdot & & \cdot & \cdot & \cdot & \cdot \\ \vdots & & & & \ddots & 0 \\ 0 & & & \cdots & 0 & \lambda_n{}^m \end{bmatrix} \tag{4.102}$$

The matrix $\mathbf{\Lambda}^m t^m$ is obtained from Equation 4.102 by multiplying each entry by t^m, and it follows that the matrix $\exp(\mathbf{\Lambda}t)$ is given by

$$e^{\mathbf{\Lambda}t} = \begin{bmatrix} e^{\lambda_1 t} & 0 & & \cdots & 0 \\ 0 & e^{\lambda_2 t} & 0 & \cdots & 0 \\ \cdot & & \cdot & \cdot & \cdot \\ \vdots & & & \ddots & 0 \\ 0 & & \cdot & 0 & e^{\lambda_n t} \end{bmatrix} \tag{4.103}$$

Substituting Equation 4.103 in Equation 4.101 gives the final expression for the transition matrix.

As an illustration of this method, consider once again the matrix $\mathbf{A}$ as given in Equation 4.89, whose eigenvalues turn out to be -1 and -2. The matrix $\mathbf{\Theta}$ may be written, by taking $\lambda_1 = -1$ and $\lambda_2 = -2$ in Equation 4.61, as

$$\mathbf{\Theta} = \begin{bmatrix} 1 & 1 \\ -1 & -2 \end{bmatrix} \tag{4.104}$$

from which the inverse may be written down directly from Equation 4.62 as

$$\mathbf{\Theta}^{-1} = \begin{bmatrix} 2 & 1 \\ -1 & -1 \end{bmatrix} \tag{4.105}$$

The matrix $\exp(\mathbf{\Lambda}t)$ may be written as

$$e^{\mathbf{\Lambda}t} = \begin{bmatrix} e^{-t} & 0 \\ 0 & e^{-2t} \end{bmatrix} \tag{4.106}$$

Substituting the above three expressions in Equation 4.101 we obtain:

$$e^{\mathbf{A}t} = \begin{bmatrix} 1 & 1 \\ -1 & -2 \end{bmatrix} \begin{bmatrix} e^{-t} & 0 \\ 0 & e^{-2t} \end{bmatrix} \begin{bmatrix} 2 & 1 \\ -1 & -1 \end{bmatrix} \tag{4.107}$$

When the right side of Equation 4.107 is multiplied out, we obtain the same expression as that obtained in method 1, namely, the expression given by Equation 4.92.

4. *By using the Cayley-Hamilton theorem* [18]. This method can perhaps be most easily explained by dealing directly with the numerical example. The characteristic equation of the matrix $\mathbf{A}$ in Equation 4.89 may be written as

$$\lambda^2 + 3\lambda + 2 = 0 \tag{4.108}$$

In view of the Cayley-Hamilton theorem, we can therefore express $\mathbf{A}^2$ in terms of $\mathbf{A}$ by the expression

$$\mathbf{A}^2 = -3\mathbf{A} - 2\mathbf{I} \tag{4.109}$$

We can then express $\mathbf{A}^3$ in terms of $\mathbf{A}$ by the expression

$$\mathbf{A}^3 = -3\mathbf{A}^2 - 2\mathbf{A} = -3(-3\mathbf{A} - 2\mathbf{I}) - 2\mathbf{A} \tag{4.110}$$

Hence any positive integral power of $\mathbf{A}$ can be expressed in the form

$$\mathbf{A}^m = a_m\mathbf{A} + b_m\mathbf{I} \quad (m = 0, 1, 2, \ldots) \tag{4.111}$$

where a_m and b_m are integers in this particular case. Now, since $\exp(\mathbf{A}t)$ is a summation of terms of the form $\mathbf{A}^m t^m/m!$, we see that $\exp(\mathbf{A}t)$ can be expressed in the form

$$e^{\mathbf{A}t} = \sum_{m=0}^{\infty} \frac{\mathbf{A}^m t^m}{m!} = \sum_{m=0}^{\infty} \frac{(a_m t^m \mathbf{A} + b_m t^m \mathbf{I})}{m!} \tag{4.112}$$

This expression can be written in the form

$$e^{\mathbf{A}t} = f_0(t)\mathbf{I} + f_1(t)\mathbf{A} \tag{4.113}$$

Now, in view of the fact that the eigenvalues λ_1 and λ_2 also satisfy the characteristic equation, all the steps from Equation 4.109 to Equation 4.113 are equally valid if we substitute either λ_1 or λ_2 for $\mathbf{A}$. Taking $\lambda_1 = -1$ and $\lambda_2 = -2$ as before, we can therefore say, in view of Equation 4.113, that

$$e^{-t} = f_0(t) + f_1(t)(-1) \tag{4.114}$$

and

$$e^{-2t} = f_0(t) + f_1(t)(-2) \tag{4.115}$$

Equations 4.114 and 4.115 can be solved for $f_0(t)$ and $f_1(t)$. Subtracting Equation 4.115 from Equation 4.114, we obtain

$$f_1(t) = e^{-t} - e^{-2t} \tag{4.116}$$

Substituting Equation 4.116 in Equation 4.114, we obtain

$$f_0(t) = 2e^{-t} - e^{-2t} \tag{4.117}$$

Therefore, substituting in Equation 4.113, we obtain

$$\mathbf{e}^{\mathbf{A}t} = (2e^{-t} - e^{-2t})\begin{bmatrix} 1 & 0 \\ 0 & 1 \end{bmatrix} + (e^{-t} - e^{-2t})\begin{bmatrix} 0 & 1 \\ -2 & -3 \end{bmatrix} \quad (4.118)$$

This gives the same result as that already obtained in Equation 4.92.

If we had had an nth-order system instead of second-order, it would mean that Equation 4.111 would have to be expressed in the form

$$\mathbf{A}^m = a_{m_0}\mathbf{I} + a_{m_1}\mathbf{A} + \cdots + a_{m_{n-1}}\mathbf{A}^{n-1} \quad (4.119)$$

Equation 4.113 would then have to be expressed in the form

$$\mathbf{e}^{\mathbf{A}t} = f_0(t)\mathbf{I} + f_1(t)\mathbf{A} + \cdots + f_{n-1}(t)\mathbf{A}^{n-1} \quad (4.120)$$

which can be written in the form of the summation

$$\mathbf{e}^{\mathbf{A}t} = \sum_{i=0}^{n-1} f_i(t)\mathbf{A}^i \quad (4.121)$$

If we are interested in finding the matrix $\exp(-\mathbf{A}t)$ instead of $\exp(\mathbf{A}t)$, it is easy to show by making the appropriate changes of sign throughout this section that this matrix is given by

$$\mathbf{e}^{-\mathbf{A}t} = \sum_{i=0}^{n-1} f_i(-t)\mathbf{A}^i \quad (4.122)$$

In certain simple cases the Cayley-Hamilton theorem provides a particularly simple result. Consider, for example, the matrix $\mathbf{A}$ given by

$$\mathbf{A} = \begin{bmatrix} 0 & 1 \\ 0 & 0 \end{bmatrix} \quad (4.123)$$

The characteristic equation is

$$\lambda^2 = 0 \quad (4.124)$$

Equation 4.124 shows that

$$\mathbf{A}^2 = \mathbf{0} \quad (4.125)$$

(a result which can be very easily verified). This means that the entire summation of $\exp(\mathbf{A}t)$ consists of only two terms, namely,

$$\mathbf{e}^{\mathbf{A}t} = \mathbf{I} + \mathbf{A}t = \begin{bmatrix} 1 & t \\ 0 & 1 \end{bmatrix} \quad (4.126)$$

5. *By numerical computation.* The transition matrix may be computed numerically, either by direct summation of the series for $\exp(\mathbf{A}t)$, or by a numerical solution of the set of differential equations of the system. The

summation of the series may not be straightforward, because in view of Equation 4.100 the magnitudes of the high-order terms in the series depend on the magnitudes of the eigenvalues, and unless t is small it may be necessary to take many terms in the series to ensure sufficient numerical accuracy. However, with suitable numerical procedures, numerical computation using a digital computer may often be the easiest method of finding the transition matrix of a high-order system.

4.8   RESPONSE OF A LINEAR SYSTEM WITH NONZERO INPUT

Let us consider the solution of the vector-matrix differential equation

$$\dot{\mathbf{x}} = \mathbf{A}\mathbf{x} + \mathbf{B}\mathbf{u} \tag{4.127}$$

Suppose the complete solution is of the form

$$\mathbf{x}(t) = e^{\mathbf{A}t}\mathbf{x}(0) + \int_0^t e^{\mathbf{A}(t-\tau)}\mathbf{B}\mathbf{u}(\tau)\,d\tau \tag{4.128}$$

In order to check whether Equation 4.128 is a solution, let us first consider the differentiation of a definite integral. It can be shown [5] that the derivative of a definite integral can be found as follows: If

$$y(t) = \int_{a(t)}^{b(t)} F(t, \tau)\,d\tau \tag{4.129}$$

then

$$\frac{dy(t)}{dt} = \int_a^b \frac{\partial F(t, \tau)}{\partial t}\,d\tau + F(t, b)\frac{db}{dt} - F(t, a)\frac{da}{dt} \tag{4.130}$$

Using these results we can find the derivatives of both sides of Equation 4.128 as follows:

$$\dot{\mathbf{x}}(t) = \mathbf{A}e^{\mathbf{A}t}\mathbf{x}(0) + \int_0^t \mathbf{A}e^{\mathbf{A}(t-\tau)}\mathbf{B}\mathbf{u}(\tau)\,d\tau + e^{\mathbf{A}\cdot0}\mathbf{B}\mathbf{u}(t) \tag{4.131}$$

Equation 4.131 can be written in the form

$$\dot{\mathbf{x}}(t) = \mathbf{A}\left[e^{\mathbf{A}t}\mathbf{x}(0) + \int_0^t e^{\mathbf{A}(t-\tau)}\mathbf{B}\mathbf{u}(\tau)\,d\tau\right] + \mathbf{B}\mathbf{u}(t) \tag{4.132}$$

The expression in brackets in Equation 4.132 is the same as the right side of Equation 4.128. Hence we see that Equation 4.132 can be written as

$$\dot{\mathbf{x}}(t) = \mathbf{A}\mathbf{x}(t) + \mathbf{B}\mathbf{u}(t) \tag{4.133}$$

which shows that expression 4.128 is a solution of the differential Equation 4.127. It also satisfies the initial conditions at $t = 0$, and is therefore the complete solution.

If the system is initially in the zero or null state $x(0) = 0$, the response is given by the second term of Equation 4.128 alone. This is a generalization of the convolution integral. The matrix $\exp(At)$ may be considered to be the impulse response of the system, in the sense that, if the ith component of the input vector $\mathbf{B}\mathbf{u}(t)$ were a unit impulse $\delta(t)$, the system output vector would be given by

$$\mathbf{x}(t) = [e^{At}] \begin{bmatrix} 0 \\ 0 \\ 0 \\ \vdots \\ 0 \\ 1 \\ 0 \\ \vdots \\ 0 \end{bmatrix} \tag{4.134}$$

where the 1 appears in the ith position of the column vector shown in the equation. In other words, the effect of such an impulsive input is to cause the state vector to behave as the ith column of the transition matrix $\exp(At)$. We have already observed this in our study of method 2 of finding the transition matrix.

EQUILIBRIUM STATES

A system characterized by Equation 4.127 may reach a state of equilibrium, in which the derivative of every state variable is zero, if the control input remains constant. For example, if the control input $\mathbf{u}$ is zero, the condition for an equilibrium state is

$$\mathbf{A}\mathbf{x} = 0 \tag{4.135}$$

Therefore $\mathbf{x} = 0$ is an equilibrium state for any system governed by the differential equation $\dot{\mathbf{x}} = \mathbf{A}\mathbf{x}$ (of course, the equilibrium may be stable or unstable). If $\mathbf{A}$ is nonsingular, then $\mathbf{x} = 0$ is the only equilibrium state for zero input, while if $\mathbf{A}$ is singular there may be others. For example, in the two-capacitor circuit shown in Fig. 4.10, any state such that $v_1 + v_2 = 0$ is an equilibrium state. The reader can easily verify that the $\mathbf{A}$ matrix of this circuit is singular.

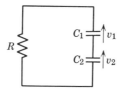

Fig. 4.10. A system with a singular matrix. The reference polarity of each voltage is represented by the arrow, the head of the arrow being adjacent to the point of higher potential.

If a constant input $\mathbf{u}$ is applied to the system (4.127), the equilibrium state can be found, if $\mathbf{A}$ is nonsingular, by setting the derivative vector to zero and solving for the steady-state vector $\mathbf{x}$ using the relationship

$$\mathbf{x} = -\mathbf{A}^{-1}\mathbf{Bu} \tag{4.136}$$

4.9   TRANSFER-FUNCTION MATRICES

Consider the system characterized by the differential equation

$$\dot{\mathbf{x}} = \mathbf{Ax} + \mathbf{Bu} \tag{4.137}$$

Taking Laplace transforms of both sides, we obtain

$$(s\mathbf{I} - \mathbf{A})\mathbf{X}(s) = \mathbf{BU}(s) \tag{4.138}$$

From Equation 4.138 we obtain the following matrix relationship between the Laplace transforms $\mathbf{X}(s)$ and $\mathbf{U}(s)$.

$$\mathbf{X}(s) = (s\mathbf{I} - \mathbf{A})^{-1}\mathbf{BU}(s) \tag{4.139}$$

The matrix quantity $(s\mathbf{I} - \mathbf{A})^{-1}\mathbf{B}$ is a matrix transfer function from the input $\mathbf{U}(s)$ to the state $\mathbf{X}(s)$. If, in addition, we have an output vector $\mathbf{y}$ specified by the relationship

$$\mathbf{y} = \mathbf{Cx} + \mathbf{Du} \tag{4.140}$$

we can write the relationship between the output $\mathbf{Y}(s)$ and the input $\mathbf{U}(s)$ as follows

$$\mathbf{Y}(s) = [\mathbf{C}(s\mathbf{I} - \mathbf{A})^{-1}\mathbf{B} + \mathbf{D}]\mathbf{U}(s) \tag{4.141}$$

It should be realized that, although the transfer-function matrix corresponding to Equations 4.137 and 4.140 is unique, the state differential equations are not necessarily specified uniquely by the transfer-function matrix. In attempting to simulate a system having a specified transfer-function matrix, by means of an analogue computer, it may be necessary to find the minimum number of state variables needed, so as to minimize the number of integrators required. For further discussion of this topic see, for example, Kalman [24].

4.10   CONTROLLABILITY AND OBSERVABILITY

The concepts of controllability and observability were introduced by Kalman [6], and are very important concepts in the study of control. Roughly speaking, a system is controllable if it is possible to cause any desired state transition in a finite time; a system is observable if the values of the state variables can be inferred from a study of the output variables.

In order to illustrate the meanings of these two concepts in a very simple way, consider the two simple systems shown in Figs. 4.11a and 4.11b. In each case we shall assume that a control signal can be applied, or a measuring instrument connected, only to the terminals at the left of the circuit. We shall assume the state of the system to be represented by the capacitor voltage in each case. In case (a), it is obviously possible to make the capacitor voltage reach any desired value in a finite time, provided that a voltage supply of sufficient magnitude is available. In case (b), however, we have a balanced bridge, and the application of a voltage signal to the terminals has no effect on the state of the system. System (a) is controllable; system (b) is not.

If the input is disconnected from system (a), it is (in theory at least) a simple matter to measure the system state. If we assume that there is no

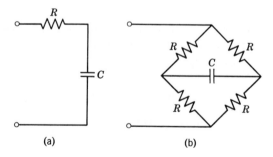

(a)   (b)

Fig. 4.11

noise, and that we have an ideal voltmeter which takes no current, the state can be measured by connecting the voltmeter to the terminals. In case (b), however, a voltmeter connected to the terminals would give a zero reading, whatever the state of the system. System (a) is observable; system (b) is not.

In typical problems of optimal control we are required to find a control input **u** which steers the system from a prescribed initial state to a prescribed final state, in some optimum way. It is obviously necessary to find out whether the final state can in fact be reached, and so the problem of controllability arises. It is also necessary to know whether or not the system state can be determined in practice by measurements made on the output of the system, and so the problem of observability arises.

Let us now make a brief study of controllability and observability of time-invariant linear systems, in order to derive some general rules for deciding whether a particular system is controllable and whether it is observable.

CONTROLLABILITY

In determining whether a system is controllable or not, we are not interested in deciding whether the control signals can be made large enough to accomplish a desired transition in a finite time, but whether the interconnections of the system are such as to permit such a transition. For example, consider the system characterized by the differential equation

$$\dot{\mathbf{x}} = \mathbf{A}\mathbf{x} + \mathbf{B}\mathbf{u} \qquad (4.142)$$

In order to find out whether this system is controllable, we wish to know whether there can be found any possible control input $\mathbf{u}(t)$, over a finite interval, which causes a prescribed state transition. As the possibility of making such a state transition depends on the interconnections of the system, we would expect the controllability to depend in some way on the properties of the matrices **A** and **B** of Equation 4.142.

Suppose, for example, we wish to find out whether the system (Equation 4.142) can be driven from an arbitrary initial state $\mathbf{x}^0$ at time t_0 to a desired final state $\mathbf{x}^1$ at time t_1, where $t_1 - t_0$ is finite. If and only if it is possible to achieve this, we shall describe the system as being controllable. We can take the initial time t_0 to be zero, and the desired final state to be the origin **0**; in this case we can express the state transition in terms of Equation 4.128 as follows

$$\mathbf{0} = e^{\mathbf{A}t_1}\mathbf{x}^0 + \int_0^{t_1} e^{\mathbf{A}(t_1 - \tau)}\mathbf{B}\mathbf{u}(\tau)\, d\tau \qquad (4.143)$$

Multiplying both sides by $\exp{(-\mathbf{A}t_1)}$, we obtain

$$\mathbf{x}^0 + \int_0^{t_1} e^{-\mathbf{A}\tau}\mathbf{B}\mathbf{u}(\tau)\, d\tau = 0 \tag{4.144}$$

Expressing $\exp{(-\mathbf{A}\tau)}$ in the form of expression 4.122, we obtain

$$-\mathbf{x}^0 = \sum_{i=0}^{n-1} \mathbf{A}^i\mathbf{B} \int_0^{t_1} f_i(-\tau)\mathbf{u}(\tau)\, d\tau \tag{4.145}$$

If we consider the $n \times nr$ matrix $\mathbf{M}$, defined by

$$\mathbf{M} \triangleq [\mathbf{B}, \mathbf{AB}, \ldots, \mathbf{A}^i\mathbf{B}, \ldots, \mathbf{A}^{n-1}\mathbf{B}] \tag{4.146}$$

we see that the right side of Equation 4.145 is a linear combination of the columns of the matrix $\mathbf{M}$. As $\mathbf{x}^0$ is assumed to be arbitrary, it must therefore be possible for any state vector to be represented by a linear combination of the columns of the matrix $\mathbf{M}$. For the system to be controllable, therefore, it is necessary that the vectors formed by the columns of $\mathbf{M}$ span the entire state space. In other words, for the system to be controllable it is necessary for the rank of the matrix $\mathbf{M}$ to be n. It is shown by Zadeh and Desoer [10] that this is also a sufficient condition for the system to be controllable.

Another way of deriving the condition for controllability is to start from the condition that it must be possible for the control input to excite all the natural modes of the system. In other words, it must be possible to make all the quantities β_i in Equation 4.60 nonzero. Since the β_i of Equation 4.60 are the components of the vector $\mathbf{\Theta}^{-1}\mathbf{B}\mathbf{u}$, the condition that all the β_i can be made nonzero means that every row of $\mathbf{\Theta}^{-1}\mathbf{B}$ must contain at least one nonzero element. Using this condition the same result can be derived [11].

As an example, let us consider the system of Equation 4.6, the $\mathbf{A}$ matrix having the numerical value specified by Equation 4.89, and the corresponding $\mathbf{B}$ matrix being

$$\mathbf{B} = \begin{bmatrix} 0 \\ 2 \end{bmatrix} \tag{4.147}$$

The matrix $\mathbf{M}$ is easily shown to be

$$\mathbf{M} = [\mathbf{B}, \mathbf{AB}] = \begin{bmatrix} 0 & 2 \\ 2 & -6 \end{bmatrix} \tag{4.148}$$

The columns of the matrix (Equation 4.148) are obviously linearly independent, showing that the system is controllable.

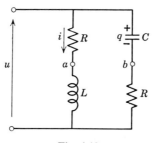

Fig. 4.12

As a second example, consider the circuit shown in Fig. 4.12. The control input u is the voltage applied at the terminals. If we define the state variables as follows

$$x_1 \triangleq q$$
$$x_2 \triangleq i \qquad (4.149)$$

where q is the charge on the capacitor, and i the current in the inductor, with the polarities shown on Fig. 4.12, the state equations may be written in the form

$$\frac{d}{dt}\begin{bmatrix} x_1 \\ x_2 \end{bmatrix} = \begin{bmatrix} -\dfrac{1}{CR} & 0 \\ 0 & -\dfrac{R}{L} \end{bmatrix}\begin{bmatrix} x_1 \\ x_2 \end{bmatrix} + \begin{bmatrix} \dfrac{1}{R} \\ \dfrac{1}{L} \end{bmatrix} u \qquad (4.150)$$

The matrix $\mathbf{M}$ turns out to be

$$\mathbf{M} = [\mathbf{B}, \mathbf{AB}] = \begin{bmatrix} \dfrac{1}{R} & -\dfrac{1}{CR^2} \\ \dfrac{1}{L} & -\dfrac{R}{L^2} \end{bmatrix} \qquad (4.151)$$

The determinant of the matrix $\mathbf{M}$ turns out to be

$$-\frac{1}{L^2} + \frac{1}{LCR^2} \qquad (4.152)$$

The system is controllable unless this determinant is equal to zero. The determinant becomes zero when

$$R^2 = \frac{L}{C} \qquad (4.153)$$

If we derive the expression for the input impedance of the circuit of Fig. 4.12, we find that, if condition 4.153 is satisfied, the input impedance is R at all frequencies. In other words, under these conditions there occurs pole-zero cancellation in the system transfer function, and it is well known that if pole-zero cancellation occurs some of the natural modes of the system may not be excited by any input. These conditions can also be interpreted as the conditions for balance of a bridge circuit, if we suppose a detector to be connected between points a and b in Fig. 4.12.

OBSERVABILITY

Suppose that the system characterized by Equation 4.142 has its output vector $\mathbf{y}$ given by the following equation

$$\mathbf{y} = \mathbf{Cx} + \mathbf{Du} \tag{4.154}$$

where $\mathbf{y}$ is a vector with p components, as in Equation 4.12. This system will be defined to be observable if and only if the initial state $\mathbf{x}^0$ at some time t_0 can be uniquely determined from the knowledge of the vector $\mathbf{y}(t)$ in some finite time interval $[t_0, t_1]$,[5] assuming the $\mathbf{A}, \mathbf{B}, \mathbf{C}, \mathbf{D}$ matrices and the input vector $\mathbf{u}(t)$ are known throughout the interval. Because the equations specify a time-invariant system ($\mathbf{A}, \mathbf{B}, \mathbf{C}$, and $\mathbf{D}$ being constant), we can take t_0 to be zero without loss of generality.

By substituting Equation 4.128 in Equation 4.154 we find the output $\mathbf{y}(t)$ during the interval 0 to t_1 to be given by

$$\mathbf{y}(t) = \mathbf{C}e^{\mathbf{A}t}\mathbf{x}^0 + \mathbf{C}\int_0^t e^{\mathbf{A}(t-\tau)}\mathbf{Bu}(\tau)\,d\tau + \mathbf{Du}(t) \tag{4.155}$$

As we have assumed the input and the system parameters to be known, the second and third terms on the right of Equation 4.155 are known. Hence the system is observable if and only if knowledge of the vector quantity

$$\mathbf{z}(t) = \mathbf{C}e^{\mathbf{A}t}\mathbf{x}^0 \tag{4.156}$$

during the interval 0 to t_1 allows the initial state vector $\mathbf{x}^0$ to be found uniquely.

Substituting Equation 4.121 into Equation 4.156 we obtain

$$\mathbf{z}(t) = \sum_{i=0}^{n-1} f_i(t)\mathbf{CA}^i\mathbf{x}^0 \tag{4.157}$$

The necessary and sufficient conditions for the system to be observable is that the columns of the $n \times np$ matrix $\mathbf{N}$, defined by

$$\mathbf{N} \triangleq [\mathbf{C}', \mathbf{A}'\mathbf{C}', \ldots, (\mathbf{A}^{n-1})'\mathbf{C}'] \tag{4.158}$$

---

[5] The notation $[t_0, t_1]$ represents the closed interval $t_0 \leqslant t \leqslant t_1$. Where appropriate, we shall use the notation (t_0, t_1) to denote the interval $t_0 < t < t_1$, and $(t_0, t_1]$ and $[t_0, t_1)$ to denote the intervals $t_0 < t \leqslant t_1$ and $t_0 \leqslant t < t_1$, respectively.

(where C' is the transpose of the matrix C) span the state space of the system. In other words, the system is observable if and only if the matrix N has rank n.

Suppose, for example, that the rank of N is less than n. This means that there is some vector a in the state space which is orthogonal to all the columns of the matrix N, which in turn means that

$$[(A^i)'C']'a = 0 \qquad (i = 0, 1, \ldots, n - 1) \qquad (4.159)$$

Equation 4.159 may be interpreted as a set of np scalar products, each of which is equal to zero. These equations may be written in the form

$$CA^i a = 0 \qquad (i = 0, 1, \ldots, n - 1) \qquad (4.160)$$

A comparison of Equations 4.160 and 4.157 shows that, if the initial state x^0 is in the direction of the vector a, the output resulting from that state is identically zero. That is, the initial state cannot be determined from the knowledge of $z(t)$; the system is not observable if the rank of N is less than n.

If the rank of N is equal to n, the initial state vector can be found from the output vector z during the interval 0 to t_1, by virtue of the fact that the $f_i(t)$ of Equation 4.121 are linearly independent over any finite interval [10]. The fact that the initial state vector can be found in this way is shown as follows: We can write the equation for the jth component of $z(t)$ from Equation 4.157 as follows:

$$z_j(t) = \sum_{i=0}^{n-1} f_i(t)c_j A^i x^0 \qquad (j = 1, \ldots, p) \qquad (4.161)$$

where c_j is the jth row of the matrix C. It should be observed that the quantity $c_j A^i x^0$ is a scalar quantity. Multiplying both sides of Equation 4.161 by $f_k(t)$ and integrating, we obtain

$$\int_0^{t_1} f_k(t)z_j(t)dt = \sum_{i=0}^{n-1} \int_0^{t_1} f_i(t)f_k(t)dt\,(c_j A^i x^0) \qquad (4.162)$$

$$(k = 0, 1, \ldots, n - 1; \qquad j = 1, \ldots, p)$$

(where p is the number of components of y, or the number of rows of C). Knowing all the $z_j(t)$ $(j = 1, 2, \ldots, p)$ and the $f_k(t)$ $(k = 0, 1, \ldots, n - 1)$, Equation 4.162 represents np equations from which the np scalar quantities $c_j A^i x^0$ can be found. Each of these scalar quantities can be expressed in the form

$$c_j A^i x^0 = [(A^i)'(c_j)']\cdot x^0 \qquad (4.163)$$

The column vector $(A^i)'(c_j)'$ is the jth column of the matrix $(A^i)'C'$. The solution of Equations 4.162 therefore gives the np scalar products of the np vectors $(A^i)'C'$ $(i = 0, \ldots, n - 1)$ and the vector x^0. These np vectors are the column vectors of $\mathbf{N}$, and we have assumed that the rank of $\mathbf{N}$ is n, so that the columns of $\mathbf{N}$ contain a set of n linearly independent vectors. Therefore, as we can calculate the scalar product of $\mathbf{x}^0$ with a set of n linearly independent vectors, we can determine the initial state $\mathbf{x}^0$ uniquely from observation of the output $\mathbf{y}$ throughout the interval 0 to t_1.

The concept of observability will be of importance if it is necessary to estimate state variables which are not directly measurable. If a system is observable, and if it is possible to make perfect noise-free measurements, it would be possible (at least in theory) to compute the state variables which are not directly measurable. For example, for the system of Fig. 4.1, with transfer function given by Equation 4.2, it would be possible to find the two state variables by taking the first derivative of the output as well as the output variable itself. More generally, the state of a linear system can be observed approximately by connecting to the system an "observer" which is itself a linear system driven by the input and output variables of the original system. Luenberger [23] has shown that, for a system of order n with p independent outputs, the state vector can be estimated by an observer of order $n - p$. The observation problem will obviously become more difficult if noise is present, and it may be necessary to use Kalman filtering techniques, as described in Chapter 3, to estimate the state of the system.

In the subsequent chapters of this book, we shall use many simple examples to illustrate optimal control. For simplicity we shall assume that all state variables are directly measurable, so that we shall not need to investigate the observability of each system. In practice, however, the problems of estimating the values of the state variables of a system are often very difficult.

4.11 ANALOGUE-COMPUTER SIMULATION OF SYSTEMS

The writing of the differential equations of the system in state form, expressing the derivative of each state variable as a definite function of the state variables and the system inputs, is ideal from the point of view of analogue-computer simulation of the system. This is because we can consider each state variable to be the output of an integrating amplifier, whose input is the appropriate function of the amplifier outputs and the independent inputs. For example, if we consider the system represented by the matrix Equation 4.6, we can represent this equation in block-diagram form, in terms of simple integrators, in the form shown in Fig. 4.13.

It is assumed for simplicity that no sign reversal takes place in the integrators of Fig. 4.13. The state variables are normally represented by the output voltages of the integrating amplifiers of the analogue computer, and thus the state variables may be associated with the energy-storage elements in a

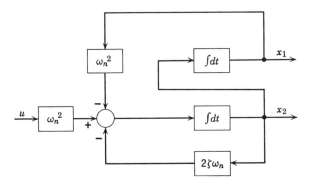

Fig. 4.13. Representation of state Equations 4.6 in terms of simple integrators.

physical system. For example, the extension of a spring, the velocity of a particle, the current in an inductor, or the charge on a capacitor may represent a state variable in a physical system. We have seen that, in the linear differential equations we have been considering, the order of the equation is the same as the number of *independent* energy-storage elements in the system. It is necessary to make the stipulation of independence; for example, if we had three capacitors connected in series around a closed loop, they would not represent three *independent* energy storages because, given the voltages of any two, we could find the third by an algebraic relationship without considering the dynamics of the system. Or, in terms of the analogue-computer representation, we could find the voltage of the third capacitor by a simple addition or subtraction instead of by integration. The finding of the exact number of state variables in a given system may be rather difficult; a method which is valid for electrical circuits is given by Fuller [7].

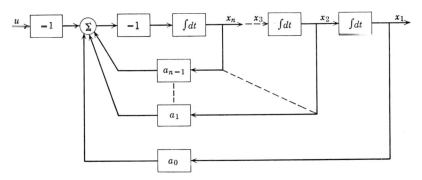

Fig. 4.14. Analogue-computer connections for simulation of nth-order system.

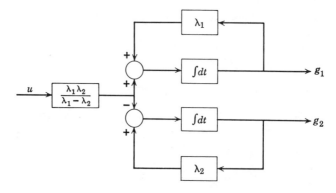

Fig. 4.15. Representation of state Equations 4.64 in terms of simple integrators.

An analogue-computer simulation of the nth-order system described by Equations 4.7, 4.9, and 4.10 is illustrated in Fig. 4.14.

We can also connect an analogue-computer circuit in such a way as to represent the normal coordinates, if these are real, as the integrator outputs. For example, the system of Equation 4.6 can, as we have shown, be expressed in terms of another pair of state variables as in Equation 4.64. Assuming the eigenvectors are real and distinct, this equation can be represented in terms of simple integrators as in Fig. 4.15.

Further details on the block-diagram representation of systems, including the cases of complex eigenvalues and repeated eigenvalues, can be found in Peschon [12].

4.12 STATE REPRESENTATION OF LINEAR SAMPLED-DATA SYSTEMS

Suppose we have a linear system represented by the vector-matrix differential equation

$$\dot{\mathbf{x}} = \mathbf{A}\mathbf{x} \qquad (4.164)$$

If we further suppose that the output of the system can only be observed at equally spaced discrete instants of time, for example at $t = 0, T, 2T$, etc., we have what is called a sampled-data system.

The response of the system governed by Equation 4.164 is known to be of the form

$$\mathbf{x}(t) = e^{\mathbf{A}t}\mathbf{x}(0) \qquad (4.165)$$

Hence the response at time T is given by

$$\mathbf{x}(T) = e^{\mathbf{A}T}\mathbf{x}(0) \tag{4.166}$$

and the response at time $2T$ is given by

$$\mathbf{x}(2T) = e^{2\mathbf{A}T}\mathbf{x}(0) = e^{\mathbf{A}T}\mathbf{x}(T) \tag{4.167}$$

We see that the response at any sampling instant may be obtained from the response at the previous sampling instant by multiplying by $\exp(\mathbf{A}t)$. Mathematically, this may be expressed as

$$\mathbf{x}[(k + 1)T] = e^{\mathbf{A}T}\mathbf{x}(kT) \tag{4.168}$$

Furthermore, it is easy to see that

$$\mathbf{x}[(k + m)T] = e^{m\mathbf{A}T}\mathbf{x}(kT) = e^{m\mathbf{A}T}e^{k\mathbf{A}T}\mathbf{x}(0) = e^{(m + k)\mathbf{A}T}\mathbf{x}(0) \tag{4.169}$$

Let us now extend this to a system with a control input. Suppose we have a system governed by the equation

$$\dot{\mathbf{x}} = \mathbf{A}\mathbf{x} + \mathbf{B}\mathbf{u} \tag{4.170}$$

and let us further suppose that the components of the input vector $\mathbf{u}$ are piecewise constant, changing values only at discrete instants of time $t = 0$, T, $2T$, and so on. For example, the control input $\mathbf{u}$ might be the output of a set of zero-order holds, which are well known in the theory of sampled-data systems [13]. In this case, the output at time T can be expressed as

$$\mathbf{x}(T) = e^{\mathbf{A}T}\mathbf{x}(0) + \int_0^T e^{\mathbf{A}(T - \tau)}\mathbf{B}\mathbf{u}(0)\,d\tau \tag{4.171}$$

where the vector $\mathbf{u}$ is assumed to retain the value $\mathbf{u}(0)$ throughout the interval $0 \leqslant t < T$. Let us define a matrix $\mathbf{H}$ by the equation

$$\mathbf{H} \triangleq \int_0^T e^{\mathbf{A}(T - \tau)}\mathbf{B}\,d\tau \tag{4.172}$$

In view of the fact that the control input vector $\mathbf{u}$ is constant throughout the interval $0 \leqslant t < T$, we can now write Equation 4.171 in the form

$$\mathbf{x}(T) = e^{\mathbf{A}T}\mathbf{x}(0) + \mathbf{H}\mathbf{u}(0) \tag{4.173}$$

In more general terms, we can write the output at $t = (k + 1)T$ as

$$\mathbf{x}[(k + 1)T] = e^{\mathbf{A}T}\mathbf{x}(kT) + \mathbf{H}\mathbf{u}(kT) \tag{4.174}$$

Equation 4.174 describes the state transition from any sampling instant to the next, in terms of the state at the first instant and the constant input during the sampling period. It is also possible to write the response at $t = kT$ in the form

$$\mathbf{x}(kT) = e^{kAT}x(0) + \sum_{i=1}^{k} e^{(k-i)AT}\mathbf{Hu}[(i-1)T] \qquad (4.175)$$

Equation 4.175 may be considered to be a sampled-data analogue of Equation 4.128. The second term on the right of Equation 4.175 is the vector form of a convolution summation for the sampled-data system described above.

Equation 4.174 can be written in the form

$$\mathbf{x}(k+1) = \mathbf{Gx}(k) + \mathbf{Hu}(k) \qquad (4.176)$$

where $\mathbf{G}$ represents the matrix $\exp(\mathbf{A}T)$, and the sampling period T is implicit in the equation. For a specified time-invariant system and a specified sampling period T, the matrices $\mathbf{G}$ and $\mathbf{H}$ are constant. A system of this type can be simulated in a similar way to a system of differential equations, except that pure-time-delay elements of T seconds delay are used instead of integrators. To be more specific, consider the system of differential equations of the form

$$\dot{\mathbf{x}} = \mathbf{Gx} + \mathbf{Hu} \qquad (4.177)$$

The block diagram of Equation 4.176 would be identical to the block diagram of Equation 4.177 (in the all-integrator form similar to Fig. 4.14) except that each integrator would be replaced by a time-delay element.

Sampled-data or discrete-time systems are typically represented by difference equations, whereas continuous-time systems are represented by differential equations. Just as a high-order differential equation can be represented by a set of first-order equations, a high-order difference equation can also be represented by a set of first-order difference equations. In order to illustrate this, let us consider the well-known difference equation associated with the Fibonacci sequence of numbers.

THE FIBONACCI SEQUENCE

A Fibonacci sequence is a sequence of numbers in which each member of the sequence is the sum of the previous two. This sequence has interesting properties which will be studied in subsequent chapters. The relationship between successive numbers of the sequence can be expressed as a second-order difference equation [5] in the following form.

$$F(n+1) = F(n) + F(n-1) \qquad (4.178)$$

where $F(n)$ is the nth number in the Fibonacci sequence. If we assume the initial conditions to be[6]

$$F(0) = 0 \\ F(1) = 1 \qquad (4.179)$$

the first few numbers of the sequence can be written as

n	0	1	2	3	4	5	6	7	8
$F(n)$	0	1	1	2	3	5	8	13	21

Let us now represent the second-order difference equation by two first-order equations. We can do this by defining two state variables f_1 and f_2 as follows.

$$f_1(n) \overset{\Delta}{=} F(n) \\ f_2(n) \overset{\Delta}{=} F(n-1) \qquad (4.180)$$

The second-order difference Equation 4.178 can now be expressed as the following two first-order equations

$$f_1(n+1) = f_1(n) + f_2(n) \\ f_2(n+1) = f_1(n) \qquad (4.181)$$

These two equations can be written in vector-matrix form as

$$\mathbf{f}(n+1) = \begin{bmatrix} 1 & 1 \\ 1 & 0 \end{bmatrix} \mathbf{f}(n) \qquad (4.182)$$

where $\mathbf{f}$ is the column vector with components f_1 and f_2.

Let us now find the eigenvalues of the matrix. These are easily shown to be the roots of the equation

$$\gamma^2 - \gamma - 1 = 0 \qquad (4.183)$$

These roots can be written as

$$\gamma_1 = \frac{1 + \sqrt{5}}{2} \simeq 1.618 \qquad (4.184)$$

$$\gamma_2 = \frac{1 - \sqrt{5}}{2} \simeq -0.618 \qquad (4.185)$$

The significance of the two eigenvalues is that the value of $F(n)$ can be expressed in the form

$$F(n) = A_1(\gamma_1)^n + A_2(\gamma_2)^n \qquad (4.186)$$

---

[6] Different initial conditions may be used. See, for example, Wilde [14].

where A_1 and A_2 depend on the initial conditions. Using the initial conditions we have chosen above in Equation 4.179, the value of $F(n)$ can be expressed in the form

$$F(n) = \frac{(\gamma_1)^n - (\gamma_2)^n}{\gamma_1 - \gamma_2} \qquad (4.187)$$

Expression 4.187 may be considered to be the sum of a sequence $\gamma_1^n/(\gamma_1-\gamma_2)$ whose members increase in magnitude as n increases, and a sequence $-\gamma_2^n/(\gamma_1 - \gamma_2)$ whose members decrease and alternate in sign as n increases. The sequence (Equation 4.187) may also be visualized as the discrete-time samples of a continuous function made up of a growing exponential and a decaying oscillation. As n becomes large and positive, the former sequence predominates, and the ratio $F(n + 1)/F(n)$ approaches the value of γ_1 given by Equation 4.184.

If the sequence is projected backwards by proceeding through the negative values of n, as if we were going backwards in time, the oscillatory component grows and the other component decays. Portion of the sequence for both positive and negative values of n is as follows:

n	-5	-4	-3	-2	-1	0	1	2	3	4	5
$F(n)$	5	-3	2	-1	1	0	1	1	2	3	5

We see that each number in the sequence is the sum of the previous two. As n becomes large and negative, the ratio $F(n + 1)/F(n)$ approaches the value of γ_2 given by Equation 4.185.

A block-diagram representation of a system for generating a sequence of Fibonacci numbers is shown in Fig. 4.16.

Figure 4.16 provides a simple illustration of the process which appears to have led Fibonacci to the discovery of his sequence, namely, the breeding of rabbits [14]. It is supposed that a rabbit takes one month to mature, and that each pair of mature rabbits produces one new pair of rabbits each month

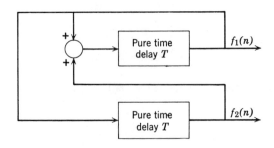

Fig. 4.16. System which generates a Fibonacci sequence.

after maturity. Therefore, in Fig. 4.16, if T is one month, we can consider $f_1(n)$ to represent the total number of pairs of rabbits alive now, and $f_2(n)$ (which now has the value which f_1 had a month ago) as the total number of pairs of *mature* rabbits alive now. The total number of rabbits which will be alive one month from now is the sum of the total number alive now (because they will still be alive in one month) and the number of mature rabbits alive now (because they will reproduce). The process can be started by taking $f_1 = 1, f_2 = 0$, representing one pair of newborn rabbits.

4.13   LINEAR TIME-VARYING SYSTEMS

Throughout the previous portions of this chapter we have assumed that the systems we are studying are time-invariant. For example, in equations of the form of Equation 4.142 we have assumed that the matrices $\mathbf{A}$ and $\mathbf{B}$ have all their entries constant. In a time-varying system, on the other hand, we might have a set of differential equations expressed in the form

$$\dot{\mathbf{x}}(t) = \mathbf{A}(t)\mathbf{x}(t) + \mathbf{B}(t)\mathbf{u}(t) \tag{4.188}$$

We shall now make a very brief study of time-varying systems. Let us first study the response of a system with zero input, governed by the differential equation

$$\dot{\mathbf{x}}(t) = \mathbf{A}(t)\mathbf{x}(t) \tag{4.189}$$

If we suppose that the initial state of the system is $\mathbf{x}(t_0)$ at time t_0, the state at some later time t may be written as

$$\mathbf{x}(t) = \mathbf{\Phi}(t, t_0)\mathbf{x}(t_0) \tag{4.190}$$

where $\mathbf{\Phi}(t, t_0)$ is the state transition matrix of the system. Because the system is time-varying, we must define the transition matrix as a function of two arguments, the initial time and the final time. We can no longer express the transition matrix in a simple form such as $\exp(\mathbf{A}t)$, because the $\mathbf{A}$ matrix is no longer constant.

The matrix $\mathbf{\Phi}(t, t_0)$ is the matrix which is the solution of the equation

$$\frac{d}{dt}[\mathbf{\Phi}(t, t_0)] = \mathbf{A}(t)\mathbf{\Phi}(t, t_0) \tag{4.191}$$

with the condition that

$$\mathbf{\Phi}(t_0, t_0) = \mathbf{I} \tag{4.192}$$

An important property of the transition matrix is that

$$[\mathbf{\Phi}(t, t_0)]^{-1} = \mathbf{\Phi}(t_0, t) \tag{4.193}$$

Let us now examine the forced response of the system, with differential equation as given by Equation 4.188. The response at time t may now be written as

$$\mathbf{x}(t) = \mathbf{\Phi}(t, t_0)\mathbf{x}(t_0) + \int_{t_0}^{t} \mathbf{\Phi}(t, \tau)\mathbf{B}(\tau)\mathbf{u}(\tau)\, d\tau \qquad (4.194)$$

We can verify that Equation 4.194 gives the response by differentiating the expression, and we obtain

$$\dot{\mathbf{x}}(t) = \mathbf{A}(t)\mathbf{\Phi}(t, t_0)\mathbf{x}(t_0) + \mathbf{A}(t)\int_{t_0}^{t} \mathbf{\Phi}(t, \tau)\mathbf{B}(\tau)\mathbf{u}(\tau)\, d\tau + \mathbf{B}(t)\mathbf{u}(t) \quad (4.195)$$

It is obvious from Equation 4.195 that expression 4.194 is a solution of Equation 4.188. It satisfies the initial conditions and is therefore the complete solution.

For obvious reasons, the transition matrix of a time-varying system cannot be computed by methods 1 to 4 described for the computation of the transition matrix of a time-invariant system in Section 4.7. In general, the response of a time-varying system must be computed by a digital computer.

ADJOINT EQUATIONS

Corresponding to a linear differential equation or a linear system, there is another differential equation called the adjoint equation. The solution of this equation is closely related to the solution of the original equation, and the adjoint equation (or the adjoint system) is frequently encountered in optimal control theory. Let us now make a brief study of the adjoint equation.

Consider the linear time-varying differential equation

$$\dot{\mathbf{x}}(t) = \mathbf{A}(t)\mathbf{x}(t) \qquad (4.196)$$

where the matrix $\mathbf{A}(t)$ varies with time. The solution of the differential equation is given by

$$\mathbf{x}(t) = \mathbf{\Phi}(t, t_0)\mathbf{x}(t_0) \qquad (4.197)$$

where $\mathbf{\Phi}(t, t_0)$ is the transition matrix defined by Equations 4.191 and 4.192. Now consider the following differential equation, which is called the *adjoint* equation of Equation 4.196:

$$\dot{\mathbf{y}}(t) = -\mathbf{A}'(t)\mathbf{y}(t) \qquad (4.198)$$

where $\mathbf{A}'$ is the transpose of $\mathbf{A}$. The two Equations 4.196 and 4.198 may be said to be adjoint to one another. The solution of Equation 4.198 can be written in the form

$$\mathbf{y}(t) = \mathbf{\Psi}(t, t_0)\mathbf{y}(t_0) \qquad (4.199)$$

where $\Psi(t, t_0)$ is the transition matrix, and is the solution of the equation

$$\frac{d}{dt}[\Psi(t, t_0)] = -A'(t)\Psi(t, t_0) \tag{4.200}$$

with the initial condition

$$\Psi(t_0, t_0) = I \tag{4.201}$$

Now consider any solution $x(t)$ of Equation 4.196, and any solution $y(t)$ of Equation 4.198. In particular, let us consider the derivative of the scalar product $x(t) \cdot y(t)$ as follows:

$$\frac{d}{dt}[x(t) \cdot y(t)] = [\dot{x}(t) \cdot y(t)] + [x(t) \cdot \dot{y}(t)] \tag{4.202}$$

The expression on the right side of Equation 4.202 can be written in the form

$$[A(t)x(t)] \cdot y(t) + x(t) \cdot [-A'(t)y(t)] \tag{4.203}$$

This can be written in the form

$$x'(t)A'(t)y(t) - x'(t)A'(t)y(t) \tag{4.204}$$

which is equal to zero. This shows that the scalar product $x(t) \cdot y(t)$ is constant. In particular, let us consider the matrix product

$$\Phi'(t, t_0)\Psi(t, t_0) \tag{4.205}$$

Because each column of Φ is a solution of Equation 4.196, and each column of Ψ is a solution of Equation 4.198, the product (expression 4.205) is constant, for all t and all t_0. If this is so, we can set $t = t_0$, in which case both Φ and Ψ are equal to the unit matrix I. We can therefore say that

$$\Phi'(t, t_0) = \Psi^{-1}(t, t_0) = \Psi(t_0, t) \tag{4.206}$$

and similarly that

$$\Psi'(t, t_0) = \Phi^{-1}(t, t_0) = \Phi(t_0, t) \tag{4.207}$$

We shall illustrate the use of the adjoint system in a computational method of optimization described in Chapter 8.

4.14 NONLINEAR SYSTEMS

In the foregoing portions of this chapter we have assumed that the derivative of each state variable at any instant is a linear function of the state variables and the input variables. This allows the set of differential equations for the system to be written in vector-matrix form. A more general way of writing a set of differential equations, for a system with n state variables, is the following:

$$\frac{dx_i}{dt} = f_i(x_1, x_2, \ldots, x_n, u_1, u_2, \ldots, u_r, t) \quad (i = 1, 2, \ldots, n) \quad (4.208)$$

or, in more compact form,

$$\dot{\mathbf{x}} = \mathbf{f}(\mathbf{x}, \mathbf{u}, t) \quad (4.209)$$

where $\mathbf{x}$ and $\mathbf{f}$ are n-dimensional vectors, and $\mathbf{u}$ is an r-dimensional vector. We have assumed that, as in the general cases we have been considering, there are r inputs $u_1, \ldots, u_r$. Equation 4.208 can cover general nonlinear systems, and also include linear systems as special cases. As in the case of time-varying linear systems, the responses of nonlinear systems must generally be solved by a digital computer.

Equations 4.208 represent a *nonautonomous* system, which means that the derivatives of the state variables are explicit functions of time t as well as of the state variables and the inputs. If, on the other hand, the time t does not appear explicitly in the expression for the derivatives, the system is said to be *autonomous*. It is possible, however, to deal with a nonautonomous system with n state variables as if it were an autonomous system with $n + 1$ state variables, by considering the time t as an extra state variable x_{n+1}. We then obtain $n + 1$ state equation as follows:

$$\frac{dx_i}{dt} = f_i(x_1, \ldots, x_n, u_1, \ldots, u_r, x_{n+1}) \quad (i = 1, \ldots, n)$$

$$\frac{dx_{n+1}}{dt} = f_{n+1}(x_1, \ldots, x_n, u_1, \ldots, u_r, x_{n+1}) \equiv 1 \quad (4.210)$$

These equations can be expressed in vector form as follows:

$$\dot{\mathbf{x}}_{n+1} = \mathbf{f}_{n+1}(\mathbf{x}_{n+1}, \mathbf{u}) \quad (4.211)$$

where $\mathbf{x}_{n+1}$ is the vector with components $x_1, \ldots, x_n, x_{n+1}$ and $\mathbf{f}_{n+1}$ is the vector with components $f_1, \ldots, f_n, f_{n+1}$. A word of caution may be appropriate here. Although we can represent an nth-order nonlinear nonautonomous system by an $(n + 1)$th-order nonlinear autonomous system, this does not necessarily mean that a given nth-order linear time-varying system can be represented by an $(n + 1)$th-order *linear* time-invariant system.

As a particular case of the state representation of nonlinear systems, the phase-plane method of studying the response of second-order systems is well known. For a second-order autonomous system with zero input, we can write the differential equations in the form

$$\dot{x}_1 = f_1(x_1, x_2)$$
$$\dot{x}_2 = f_2(x_1, x_2)$$

(4.212)

From these equations we can express the slope of the trajectory on the phase plane as

$$\frac{dx_2}{dx_1} = \frac{f_2(x_1, x_2)}{f_1(x_1, x_2)} = g(x_1, x_2)$$

(4.213)

Equation 4.213 gives an expression for the slope of the trajectory in the phase plane at any point, as a function of the coordinates of the point. Knowing the slope corresponding to every point in the phase plane, the response of the system for any initial state can be determined. A particular way of doing this is to find the isoclines, or the loci of points at which the trajectory slopes are equal, and use these isoclines in finding the response of the system. A description of this method of finding the response of a nonlinear system can be found in almost any textbook dealing with nonlinear systems.[7] Similar considerations apply in principle to higher-order systems, except that we cannot then use simple graphical methods to sketch the response of higher-order systems.

SUMMARY

This chapter has introduced some of the principal ideas and concepts involved in the state representation of systems. This knowledge will be used in later chapters, where we are dealing with the optimal control of systems.

For the reader who wishes to study the state representation of systems in more detail, there are several books available for further study [10, 15, 16, 17]. Papers by Fuller [7, 8, 9] and Kuh and Rohrer [18] are also recommended for further study.

The material of this chapter, together with the simplified outline of Kalman filter theory in Chapter 3, may enable the reader to proceed with a study of the original papers on the Kalman filter [19, 20].

---

[7] See, for example, Truxal [22].

REFERENCES

[1] Kalman, R. E., "The Theory of Optimal Control and the Calculus of Variations," in *Mathematical Optimization Techniques*, R. Bellman, ed., 1963, Chap. 16, pp. 309–331, University of California Press, Berkeley and Los Angeles.

[2] Guillemin, E. A., *The Mathematics of Circuit Analysis*, Wiley, New York, 1949.

[3] Coddington, E. A., and N. Levinson, *Theory of Ordinary Differential Equations*, McGraw-Hill, New York, 1955.

[4] Kuo, B. C., *Automatic Control Systems*, 2nd ed., Prentice-Hall, Englewood Cliffs, N.J., 1967.

[5] Pipes, L. A., *Applied Mathematics for Engineers and Physicists*, 2nd ed., McGraw-Hill, New York, 1958.

[6] Kalman, R. E., "On the General Theory of Control Systems," *Automatic and Remote Control (Proc. IFAC Moscow 1960)*, Vol. I, Butterworth, London, 1961, pp. 481–492.

[7] Fuller, A. T., "Phase Space in the Theory of Optimum Control," *J. Electron. Control*, **8**, 381–400 (1960).

[8] Fuller, A. T., "Optimization of Non-Linear Control Systems with Transient Inputs," *J. Electron. Control*, **8**, 465–479 (1960).

[9] Fuller, A. T., "Optimization of Non-Linear Control Systems with Random Inputs," *J. Electron. Control*, **9**, 65–80 (1960).

[10] Zadeh, L. A., and C. A. Desoer, *Linear System Theory: The State Space Approach*, McGraw-Hill, New York, 1963.

[11] Schwarz, R. J., and B. Friedland, *Linear Systems*, McGraw-Hill, New York, 1965.

[12] Peschon, J., ed., *Disciplines and Techniques of Systems Control*, Blaisdell Pub., New York, 1965.

[13] Freeman, H., *Discrete-Time Systems*, Wiley, New York, 1965.

[14] Wilde, D. J., *Optimum Seeking Methods*, Prentice-Hall, Englewood Cliffs, N.J., 1964.

[15] DeRusso, P. M., R. J. Roy, and C. M. Close, *State Variables for Engineers*, Wiley, New York, 1965.

[16] Gupta, S. C., *Transform and State Variable Methods in Linear Systems*, Wiley, New York, 1966.

[17] Ogata, K., *State Space Analysis of Control Systems*, Prentice-Hall, Englewood Cliffs, N.J., 1967.

[18] Kuh, E. S., and R. A. Rohrer, "The State-Variable Approach to Network Analysis," *Proc. IEEE*, **53**, No. 7, 672–686 (July 1965).

[19] Kalman, R. E., "A New Approach to Linear Filtering and Prediction Problems," *ASME Trans., Series D (J. Basic Eng.)*, **82**, 35–45 (1960).

[20] Kalman, R. E., and R. S. Bucy, "New Results in Linear Filtering and Prediction Theory," *ASME Trans., Series D (J. Basic Eng.)*, **83**, 95–108 (1961).

[21] Tou, J. T., *Modern Control Theory*, McGraw-Hill, New York, 1964.

[22] Truxal, J. G., *Automatic Feedback Control System Synthesis*, McGraw-Hill, New York, 1955.

[23] Luenberger, D. G., "Observers for Multivariable Systems," *IEEE Transactions on Automatic Control*, **AC-11**, 190–197 (1966).

[24] Kalman, R. E., "On Structural Properties of Linear, Constant, Multivariable Systems," Proceedings of the I.F.A.C. Congress, London, 1966, Paper 6.A.

PROBLEMS

1. (a) Derive a set of state equations for the electrical circuit shown in Fig. 4.17, in which the control input u is an applied voltage, and the capacitor voltage x_1 and the inductor current x_2 are the state variables.

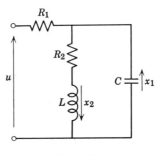

Fig. 4.17

(b) Derive a set of state equations for the circuit shown in Fig. 4.18, using the capacitor voltage and the inductor current as state variables.

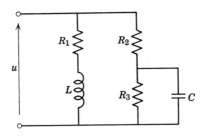

Fig. 4.18

(c) Investigate the controllability of both the above systems.

2. Write a set of state equations for the mechanical system shown in Fig. 4.19, in which the control input u is the angle of the input shaft, the spring stiffnesses are K_1 and K_2 newton-meters per radian, and the moments of inertia are J_1 and J_2 kilogram-meters^2.

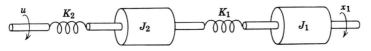

Fig. 4.19

3. For the system shown in Fig. 4.20:
   (a) Write the differential equations in matrix form.
   (b) Find the eigenvalues and eigenvectors of the matrix.
   (c) Find the transition matrix, exp $(\mathbf{A}t)$.
   (d) Find the vector response to a unit impulse at the input.

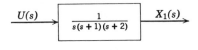

Fig. 4.20

4. For the circuit of Fig. 4.21, derive a set of state equations using the three
   capacitor voltages as state variables. Assuming for simplicity that $RC = 1$,
   find the eigenvalues and eigenvectors of the matrix, and the transition matrix
   exp $(\mathbf{A}t)$.

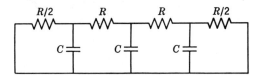

Fig. 4.21

5. (a) Derive state equations for the circuit shown in Fig. 4.22, taking as the
       state variables the charge on the capacitor and the current in the inductor.
       Assume for simplicity that $R = 3$ ohms, $C = 0.5$ farads, and $L = 1$ henry.
       Find the eigenvalues and eigenvectors of the matrix, and show the directions
       of the eigenvectors on a phase-plane diagram. Sketch the phase-plane
       trajectories starting from various initial states.
   (b) Find the limiting directions of the eigenvectors as L approaches zero, and
       hence show the degenerate phase-plane trajectories for the condition $L = 0$.

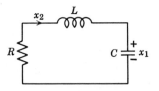

Fig. 4.22

(c) Use the results of (a) and (b) to sketch the phase-plane trajectories for the circuit of Fig. 4.22, for the case where the inductance L is nonlinear due to magnetic saturation, being 1 henry for $|x_2| < I_s$ and zero for $|x_2| > I_s$, where I_s is the magnitude of the saturating current.

6. For the system shown in Fig. 4.23, use the method of isoclines or other suitable method to sketch the state trajectories for an input $u = +1$. Assume that a is positive.

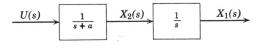

Fig. 4.23

7. In Fig. 4.24, each of the four resistances is 1 megohm and each of the three capacitances is 1 microfarad.

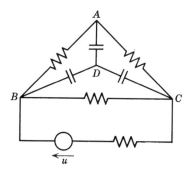

Fig. 4.24

(a) Write a set of first-order differential equations for this system, taking the state variables to be v_{AD}, v_{BD}, and v_{CD}, where v_{AD} represents the potential of A with respect to D. The control input u is a voltage source; the reference polarity is represented by the arrow, the head of the arrow being adjacent to the point of higher potential.

Write the differential equations of the system as a single first-order vector-matrix differential equation of the form $\dot{x} = Ax + bu$.

(b) Find the eigenvalues and eigenvectors of the A matrix.

(c) Find the transition matrix $\exp{(At)}$. Hence find the final steady values of the three state variables if the initial values are $v_{AD} = 30$ volts, $v_{BD} = 0$, $v_{CD} = 0$, and if the control input u has a steady value equal to zero.

(d) (i) If the control input u is fixed at zero, is it possible to specify the final steady state uniquely if the initial state is not known?

(ii) If an extra 1-megohm resistor is available and can be connected between any two of the points denoted by letters in Fig. 4.24, is it possible to alter the answer to the question asked in part (d)(i)? If so, name all the possible pairs of lettered points to which the resistor could be connected to cause such an alteration.

(e) (i) Is the system of Fig. 4.24 controllable?

(ii) Of the six different systems which can be formed by connecting a single 1-megohm resistor between a pair of lettered points in Fig. 4.24, which ones are controllable?

8. Consider the system represented by the input-output transfer function shown in Fig. 4.25, where the symbol α represents a constant whose value will be specified below.

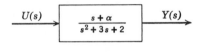

Fig. 4.25

(a) By using the two methods for handling systems with transfer-function zeros, as suggested in this chapter, derive two different state differential equations and output equations for the system, in the forms

$$\dot{\mathbf{x}} = \mathbf{A}\mathbf{x} + \mathbf{b}u \qquad \dot{\mathbf{z}} = \mathbf{F}\mathbf{z} + \mathbf{g}u$$
$$y = \mathbf{c}'\mathbf{x} \qquad\qquad y = \mathbf{h}'\mathbf{z} \qquad\qquad (4.214)$$

where $\mathbf{b}$ and $\mathbf{g}$ are column vectors, and $\mathbf{c}'$ and $\mathbf{h}'$ are row vectors.

(b) Taking the value of α to be 3, show that the two sets of Equations 4.214 are related by a matrix $\mathbf{T}$ such that

$$\mathbf{F} = \mathbf{T}\mathbf{A}\mathbf{T}^{-1} \qquad \mathbf{g} = \mathbf{T}\mathbf{b} \qquad \mathbf{h}' = \mathbf{c}'\mathbf{T}^{-1} \qquad (4.215)$$

Find the matrices $\mathbf{T}$ and $\mathbf{T}^{-1}$.

(c) Taking the value of α to be unity, investigate the controllability and observability of *both* forms of the system equations. (This part illustrates the fact that the state equations are not necessarily uniquely defined by the input-output transfer function.)

9. (a) Express the second-order difference equation

$$2F(k + 1) = F(k) + F(k - 1) \qquad (4.216)$$

as a first-order difference equation in an appropriately-specified two-dimensional vector. Find the eigenvalues and eigenvectors of the matrix which is involved in the resulting equation.

(b) If the solution of the vector-matrix difference equation of part (a) can be expressed in the form

$$\mathbf{f}(k) = \mathbf{G}^k \mathbf{f}(0) \qquad\qquad (4.217)$$

find the matrix $\mathbf{G}^k$ as a function of k. What is the limit of the matrix as k approaches infinity?

(c) If the initial values of the sequence $F(k)$ are $F(0) = 0$, $F(1) = 15$, find the limiting value of $F(k)$ as k approaches infinity.

5

Calculus of Variations

A knowledge of the calculus of variations is very helpful as an aid to the understanding of problems in optimal control. This chapter is devoted to a simple, non-rigorous introduction to the calculus of variations, in which an attempt is made to relate the subject to control problems.

The reader is assumed to be familiar with the use of differential calculus to find the necessary conditions for a maximum or minimum value of a continuous function of one variable or of a finite number of variables. Simple problems of this type have been reviewed in Chapter 2. The calculus of variations may be considered to be a more general kind of calculus, which allows us to find the conditions for a maximum or minimum value of a quantity whose value is determined by a continuous function. For example, the area enclosed by a loop of thread of a specified length, lying on a flat surface, depends on the shape of the curve in which the thread is arranged. It is fairly obvious that maximum area would be enclosed if the thread were arranged in the shape of a circle; the calculus of variations could be used to derive this result.

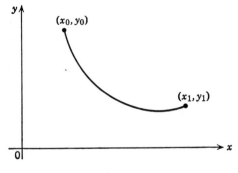

Fig. 5.1

The quantity to be maximized or minimized, using the calculus of variations, is called a *functional*. A functional may be defined as a relationship by which we associate a definite real number with each function or curve belonging to a certain class. The concept of a functional may be illustrated by a few simple examples. The area enclosed by a closed curve, such as the loop of thread referred to in the previous paragraph, is a functional which depends on the curve. The length of a smooth curve joining two points, such as the curve joining the points (x_0, y_0) and (x_1, y_1) of Fig. 5.1, is a functional which depends on the curve. The volume of the surface of revolution obtained by rotating the curve about the x axis is also a functional.

5.1 MAXIMIZATION OR MINIMIZATION OF A FUNCTIONAL

Suppose, for example, we study the simple problem of finding the curve, of minimum length, joining two fixed points. Referring to Fig. 5.1, the length of the curve joining (x_0, y_0) to (x_1, y_1) can be expressed in the form

$$L = \int_{x_0}^{x_1} \sqrt{1 + y'^2} \, dx \qquad (5.1)$$

where y' represents dy/dx. The functionals which are studied in the calculus of variations are frequently expressed in an integral form somewhat similar to that of Equation 5.1. We shall now consider a more general form of the functional, find the conditions for maximization or minimization of the functional, and then interpret the result in terms of the length functional (Equation 5.1). Consider, for example, the more general functional

$$I = \int_{x_0}^{x_1} f(x, y, y') \, dx \qquad (5.2)$$

where f is some prescribed function of the arguments shown. It is required to find the curve[1] $y(x)$, joining two specified points (x_0, y_0) and (x_1, y_1) as shown in Fig. 5.1, which makes the functional 5.2 take on a maximum or minimum value. It is obvious that integral 5.1 is a special case of Equation 5.2; Equation 5.2 also includes a wide range of possible optimization criteria, and is used in most textbooks of the calculus of variations as a basic example of a functional to be maximized or minimized.

We shall now derive, in a simple non-rigorous way, the conditions which the function $y(x)$ must satisfy in order to make Equation 5.2 take on its minimum

---

[1] With this form of functional, the curve $y(x)$ will be restricted to the class of functions which are continuous and have continuous first derivatives. For a more thorough discussion of restrictions of this kind, see, for example, Gelfand and Fomin [1].

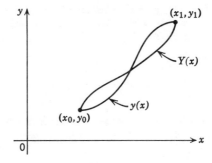

Fig. 5.2

value. Suppose, for example, that $y(x)$ in Fig. 5.2 is the curve which minimizes the integral (Equation 5.2), and that $Y(x)$ is another curve whose equation can be expressed in the form

$$Y(x) = y(x) + \alpha\eta(x) \tag{5.3}$$

where α is a constant, and $\eta(x)$ is a function that is continuous and has a continuous first derivative, that has the value $\eta(x_0) = \eta(x_1) = 0$ at the endpoints, but is otherwise of arbitrary form. If α changes, the curve specified by Equation 5.3 still passes through the specified endpoints.

The value of the integral I of Equation 5.2, corresponding to the function $Y(x)$ as given by Equation 5.3, can be written in the form

$$I(\alpha) = \int_{x_0}^{x_1} f(x, Y, Y')\, dx \tag{5.4}$$

where it is assumed that $\eta(x)$ of Equation 5.3 is a fixed function (although of arbitrary form) and α is a variable. If α is varied, the behavior of the integral $I(\alpha)$ of Equation 5.4 will be of the form shown in Fig. 5.3, reaching a minimum value at $\alpha = 0$. This is because the curve $y(x)$ is assumed to be the curve which makes the integral a minimum, and means that the derivative $dI(\alpha)/d\alpha$ must be zero at $\alpha = 0$. Differentiating Equation 5.4 with respect to α, we obtain the following result.

$$\frac{dI}{d\alpha} = \int_{x_0}^{x_1} \frac{\partial}{\partial\alpha} [f(x, Y, Y')]\, dx \tag{5.5}$$

Equation 5.5 can be written as

$$\frac{dI}{d\alpha} = \int_{x_0}^{x_1} \left[\frac{\partial f}{\partial Y} \frac{\partial Y}{\partial\alpha} + \frac{\partial f}{\partial Y'} \frac{\partial Y'}{\partial\alpha} \right] dx \tag{5.6}$$

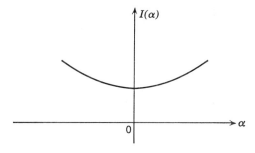

Fig. 5.3

In view of Equation 5.3, we can write Equation 5.6 in the form

$$\frac{dI}{d\alpha} = \int_{x_0}^{x_1} \left[\frac{\partial f}{\partial Y} \eta(x) + \frac{\partial f}{\partial Y'} \eta'(x) \right] dx \tag{5.7}$$

Integrating the second term in the integrand of Equation 5.7 by parts, we obtain

$$\int_{x_0}^{x_1} \frac{\partial f}{\partial Y'} \eta'(x)\, dx = \left[\frac{\partial f}{\partial Y'} \eta(x) \right]_{x_0}^{x_1} - \int_{x_0}^{x_1} \frac{d}{dx} \left(\frac{\partial f}{\partial Y'} \right) \eta(x)\, dx \tag{5.8}$$

The first term on the right side of Equation 5.8 is zero, because $\eta(x_0)$ and $\eta(x_1)$ are both zero. Substituting Equation 5.8 in Equation 5.7, we obtain

$$\frac{dI}{d\alpha} = \int_{x_0}^{x_1} \left(\frac{\partial f}{\partial Y} - \frac{d}{dx} \frac{\partial f}{\partial Y'} \right) \eta(x)\, dx \tag{5.9}$$

Setting $\alpha = 0$, the derivative $dI/d\alpha$ becomes zero and Y is replaced by y, giving

$$\int_{x_0}^{x_1} \left[\frac{\partial f}{\partial y} - \frac{d}{dx} \left(\frac{\partial f}{\partial y'} \right) \right] \eta(x)\, dx = 0 \tag{5.10}$$

As the form of $\eta(x)$ is arbitrary, the integral 5.10 can only be zero if the quantity inside the brackets is zero for all x in the interval between x_0 and x_1.[2] There results the equation

$$\frac{\partial f}{\partial y} = \frac{d}{dx} \left(\frac{\partial f}{\partial y'} \right) \tag{5.11}$$

---

[2] This statement assumes the truth of the fundamental lemma of the calculus of variations. This lemma may be stated as follows: "If a function $g(x)$ is continuous in the interval $[x_0, x_1]$, and if the integral $\int_{x_0}^{x_1} g(x)\eta(x)\, dx$ is equal to zero for all $\eta(x)$ which are continuous and have continuous first derivatives in $[x_0, x_1]$ and have $\eta(x_0) = \eta(x_1) = 0$, then $g(x) \equiv 0$ throughout the interval $[x_0, x_1]$." For a proof of this lemma see, for example, Elsgolc [2].

Equation 5.11 is usually called the Euler-Lagrange equation. It is an ordinary differential equation whose solution gives y as a function of x. This equation could also be derived by representing the function $y(x)$ approximately by the value of y at n equally spaced ordinates within the appropriate interval, expressing the integral approximately as a function of the n variables $y_1, \ldots, y_n$, and finding the condition for a minimum of the integral. If n is then allowed to become very large, we derive the Euler-Lagrange equation [1, 2].

Using the abbreviated notation $f_y \triangleq \partial f/\partial y$, the Euler-Lagrange equation can be written in the form

$$f_y = \frac{df_{y'}}{dx} \qquad (5.12)$$

It should be noted that the Euler-Lagrange Equation 5.11 or 5.12 gives only a necessary condition for a maximum or minimum. As in simple maximization problems in ordinary calculus, we may have to investigate further to decide whether we have found a maximum or a minimum. However, our knowledge of the nature of the problem often shows whether the result is a maximum or a minimum without further investigation.

Let us now return to the problem of finding the equation to the curve, joining (x_0, y_0) and (x_1, y_1), which has the shortest length. In this case, f is the integrand of expression 5.1, and the quantities required for the Euler-Lagrange equation are

$$f_y = 0 \qquad (5.13)$$

$$f_{y'} = y'(1 + y'^2)^{-1/2} \qquad (5.14)$$

In this case the Euler-Lagrange equation shows that the derivative of $f_{y'}$ with respect to x is zero. Hence $f_{y'}$ is a constant, and from Equation 5.14 this means that y' is a constant. This shows that the curve of shortest length must have a constant slope, which means that it must be a straight line, as expected. The complete solution of y as a function of x can be written in the form

$$\frac{dy}{dx} = a \qquad (5.15)$$

$$y = ax + b \qquad (5.16)$$

We have two arbitrary constants a and b, which arise because the Euler-Lagrange equation, involving the derivative of expression 5.14, is a second-order differential equation. The values of these two constants can be found from the specified initial and final values y_0 and y_1 at the values x_0 and x_1 respectively.

It should be noted that the complete solution of the problem requires the solution of a two-point boundary-value problem. The problem is a "two-point" one in the sense that some of the boundary-condition information is available at one stage of the process (in this case, the left-hand end of the curve) and the remainder at another point (the right-hand end). The more familiar one-point boundary-value problem assumes a knowledge of all necessary boundary conditions at one point, such as the left-hand end of the curve in this example. For example, if the values of y and its first derivative were known, for $x = x_0$, the values of the two arbitrary constants in the solution could be found. In the present example we have the solution of the differential equation in analytic form in Equation 5.16, and it is no more difficult to solve the two-point boundary-value problem than the one-point problem. However, as we shall see later, the solution of a two-point boundary-value problem presents severe computational difficulties if the equations are being solved numerically.

5.2 VARIABLE ENDPOINTS

The development in the previous section is based on the assumption that the two ends of the curve $y(x)$ are firmly fixed in advance. Another possible type of problem is that in which one end or both ends of the curve $y(x)$ may have some freedom to vary. For example, if we wish to find the curve which joins a fixed point to a specified smooth curve, and which has the shortest possible length, the situation might be illustrated as shown in Fig. 5.4. In the diagram, all the curves starting at (x_0, y_0) satisfy the requirement that the right-hand endpoint lies on the specified smooth curve. This makes the derivation of the necessary conditions more difficult than in the previous

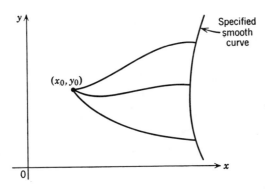

Fig. 5.4

case, for we cannot now represent every admissible curve by an equation of the form of Equation 5.3 in terms of an $\eta(x)$ which is zero at both endpoints. We shall not attempt to derive the necessary conditions here but shall indicate the principles involved and quote the appropriate results.

To begin with, the curve which minimizes the length (or a more general functional) must again satisfy the appropriate Euler-Lagrange equation. This is obviously true because, if we imagine the problem to be completely solved, we can note the right-hand endpoint reached by the optimal curve and then re-solve the problem as a fixed-endpoint problem. Obviously the Euler-Lagrange equation would have to be satisfied by the optimal curve.

The difference between the free-endpoint problem and the fixed-endpoint problem is the finding of the unknown constants in the solution of the differential equation. We no longer have two specified endpoints to find the two constants. One further condition is, however, known from simple geometrical considerations, namely, that the straight line of minimum length which joins the specified point to the smooth curve must meet the smooth curve at right angles. This information makes up for the information lost by allowing the right-hand endpoint to be free to vary.

In order to illustrate how this information can be used in finding the equation to the straight line of shortest distance between a point and a curve, consider the problem of finding the shortest distance between the point $(0, 1)$ and the parabola $y = x^2$, as illustrated in Fig. 5.5. The straight line has an equation of the form of Equation 5.16, and it is required to find a and b.

The slope of the parabola is given by

$$\frac{dy}{dx} = 2x \tag{5.17}$$

The slope of the straight line which meets the parabola at right angles at $x = x_1$ is therefore

$$\frac{dy}{dx} = \frac{-1}{2x_1} \tag{5.18}$$

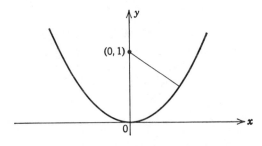

Fig. 5.5

Substituting the value of slope given by Equation 5.18 in Equation 5.16, for the straight line, we have

$$y_1 = \left(\frac{-1}{2x_1}\right)x_1 + b = -\frac{1}{2} + b \tag{5.19}$$

where x_1 and y_1 are the (as yet unknown) coordinates of the right-hand endpoint. From the coordinates of the fixed left-hand endpoint, we know that

$$1 = 0 + b \tag{5.20}$$

Substituting Equation 5.20 in Equation 5.19, we obtain the result

$$y_1 = \frac{1}{2} \tag{5.21}$$

From the requirement that (x_1, y_1) lie on the parabola $y = x^2$, we find the coordinates of the right-hand endpoint to be $(\sqrt{2}/2, 1/2)$. The required straight line is therefore

$$y = \frac{-1}{\sqrt{2}}x + 1 \tag{5.22}$$

This example has shown that, for the straight line which is the shortest possible path between a fixed point and a specified smooth curve, the fact that the minimum-distance line meets the curve orthogonally (that is, at right angles) allows us to find the equation to the straight line. Similarly, if we wished to find the line of shortest length which joined two smooth curves, the line would be orthogonal to both curves. In other words, information lost because of the freedom of the endpoints is replaced by information about the orthogonality relationships.

In dealing with the minimization of more general functionals, we must deal with a generalization of the orthogonality conditions, known as transversality conditions. We shall not derive the general conditions here but shall merely state the relationships in a simple, non-rigorous way and give references to sources of further information.[3] Suppose, for example, that the integral to be minimized is of the general form of Equation 5.2, that the left-hand endpoint (x_0, y_0) is fixed, and that the right-hand endpoint is free to lie anywhere on a specified curve. If dx and dy are allowable infinitesimal variations in the coordinates of the right-hand endpoint [in the sense that, if (x, y) lies on the

---

[3] A derivation of the transversality conditions can be found in almost any textbook of the calculus of variations, a selection of which is listed at the end of this chapter. For a helpful geometrical interpretation of the results, the books by Elsgolc [2] and Halfman [3] are recommended.

specified curve, then $(x + dx, y + dy)$ also lies on the curve], then dx and dy are related by the transversality condition

$$[(f - y'f_{y'})\, dx + f_{y'}\, dy]_1 = 0 \qquad (5.23)$$

where the subscript 1 shows that this relationship is satisfied at the right-hand endpoint. If the left-hand endpoint were also free to lie on a separate and independent curve, a similar transversality condition would have to be independently satisfied at the left-hand endpoint. The fixed-endpoint case may be considered as a special case of the free-endpoint case, with dx and dy both zero.

If the curve on which the right-hand endpoint is to lie can be expressed by an equation of the form $y = h_1(x)$, we can express the transversality condition in the form

$$[(f - y'f_{y'})\, dx + f_y h_1'(x)\, dx]_1 = 0 \qquad (5.24)$$

which can be expressed as

$$[f - y'f_{y'} + h_1'(x)f_{y'}]_1 = 0 \qquad (5.25)$$

In addition to the transversality conditions, the Euler-Lagrange Equation 5.11 must also be satisfied. The Euler-Lagrange equation is the differential equation which provides the solution in a general form; the transversality conditions supply information concerning the boundary conditions of the problem.

Let us now illustrate the use of the transversality conditions by checking that they provide the correct information concerning the minimum-distance line from a point to a curve. The integral to be minimized is given by Equation 5.1, and we shall assume that the problem is to find the line of shortest length between the point $(0, 1)$ and the parabola $y = x^2$ as before. Equation 5.25 can in this case be written in the form

$$\left[\sqrt{1 + y'^2} - \frac{y'^2}{\sqrt{1 + y'^2}} + \frac{2xy'}{\sqrt{1 + y'^2}}\right]_1 = 0 \qquad (5.26)$$

Simplification of Equation 5.26 yields the result that, at the right-hand endpoint

$$y' = \frac{-1}{2x} \qquad (5.27)$$

which is the same result as previously found by Equation 5.18, and which allows the complete solution of the problem to be obtained.

Let us now consider a very simple example which illustrates the use of Equation 5.23 directly. Suppose, for example, that we wish to find the curve of minimum length from the origin to the straight line $x = 1$. Allowable variations dx and dy in the coordinates of the right-hand endpoint may now be specified by saying that dx must be zero, whereas dy may be nonzero. In this case, Equation 5.23 reduces to

$$[f_{y'}]_1 = 0 \tag{5.28}$$

Equation 5.28 gives, at the right-hand endpoint,

$$y'(1 + y'^2)^{-1/2} = 0 \tag{5.29}$$

which gives the result $y' = 0$ at the right-hand endpoint. As expected, the minimum-distance line is horizontal.

We shall find that the transversality conditions are frequently encountered in the study of optimal control.

5.3 A PROBLEM IN OPTIMAL CONTROL

Having outlined some of the basic theory of the calculus of variations, let us now turn to optimal control problems. The type of control problem with which we shall most frequently deal in this book is the problem of finding the control input, as a function of time, which steers a system from a prescribed initial state to some final state so as to maximize or minimize some performance index. In some cases, we shall be able to show how to connect a closed-loop system in such a way as to obtain the desired control input as an instantaneous function of the state variables of the system; in other cases the optimal control input will be found as a function of time, and this can then be applied to the system in an open-loop way. Even if it is not possible to synthesize a controller that provides a control input that is exactly optimal, the derivation of the optimum result does tell us what it is possible to achieve, so that the performance of a practical controller can be compared with this optimum. This is perhaps one of the most valuable potential benefits of optimal control theory, in that it tells us how far our real systems fall short of what is theoretically possible.

Consider a simple optimal control problem, defined in terms of the simple linear integrator shown in Fig. 5.6 with a single input u and a single state variable x. We shall suppose that it is desired to transfer the system from

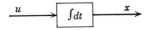

Fig. 5.6. A simple linear integrator.

state x^0 at time t_0 to state x^1 at a time t_1, in such a way as to minimize the integral

$$I = \int_{t_0}^{t_1} (x^2 + \dot{x}^2)\, dt \qquad (5.30)$$

Let us consider the fixed-endpoint problem first. In other words, let us assume that x^0, x^1, t_0, and t_1 are all specified in advance. The Euler-Lagrange equation can in this case be written in the form

$$\frac{\partial f}{\partial x} = \frac{d}{dt}\left(\frac{\partial f}{\partial \dot{x}}\right) \qquad (5.31)$$

where f represents the integrand in Equation 5.30. Equation 5.31 can be written in the form

$$2x = \frac{d}{dt}(2\dot{x}) \qquad (5.32)$$

Equation 5.32 is a second-order differential equation whose solution can be written in the form

$$x(t) = Ae^t + Be^{-t} \qquad (5.33)$$

where A and B are constants, which can be found from the specified endpoints x^0 at time t_0 and x^1 at time t_1. When these quantities are found, this allows the control input $u(t)$ to be written as

$$u(t) = \dot{x}(t) = Ae^t - Be^{-t} \qquad (5.34)$$

If the right-hand[4] endpoint is free to occur at any point on a specified curve, we obtain a transversality condition of the form

$$[(f - \dot{x}f_{\dot{x}})\, dt + f_{\dot{x}}\, dx]_1 = 0 \qquad (5.35)$$

where Equation 5.35 is obtained by analogy with Equation 5.23. If, for example, the initial state x^0 and the times t_0 and t_1 are fixed as before, and the final state x^1 is free to take on any value,[5] the transversality condition 5.35 allows us to write

$$[f_{\dot{x}}]_1 = 0 \qquad (5.36)$$

---

[4] The terms "left-hand" and "right-hand" endpoints are frequently used to refer to the starting and finishing points, respectively, implying a visualization of the coordinate space with the time axis pointing to the right.

[5] For simplicity we shall assume throughout this book that the left-hand endpoint (or initial state) is fixed, though the final state (or possibly the final time) may be free.

This means that the quantity $\dot{x}(t_1)$ is zero, and the values of A and B in Equations 5.33 and 5.34 can then be found using the known values of $x(t_0)$ and $\dot{x}(t_1)$.

The simple optimal control problem studied in this section will be used as an example in later portions of the book to illustrate other methods of approach.

5.4   PROBLEMS WITH ISOPERIMETRIC CONSTRAINTS

Problems with isoperimetric constraints are problems in which we are required to maximize or minimize the value of a specified functional, while making another functional take on a definite value. For example, the problem of finding the shape of a closed curve that encloses maximum area (the first functional), while keeping the length of the curve (the second functional) fixed at a specific value, is a problem with an isoperimetric constraint. Another example is the problem of finding the shape assumed by a rope of fixed length, with its ends attached to two fixed supports, such that the potential energy of the rope is a minimum.

A TYPICAL ISOPERIMETRIC PROBLEM

Let us consider the problem of finding the function $x(t)$, joining two specified points (t_0, x_0) and (t_1, x_1), which minimizes the functional

$$I = \int_{t_0}^{t_1} f(t, x, \dot{x}) \, dt \tag{5.37}$$

and which gives a specified value C to the functional

$$J = \int_{t_0}^{t_1} g(t, x, \dot{x}) \, dt \tag{5.38}$$

The method of Lagrange multipliers can be used here, as it was used in Chapter 2 in dealing with a problem in ordinary calculus. We shall omit the details of the derivation of the method, which can easily be found elsewhere [3], and shall merely describe the procedure.

We shall introduce a Lagrange multiplier λ, and define a new functional $\tilde{I}$ by the expression

$$\tilde{I} = I + \lambda J \tag{5.39}$$

This functional can be expressed in the form

$$\tilde{I} = \int_{t_0}^{t_1} F(t, x, \dot{x}) \, dt \tag{5.40}$$

where the function F is defined by the equation

$$F(t, x, \dot{x}) = f(t, x, \dot{x}) + \lambda g(t, x, \dot{x}) \tag{5.41}$$

As in the case of the problem in ordinary calculus, the use of the Lagrange multiplier allows the problem to be treated as if it were an unconstrained optimization problem. The condition for $\tilde{I}$ to be a maximum or minimum is the Euler-Lagrange equation

$$F_x = \frac{d}{dt}(F_{\dot{x}}) \tag{5.42}$$

Equation 5.42, together with the equation

$$J = \int_{t_0}^{t_1} g(t, x, \dot{x})\, dt = C \tag{5.43}$$

(where C is the specified value of the integral), allows us to find $x(t)$ and the value of the Lagrange multiplier λ.

GEOMETRIC INTERPRETATION OF LAGRANGE MULTIPLIER IN AN ISOPERIMETRIC PROBLEM

We shall now present a geometrical interpretation of the use of the Lagrange multiplier in an isoperimetric problem. The development is due to Bellman [4] and is intended to be explanatory rather than rigorous.

For an arbitrary function $x(t)$, which satisfies the endpoint conditions of the isoperimetric problem described above, there is a definite value of the functional I and a definite value of the functional J. We can suppose these values I and J to be represented by the coordinates of a point in a Euclidean plane. If we consider all functions $x(t)$ satisfying the endpoint conditions, the corresponding values of I and J can then be represented as a set of points in the Euclidean plane. Let us suppose that the set of points forms a closed convex[6] set in the IJ plane, as shown in Fig. 5.7. It is obvious that the maximum or minimum value of I, for any value of J, is a point on the boundary of the convex set. The boundary can theoretically be determined by taking a straight line of the form

$$pI + qJ = r \tag{5.44}$$

and moving it parallel to itself until it is tangential to the set. Or, in other words, we fix p and q and find the maximum and minimum values of r such that at least one point on the straight line (Equation 5.44) is a member of

---

[6] A convex set is a set of points such that, if a straight line is drawn between any two points of the set, every point on the straight line is a member of the set.

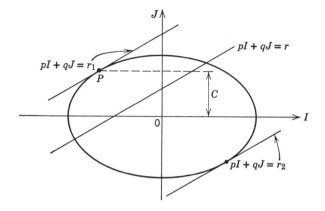

Fig. 5.7. Set of points IJ corresponding to functions $x(t)$.

the convex set. For example, the straight lines tangential to the curve in Fig. 5.7 illustrate the conditions for maximum and minimum values of r, for a definite pair of values p and q. The condition for an extreme value of r is the condition that the expression

$$pI + qJ = p \int_{t_0}^{t_1} f(t, x, \dot{x}) \, dt + q \int_{t_0}^{t_1} g(t, x, \dot{x}) \, dt \qquad (5.45)$$

has an extreme value. If p is not zero, we can divide through by p and we find that the condition for an extreme value of r is that the expression

$$\int_{t_0}^{t_1} f(t, x, \dot{x}) \, dt + \lambda \int_{t_0}^{t_1} g(t, x, \dot{x}) \, dt \qquad (5.46)$$

has an extreme value, where $\lambda = q/p$. As can be observed in Fig. 5.7, the minimum value of I, subject to the condition that $J = C$, is represented by the point P on the IJ plane, which represents an extreme value of the functional (Expression 5.46).

EXAMPLE OF A PROBLEM WITH AN ISOPERIMETRIC CONSTRAINT

As an example of a problem with an isoperimetric constraint, consider once again the control problem discussed in Section 5.3. Suppose that, as before, the integral to be minimized is as given in Equation 5.30. Suppose also that, for some reason, the input u is such that a definite integral square value of u is available for the control of the process and must all be used up. Mathematically speaking, this may be expressed by introducing a second functional of the form

$$J = \int_{t_0}^{t_1} \dot{x}^2 \, dt = C \qquad (5.47)$$

where C is the prescribed integral squared value of the input.

Following the procedure described in this section, we introduce a Lagrange multiplier and form the function F as follows

$$F = x^2 + \dot{x}^2 + \lambda \dot{x}^2 \qquad (5.48)$$

The Euler-Lagrange equation is

$$2x = 2\ddot{x} + 2\lambda\ddot{x} \qquad (5.49)$$

The solution for $x(t)$ is of the form

$$x(t) = A e^{t/\sqrt{1+\lambda}} + B e^{-t/\sqrt{1+\lambda}} \qquad (5.50)$$

From Equation 5.50 the derivative of x can be found, and this allows the integral J of Equation 5.47 to be expressed in terms of A, B, λ, t_0, and t_1. Knowing x^0 at t_0, x^1 at t_1, and the value of C, the values of A, B, and λ can be evaluated. Having done this, the isoperimetric problem is completely solved.

5.5   PROBLEMS WITH MORE THAN ONE DEPENDENT VARIABLE

Variational problems with several dependent variables occur, for example, when we wish to find an optimal state trajectory for a higher-order system. Once again, we shall merely state the procedures to be followed in solving such problems, and shall not attempt a rigorous derivation of the conditions.

Suppose, for example, we wish to find the two functions $x(t)$ and $y(t)$ which minimize a functional of the following form,

$$I = \int_{t_0}^{t_1} f(t, x, \dot{x}, y, \dot{y}) \, dt \qquad (5.51)$$

It turns out that the functions $x(t)$ and $y(t)$ must both satisfy Euler-Lagrange equations; that is, the necessary conditions for an extreme value of I are the Euler-Lagrange equations

$$f_x = \frac{df_{\dot{x}}}{dt}$$

$$\qquad (5.52)$$

$$f_y = \frac{df_{\dot{y}}}{dt}$$

If, in addition, the right-hand endpoint is variable, we also have a transversality condition which may be expressed in the form[7]

$$[(f - \dot{x}f_{\dot{x}} - \dot{y}f_{\dot{y}}) \, dt + f_{\dot{x}} \, dx + f_{\dot{y}} \, dy]_1 = 0 \tag{5.53}$$

See, for example, Halfman [3].

Extending this to n dependent variables, we find that the necessary conditions for an extreme value of

$$I = \int_{t_0}^{t_1} f(t, x_1, \dot{x}_1, \ldots, x_n, \dot{x}_n) \, dt \tag{5.54}$$

are

$$f_{x_i} = \frac{df_{\dot{x}_i}}{dt} \qquad \text{for } i = 1, 2, \ldots, n \tag{5.55}$$

If the right-hand endpoint is variable, we have in addition the transversality condition

$$\left[\left(f - \sum_{i=1}^{n} \dot{x}_i f_{\dot{x}_i} \right) dt + \sum_{i=1}^{n} f_{\dot{x}_i} \, dx_i \right]_1 = 0 \tag{5.56}$$

AUXILIARY CONDITIONS OR CONSTRAINTS

In Section 5.4 we studied problems with isoperimetric constraints, in which it was required to find an extreme value of one functional while another functional remained at a fixed value. Another type of constraint may arise in problems with more than one dependent variable; in this type of "instantaneous constraint" a prescribed relationship or relationships between the dependent variables must be satisfied at every instant.

Problems of this kind may also be treated by the introduction of a Lagrange multiplier, but in this case the multiplier must be treated as a function of time $\lambda(t)$ instead of being a constant. We can explain this in a nonrigorous way by considering an instantaneous constraint to be equivalent to an infinite number of isoperimetric constraints. Suppose that we have a relationship which is to be satisfied at one particular instant of time only, for example a relationship of the form $x_1(\tau)x_2(\tau) = C_\tau$, where τ is some instant of time between t_0 and t_1, x_1 and x_2 are two dependent variables, and C_τ is a constant. This relationship can be expressed as an integral of the following form

$$\int_{t_0}^{t_1} x_1(t)x_2(t)\delta(t - \tau) \, dt = C_\tau \tag{5.57}$$

---

[7] In many cases, the separate terms involved in the transversality condition will themselves be zero. For example, suppose that the final time t_1 is fixed but that the final values of x and y are completely free and independent of one another. In this case the terms $f_{\dot{x}} \, dx$ and $f_{\dot{y}} \, dy$ in Equation 5.53 must both be zero.

where $\delta(t)$ is the Dirac delta function. If such a relationship is to be satisfied at every time τ between t_0 and t_1, we can visualize this constraint as being equivalent to an infinite number of isoperimetric constraints. If each iso-perimetric constraint is introduced with its own Lagrange multiplier, it can be seen that there will be an infinite set of Lagrange multipliers, each valid for one instant of time. Or, in other words, we shall have a Lagrange multiplier which is a function of time.

The procedure for solving a problem with auxiliary constraints may be described as follows. Suppose, for example, we wish to find the functions $x(t)$ and $y(t)$ which minimize the functional

$$I = \int_{t_0}^{t_1} f(t, x, \dot{x}, y, \dot{y}) \, dt \tag{5.58}$$

subject to the constraining equation

$$\phi(t, x, \dot{x}, y, \dot{y}) = 0 \tag{5.59}$$

We introduce the Lagrange multiplier $\lambda(t)$, and form an augmented integrand F, defined by

$$F \triangleq f + \lambda\phi \tag{5.60}$$

In this case it turns out that $x(t)$ and $y(t)$ must satisfy the Euler-Lagrange equations

$$F_x = \frac{dF_{\dot{x}}}{dt} \tag{5.61}$$

and

$$F_{\dot{y}} = \frac{dF_{\dot{y}}}{dt} \tag{5.62}$$

These, together with Equation 5.59, allow the three unknown functions $x(t)$, $y(t)$, and $\lambda(t)$ to be found. It should be noted that, if we treated λ as a third dependent variable, we could write a third Euler-Lagrange equation in the form

$$F_\lambda = \frac{dF_{\dot{\lambda}}}{dt} \tag{5.63}$$

Because F is not an explicit function of $\dot{\lambda}$, the right side of Equation 5.63 is zero.[8] From Equation 5.60 we see that $F_\lambda = \phi$ so that Equation 5.63 reduces to Equation 5.59.

---

[8] The partial derivative $F_{\dot{\lambda}}$ is to be interpreted as the result of differentiating the function F with respect to $\dot{\lambda}$, keeping all other quantities (including λ) fixed. The reader may find it helpful to consult the careful discussion of partial differentiation which appears in Chapter 7 of reference [5].

If the right-hand endpoint is free we obtain, in addition, the transversality condition

$$[(F - \dot{x}F_{\dot{x}} - \dot{y}F_{\dot{y}})\,dt + F_{\dot{x}}\,dx + F_{\dot{y}}\,dy]_1 = 0 \tag{5.64}$$

which is similar in form to Equation 5.53.

Extending this to the case of n dependent variables, we may wish to find the extreme value of the functional (Equation 5.54), in the presence of m constraints, where m is less than n, of the form

$$\phi_j(t, x_1, \dot{x}_1, \ldots, x_n, \dot{x}_n) = 0 \tag{5.65}$$

for $j = 1, 2, \ldots, m < n$. In this case the procedure is to form an augmented integrand

$$F = f + \sum_{j=1}^{m} \lambda_j \phi_j \tag{5.66}$$

where the λ_j are Lagrange multipliers, which are functions of time. Having formed the augmented integrand, we find the functions $x_i(t)$ and $\lambda_j(t)$ which satisfy the Euler-Lagrange equations of the form of Equation 5.55 and a transversality condition of the form of Equation 5.56, with f replaced by F in all cases. Note that the transversality condition need not include summations involving $F_{\dot{\lambda}_j}$, because these quantities are zero.

A CONTROL PROBLEM WITH AN AUXILIARY CONSTRAINT

As an example of a problem with an auxiliary constraint, consider once again the simple control problem studied in Section 5.3. We can state the same problem in two dependent variables u and x, and express the relationship between u and $\dot{x}$ as a constraint. The problem may therefore be stated as follows: Find an expression for the control input $u(t)$, and for the state variable $x(t)$, so as to transfer the system state from x^0 at time t_0 to x^1 at time t_1 (with x^0, t_0, x^1, t_1 all fixed in advance) in such a way as to minimize the integral

$$I = \int_{t_0}^{t_1} (x^2 + u^2)\,dt \tag{5.67}$$

The constraining relationship can be written in the form

$$\dot{x} - u = 0 \tag{5.68}$$

We introduce a Lagrange multiplier λ, and form the function F in the form

$$F = x^2 + u^2 + \lambda(\dot{x} - u) \tag{5.69}$$

The following two Euler-Lagrange equations are obtained for the two dependent variables x and u

$$2x = \dot{\lambda} \tag{5.70}$$

$$2u - \lambda = 0 \tag{5.71}$$

If desired, a third Euler-Lagrange equation may be written for λ, but this will just give Equation 5.68 again. From Equations 5.70 and 5.71 we obtain

$$2x = \dot{\lambda} = 2\dot{u} = 2\ddot{x} \tag{5.72}$$

Comparing the extreme left and right sides of Equation 5.72, we have an equation which is the same as Equation 5.32, and therefore the same solution of the problem. Strictly speaking, we should also investigate the transversality condition because the endpoint values of the dependent variable u are unspecified. However, we see from Equation 5.64 (with y replaced by u) that all terms in the transversality condition would disappear because $F_{\dot{u}}$ is zero. We have, in fact, enough boundary values for x to obtain the complete solution of Equation 5.72 as before, and u is then found as the derivative of x.

5.6 THE MAYER PROBLEM

Suppose that, instead of expressing our optimization problem in terms of the minimization of an integral of the form of Equation 5.54, we study the problem of minimizing a specified function of the final values of the independent and dependent variables, or the difference between a specified function of the final values and a specified function of the initial values. To be specific, suppose that we wish to minimize the quantity defined by

$$I = g(t_1, x_1^{\,1}, x_2^{\,1}, \ldots, x_n^{\,1}) \tag{5.73}$$

subject to the auxiliary conditions

$$\phi_j(t, x_1, \dot{x}_1, \ldots, x_n, \dot{x}_n) = 0 \tag{5.74}$$

for $j = 1, 2, \ldots, m < n$. This type of problem is usually known as the Mayer problem, whereas the problem in which an integral is to be minimized may be called the Lagrange problem. As we shall see, the two problems are not really different but may be treated as alternative formulations of the same problem.

The method of solution of the Mayer problem is as follows [3]. We form the function F, defined by

$$F \triangleq \sum_{i=1}^{m} \lambda_i \phi_i \qquad (5.75)$$

and solve the $n + m$ Euler-Lagrange equations

$$F_{x_i} = \frac{dF_{\dot{x}_i}}{dt} \qquad (i = 1, 2, \ldots, n) \qquad (5.76)$$

$$\phi_j = F_{\lambda_j} = 0 \qquad (j = 1, \ldots, m) \qquad (5.77)$$

subject to the specified boundary conditions, and the following transversality condition at the right-hand endpoint

$$\left[dg + \left(F - \sum_{i=1}^{n} \dot{x}_i F_{\dot{x}_i} \right) dt + \sum_{i=1}^{n} F_{\dot{x}_i}\, dx_i \right]_1 = 0 \qquad (5.78)$$

It may be noted that, as the performance index is a function of the final values of the variables and time in Equation 5.73, at least some of these final values must be free; we should therefore expect to encounter transversality conditions in all problems in Mayer form.

Let us now consider an example of the Mayer problem, which will illustrate the method of solution and will also show that the Lagrange and Mayer forms of the problem are not essentially different from each other. Consider once again the control problem studied in Section 5.3. In order to put this problem in the Mayer form, we change the notation of the problem as follows.

1. Use the symbol x_1 to denote the system state variable (formerly called x).
2. Introduce a new dependent variable x_0, characterized by the differential equation

$$\dot{x}_0 = x_1{}^2 + u^2 \qquad (5.79)$$

with the initial condition $x_0(t_0) = 0$. The value of $x_0(t_1)$ is therefore the same as the value of the integral I of Equation 5.30 or 5.67. The optimal control problem may therefore be stated as follows: "For the system whose state is represented by the vector (x_0, x_1), find the control input $u(t)$ which steers the system, starting from the state $x_0 = 0$, $x_1 = x_1{}^0$ at a specified time t_0, in such a way that the variable x_1 reaches a specified value $x_1{}^1$ at a time t_1, and which makes $x_0(t_1)$ take on the minimum possible value." This is exactly the same problem as that formulated in Section 5.3 (using $x_1{}^0$ and $x_1{}^1$ for x^0 and x^1, respectively), but the problem is now in the Mayer form because the performance index is specified as a function of the final state of the system.

Let us proceed with the solution of this problem. The two constraints may be expressed in the form

$$\phi_0 = \dot{x}_0 - x_1{}^2 - u^2 = 0 \tag{5.80}$$

$$\phi_1 = \dot{x}_1 - u = 0 \tag{5.81}$$

Equation 5.75 may therefore be written in the form

$$\mathscr{F} = \lambda_0(\dot{x}_0 - x_1{}^2 - u^2) + \lambda_1(\dot{x}_1 - u) \tag{5.82}$$

The symbol $\mathscr{F}$ is used here to identify a summation of the form $\sum_{i=0}^{n} \lambda_i \phi_i$, as distinct from the summation (Equation 5.75) starting from $i = 1$. While the handling of the two summations is the same, it will be helpful in later work to maintain the distinction between them. From Equation 5.82 we derive three Euler-Lagrange equations in the three dependent variables x_0, x_1, and u, as follows.[9]

$$0 = \frac{d\lambda_0}{dt} \tag{5.83}$$

$$-2\lambda_0 x_1 = \frac{d\lambda_1}{dt} \tag{5.84}$$

$$-2\lambda_0 u - \lambda_1 = 0 \tag{5.85}$$

Equation 5.83 shows that λ_0 is a constant; the value of this constant can be found from the transversality condition (Equation 5.78)[10] which gives

$$[dx_0 + \lambda_0 \, dx_0]_1 = 0 \tag{5.86}$$

This gives the value of λ_0 to be

$$\lambda_0(t) \equiv -1 \tag{5.87}$$

Substituting this value in Equations 5.84 and 5.85, we obtain the equations

$$2x_1 = \frac{d\lambda_1}{dt} \tag{5.88}$$

$$2u - \lambda_1 = 0 \tag{5.89}$$

These two equations are the same as Equations 5.70 and 5.71, with the minor notational changes we have introduced. The solution of the problem is therefore the same as that previously obtained.

---

[9] As before, writing the Euler-Lagrange equations for λ_0 and λ_1 merely gives us Equations 5.80 and 5.81 again.

[10] Equation 5.78 should be interpreted, for this purpose, in terms of $\mathscr{F}$ instead of F, and in terms of summations from $i = 0$ to n.

5.7   A HIGH-ORDER CONTROL PROBLEM

Let us now generalize this simple control problem to take account of a higher-order system with n state variables and r inputs. Suppose, for example, that we have a system characterized by the vector differential equation[11]

$$\dot{\mathbf{x}} = \mathbf{f}(\mathbf{x}, \mathbf{u}) \tag{5.90}$$

where $\mathbf{x}$ is the vector with components $x_1, \ldots, x_n$, $\mathbf{f}$ is the vector with components $f_1, \ldots, f_n$, and $\mathbf{u}$ is the vector with components $u_1, \ldots, u_r$. Suppose that it is desired to find the control input $\mathbf{u}(t)$, in the interval $[t_0, t_1]$, which transfers the system state from $\mathbf{x}^0$ at time t_0 to $\mathbf{x}^1$ at time t_1, and gives a minimum value to the integral

$$I = \int_{t_0}^{t_1} f_0(\mathbf{x}, \mathbf{u}) \, dt \tag{5.91}$$

This can be solved by formulating the problem in the Mayer form; the following procedure may be used:

1. Introduce a new state variable x_0, characterized by the equation

$$\dot{x}_0 = f_0(\mathbf{x}, \mathbf{u}) \tag{5.92}$$

2. Express the differential equations as constraining equations of the form

$$\phi_i = \dot{x}_i - f_i(\mathbf{x}, \mathbf{u}) = 0 \tag{5.93}$$

for $i = 0, 1, \ldots, n$.[12]

3. Form the function $\mathscr{F}$, defined by

$$\mathscr{F} \triangleq \sum_{i=0}^{n} \lambda_i \phi_i = \sum_{i=0}^{n} \lambda_i [\dot{x}_i - f_i(\mathbf{x}, \mathbf{u})] \tag{5.94}$$

---

[11] As has been pointed out in Chapter 4, the form of Equation 5.90 can still be used even if the derivatives are explicit functions of time, provided that the state vector is augmented by a component which represents the time.

[12] It is noted in Equation 5.74 that the number of constraints is less than the number of dependent variables. The present problem may be interpreted as one with $n + r + 1$ dependent variables ($n + 1$ state variables and r input variables) and the $n + 1$ constraints given by Equation 5.93.

4. Write the Euler-Lagrange equations for the dependent variables x_i, λ_i, and u_j. These are

$$\mathscr{F}_{x_i} = \frac{d}{dt}\mathscr{F}_{\dot{x}_i} \qquad (i = 0, 1, \ldots, n) \tag{5.95}$$

$$\mathscr{F}_{\lambda_i} = \frac{d}{dt}\mathscr{F}_{\dot{\lambda}_i} = 0 \qquad (i = 0, 1, \ldots, n) \tag{5.96}$$

$$\mathscr{F}_{u_j} = \frac{d}{dt}\mathscr{F}_{\dot{u}_j} = 0 \qquad (j = 1, \ldots, r) \tag{5.97}$$

The quantities $\mathscr{F}_{\dot{\lambda}_i}$ and $\mathscr{F}_{\dot{u}_j}$ are zero because $\mathscr{F}$ is not an explicit function of $\dot{\lambda}_i$ or $\dot{u}_j$. Equations 5.96 give Equations 5.93 again, and the solutions of all these equations, together with the boundary and transversality conditions, give the functions $\mathbf{u}(t)$, $^0\mathbf{x}(t)$, and $^0\boldsymbol{\lambda}(t)$ (where $^0\mathbf{x}$ represents the vector with components $x_0, x_1, \ldots, x_n$, and $^0\boldsymbol{\lambda}$ the vector with components $\lambda_0, \lambda_1, \ldots, \lambda_n$). The transversality condition, in this case, may be written in the form

$$\left[dx_0 + \left(\mathscr{F} - \sum_{i=0}^{n} \dot{x}_i \mathscr{F}_{\dot{x}_i} \right) dt + \sum_{i=0}^{n} \mathscr{F}_{\dot{x}_i}\, dx_i \right]_1 = 0 \tag{5.98}$$

The quantities $\mathscr{F}_{\dot{u}_j}$ and $\mathscr{F}_{\dot{\lambda}_j}$ are all zero as before, and need not be written in the transversality condition.

5.8 THE HAMILTONIAN FORMULATION

We have now studied several methods of formulating and solving a simple optimal control problem. Let us now consider one more method, which describes the problem in a highly appropriate way for a system represented by state equations, and which will help us to relate the calculus of variations to the maximum principle which we shall meet in the next chapter.

Referring to the optimal control problem discussed in Section 5.7, let us introduce a function $\mathscr{H}$, defined by

$$\mathscr{H} \triangleq \sum_{i=0}^{n} \lambda_i f_i(\mathbf{x}, \mathbf{u}) \tag{5.99}$$

where the script $\mathscr{H}$ denotes a summation including the term $i = 0$. It should be noted that $\mathscr{H}$ is an explicit function of $\lambda_0, \lambda_1, \ldots, \lambda_n$; $x_1, x_2, \ldots, x_n$; and $u_1, \ldots, u_r$. The quantity $\mathscr{F}$ can be written in the form

$$\mathscr{F} = \sum_{i=0}^{n} \lambda_i \dot{x}_i - \mathscr{H} \tag{5.100}$$

Expressing the three sets of Euler-Lagrange Equations 5.95 to 5.97 in terms of $\mathscr{F}$ as given by Equation 5.100 we obtain, respectively,

$$-\frac{\partial \mathscr{H}}{\partial x_i} = \frac{d\lambda_i}{dt} \qquad (i = 0, 1, \ldots, n) \tag{5.101}$$

$$\frac{dx_i}{dt} - \frac{\partial \mathscr{H}}{\partial \lambda_i} = 0 \qquad (i = 0, 1, \ldots, n) \tag{5.102}$$

$$\frac{\partial \mathscr{H}}{\partial u_j} = 0 \qquad (j = 1, \ldots, r) \tag{5.103}$$

Equations 5.101 to 5.103 may be considered as the equivalent of the Euler-Lagrange equations for this problem, and it is a necessary condition for optimal control that they be satisfied at every instant in the interval $[t_0, t_1]$. Equations 5.101 and 5.102 are analogous to Hamilton's equations of motion, the quantity $\mathscr{H}$ being analogous to the quantity known as the Hamiltonian. In other words, we can visualize the functions λ_i (the Lagrange multipliers) as if they were momentum variables for a fictitious mechanical system for which the x_i are the position variables. We can now work the problem in terms of the Hamiltonian $\mathscr{H}$, without using the function $\mathscr{F}$. The transformation by which we derive one form from the other is called the Legendre dual transformation. This transformation is described in the context of mechanics by Lanczos [6], and in a control context by McCann [7, 8] and Pagurek [9].

The transversality condition, for the Hamiltonian formulation of the problem, can easily be shown to be

$$\left[dx_0 - \mathscr{H}\, dt + \sum_{i=0}^{n} \lambda_i \, dx_i\right]_1 = 0 \tag{5.104}$$

Let us now illustrate the solution of our simple optimal control problem of Section 5.3, using the Hamiltonian formulation. As before, we introduce an extra state variable x_0 (characterized by Equation 5.79), and two auxiliary variables (Lagrange multipliers) λ_0 and λ_1. We form the function $\mathscr{H}$, which in this case is

$$\mathscr{H} = \lambda_0(x_1{}^2 + u^2) + \lambda_1 u \tag{5.105}$$

Equations 5.101 give differential equations for λ_0 and λ_1 as follows:

$$\dot{\lambda}_0 = \frac{-\partial \mathscr{H}}{\partial x_0} = 0 \tag{5.106}$$

$$\dot{\lambda}_1 = -\frac{\partial \mathscr{H}}{\partial x_1} = -2\lambda_0 x_1 \tag{5.107}$$

The condition for u to be an optimal control input is given by Equation 5.103, which may be written as

$$\frac{\partial \mathcal{H}}{\partial u} = 2\lambda_0 u + \lambda_1 = 0 \qquad (5.108)$$

The transversality condition (assuming a fixed-time, fixed x_1 endpoint problem) is

$$[dx_0 + \lambda_0 \, dx_0]_1 = 0 \qquad (5.109)$$

From Equations 5.106 and 5.109, λ_0 is constant and equal to -1 as before in Equation 5.87. Hence Equations 5.107 and 5.108 can be written in the form

$$\dot{\lambda}_1 = 2x_1 \qquad (5.110)$$

$$-2u + \lambda_1 = 0 \qquad (5.111)$$

These equations are the same as Equations 5.88 and 5.89, and therefore provide the same solution as before.

SUMMARY

In this chapter we have introduced the calculus of variations by studying its application to a simple problem in optimal control. As we have only covered a small portion of the theory of calculus of variations, in a highly simplified way, the reader may wish to continue his study by referring to some of the books on the subject in the list of references below. In particular, the books by Gelfand and Fomin [1], Elsgolc [2], Halfman [3], and Lanczos [6] are recommended. For an account of the calculus of variations, with particular reference to optimal control, the books by Tou [10], Noton [11], and Hestenes [12] may be consulted.

The material studied in this chapter is intended to help the reader in his understanding of the maximum principle, which is studied in the next chapter. In the next two chapters we shall see that a close relationship exists between the calculus of variations, the maximum principle, and dynamic programming.

REFERENCES

[1] Gelfand, I. M., and S. V. Fomin, *Calculus of Variations*, Prentice-Hall, Englewood Cliffs, N.J., 1963.

[2] Elsgolc, L. E., *Calculus of Variations*, Pergamon Press, London, and Addison-Wesley, Reading, Mass., 1962.

[3] Halfman, R. L., *Dynamics. Volume II, Systems, Variational Methods, and Relativity*, Addison-Wesley, Reading, Mass., 1962.

[4] Bellman, R., *Adaptive Control Processes: A Guided Tour*, Princeton University Press, Princeton, 1961.

[5] Hildebrand, F. B., *Advanced Calculus for Applications*, Prentice-Hall, Englewood Cliffs, N.J., 1962.

[6] Lanczos, C., *The Variational Principles of Mechanics*, 2nd ed., University of Toronto Press, Toronto, 1962.

[7] McCann, M. J., "Introduction to Variational Methods for Optimal Control," *Trans. Soc. Instrument Technology*, 13, No. 4, 232–237 (1961).

[8] McCann, M. J., "Variational Approaches to the Optimal Trajectory Problem," in *An Exposition of Adaptive Control*, J. H. Westcott, ed., Pergamon Press, Oxford, 1962, pp. 93–107.

[9] Pagurek, B., "The Classical Calculus of Variations in Optimal Control Problems: An Introduction to the Maximum Principle of Pontryagin," University of Toronto, Dept. of Electrical Engineering, Research Rep. No. 26, October, 1962.

[10] Tou, J. T., *Modern Control Theory*, McGraw-Hill, New York, 1964.

[11] Noton, A. R. M., *Introduction to Variational Methods in Control Engineering*, Pergamon Press, Oxford, 1965.

[12] Hestenes, M. R., *Calculus of Variations and Optimal Control Theory*, Wiley, New York, 1966.

[13] Bliss, G. A., *Lectures on the Calculus of Variations*, University of Chicago Press, Chicago, 1946.

[14] Bolza, O., *Lectures on the Calculus of Variations*, Dover Pub., New York, 1960 (Paperback.)

[15] Weinstock, R., *Calculus of Variations with Applications to Physics and Engineering*, McGraw-Hill, New York, 1952.

PROBLEMS

1. For the simple integrator shown in Fig. 5.8, find the control input $u(t)$ which transfers the system from a specified initial state $x(0)$ to a final state $x(t_1)$, in such a way as to minimize the integral

$$I = \int_0^{t_1} (u^2 + x^2)\, dt \qquad (5.112)$$

subject to each of the following conditions:

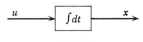

Fig. 5.8

(a) $x(0) = 1$, $x(t_1) = 0$, $t_1 = 1$.
(b) $x(0) = 1$, $x(t_1)$ unspecified, $t_1 = 1$.
(c) $x(0) = 1$, $x(t_1) = 0$, t_1 unspecified.

Calculate the minimum value of the integral corresponding to each case.

2. Repeat Problem 1 for the system shown in Fig. 5.9.

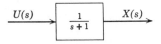

Fig. 5.9

3. For the double integrator shown in Fig. 5.10, find the control input $u^*(t)$ which controls the system in such a way as to minimize the integral

$$I = \int_0^\infty (u^2 + x^2)\, dt \qquad (5.113)$$

Assuming that the initial state is $x(0) = 1$, $\dot{x}(0) = 0$, express $x(t)$ and $u^*(t)$ as functions of time.

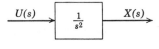

Fig. 5.10

4. For the systems shown in Figs. 5.8, 5.9, and 5.10, show that, if each system is to be controlled in such a way as to minimize the integral in Equation 5.113, the optimum control input $u(t)$ can in each case be expressed as a linear function of the state variables. Find the appropriate function in each case.

5. For the double integrator shown in Fig. 5.10, find the control input $u(t)$ which transfers the system state from $x(0) = 1$, $\dot{x}(0) = 1$ to the state $x(t_1) = 0$, $\dot{x}(t_1) = 0$, in such a way as to minimize the integral

$$I = \int_0^{t_1} u^2\, dt \qquad (5.114)$$

where the value of t_1 is 4 seconds. Calculate the value of the integral I.

6. An electric motor, as represented by the equivalent circuit in Fig. 5.11, is running at a speed ω^0 and has an instantaneous shaft angle θ^0 at time t_0.

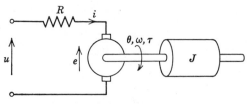

Fig. 5.11

The equations of motion are as follows:

$$u = e + iR$$
$$\tau = J\dot{\omega}$$
$$e = k\omega \qquad\qquad (5.115)$$
$$\tau = ki$$

where u is the applied voltage, e is the generated voltage, i is the armature current, τ is the torque, and k is a parameter of the machine. It is required to find the control input $u(t)$ which will transfer the system to the state $\theta = 0$, $\omega = 0$, in a fixed time, in such a way that the energy lost in the resistance R is a minimum. For simplicity, the following values may be assumed:

$$k = 1, J = 1, R = 1, t_0 = 0, t_1 = 1, \omega^0 = 1, \theta^0 = 1.$$

Write the state equations of the system, and find the optimum control input $u(t)$.

7. The system shown in Fig. 5.12 has an impulse response e^{-t}. If the initial state $x(0)$ is zero, find the control input $u(t)$, in the interval $0 \leqslant t \leqslant 1$, which, while satisfying the constraint

$$\int_0^1 [u(t)]^2 \, dt \leqslant k^2 \qquad\qquad (5.116)$$

gives the maximum value of $x(1)$.

u → [e^{-t}] → x

Fig. 5.12

8. An inclined plane has a rectangular coordinate system such that the x axis is horizontal and the y axis points directly uphill. A trolley, which can be steered but which has no motive power other than the gravitational force associated with the inclined plane, starts with zero velocity at the origin of the coordinate system. Derive a general expression for the path along which the trolley should be steered in order to reach a specified point on the plane in minimum time.

6

The Maximum Principle

This chapter deals with Pontryagin's maximum principle,[1] which may be considered as an extension or generalization of the calculus of variations, to enable us to take account of systems whose input signals have constraints of certain types. It will be recalled that in Section 5.8, where we studied the Hamiltonian formulation of a problem in the calculus of variations, one of the conditions which had to be satisfied for optimal control was that the partial derivative of the Hamiltonian $\mathscr{H}$, with respect to each component of the control input vector, was zero at every instant during the process. We did not, however, consider the possibility that the instantaneous value of the control input vector might be limited in some way which might prevent that value of $\mathbf{u}$, which makes the partial derivatives $\partial \mathscr{H}/\partial u_j$ equal to zero, from being attained. The maximum principle allows us to deal with situations in which these limitations occur.

As in the chapter on the calculus of variations, the treatment in this chapter is non-rigorous, and we do not attempt to prove the theorems involved. For the reader who wishes to study this subject in greater depth, references to material for further study are given at the end of the chapter.

6.1 CONSTRAINTS ON THE CONTROL INPUTS

As we have indicated in the previous section, the maximum principle is used to study the optimal control of systems in which there is a constraint or limitation of some kind on the instantaneous value of the control input. Let

---

[1] The same principle is sometimes referred to as the minimum principle [1]. As pointed out in Chapter 1, the maximization of a quantity is equivalent to the minimization of some complementary quantity; the reader may therefore choose whichever designation he thinks more appropriate.

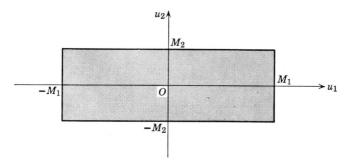

Fig. 6.1. The closed bounded region (Equation 6.2.)

us now consider some of the typical constraints which can be handled by the maximum principle.

In particular, suppose we consider a system whose behavior is governed by the differential equations

$$\frac{dx_i}{dt} = f_i(x_1, x_2, \ldots, x_n, u_1, \ldots, u_r) \qquad (i = 1, 2, \ldots, n) \qquad (6.1)$$

The typical problem which can be solved by the maximum principle is one in which the control vector $\mathbf{u}$, with components $u_1, \ldots, u_r$, is constrained so as to lie in a closed bounded region $\mathbf{U}$ in the r-dimensional vector space of the control inputs. As examples illustrating this type of constraint, let us consider the following two cases, in both of which $r = 2$.

1. A closed bounded region $\mathbf{U}$ may be specified by the inequalities

$$|u_1| \leqslant M_1 \qquad |u_2| \leqslant M_2 \qquad (6.2)$$

The region $\mathbf{U}$ is illustrated in Fig. 6.1; the control vector $\mathbf{u}$ is constrained to lie in or on the boundary of the rectangle shown shaded in the diagram.

2. A closed bounded region $\mathbf{U}$ may be specified by the inequality

$$u_1{}^2 + u_2{}^2 \leqslant R^2 \qquad (6.3)$$

The region $\mathbf{U}$ in this case is illustrated in Fig. 6.2; the control vector $\mathbf{u}$ is constrained to lie in or on the boundary of the circle shown shaded in the diagram.

It is possible that the region $\mathbf{U}$ may vary with time; for example, the radius R of the circle in Fig. 6.2 might be a variable. In this chapter, however, we shall consider $\mathbf{U}$ to be fixed in all cases. Any control vector $\mathbf{u}$ which satisfies the requirement that $\mathbf{u}$ lies in the closed bounded region $\mathbf{U}$ at every instant will be called an *admissible* control input.

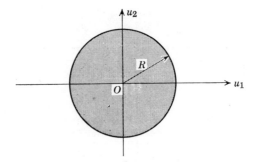

Fig. 6.2. The closed bounded region (Equation 6.3).

6.2 THE MAXIMUM PRINCIPLE

FIXED TIME, FIXED ENDPOINTS

Let us illustrate the use of the maximum principle by considering once again the problem in optimal control which was studied in Section 5.7. The problem is to find the optimal control vector $\mathbf{u}(t)$, applied to a system whose differential equations are of the form of Equations 6.1 (which are the same as Equation 5.90), in order to achieve a transition of the system state from a given initial state $\mathbf{x}^0$ at time t_0 to a specified final state $\mathbf{x}^1$ at a specified time t_1 and at the same time give the minimum possible value of a specified functional of the form

$$I = \int_{t_0}^{t_1} f_0(\mathbf{x}, \mathbf{u}) \, dt \tag{6.4}$$

In the previous consideration of this problem, we made no restriction on the control vector $\mathbf{u}$. In our present study of the problem, we shall assume that the vector $\mathbf{u}$ is constrained so as to lie within a specified closed bounded region $\mathbf{U}$ at every instant.

As before, we put the problem in the Mayer form by introducing an extra state variable x_0, such that

$$\begin{aligned} \dot{x}_0 &= f_0(\mathbf{x}, \mathbf{u}) \\ x_0(t_0) &= 0 \end{aligned} \tag{6.5}$$

where $f_0(\mathbf{x}, \mathbf{u})$ is the same function as in Equation 6.4. The value of $x_0(t_1)$ therefore gives the value of the functional I. As before, we introduce a set of auxiliary dependent variables or Lagrange multipliers; in this chapter we shall use the notation $p_0, p_1, \ldots, p_n$ to refer to the auxiliary variables, as this notation is more commonly used in the study of the maximum principle.

As we did in Section 5.8, we define a Hamiltonian $\mathscr{H}$, in terms of the system state variables and the auxiliary variables, in the form

$$\mathscr{H} \triangleq \sum_{i=0}^{n} p_i f_i(\mathbf{x}, \mathbf{u}) \tag{6.6}$$

The differential equations governing the behavior of the auxiliary variables and the system state variables can now be written in the forms

$$\frac{dp_i}{dt} = -\frac{\partial \mathscr{H}}{\partial x_i} \qquad (i = 0, 1, \ldots, n) \tag{6.7}$$

$$\frac{dx_i}{dt} = \frac{\partial \mathscr{H}}{\partial p_i} \qquad (i = 0, 1, \ldots, n) \tag{6.8}$$

It should be noted that, in view of Equation 6.6, Equations 6.7 may be written in the form

$$\frac{dp_i}{dt} = -\sum_{j=0}^{n} p_j \frac{\partial f_j}{\partial x_i} \qquad (i = 0, 1, \ldots, n) \tag{6.9}$$

Equations 6.9 are linear and homogeneous. This means that if, for example, a certain vector function $\mathbf{q}(t)$ is a solution of Equations 6.9, then any vector function $a\mathbf{q}(t)$, where a is any scalar constant, is also a solution of Equations 6.9 (but would not, except in a trivial case, satisfy the same initial conditions). The significance of this fact will be pointed out later.

Having introduced the auxiliary variables and the Hamiltonian as described above, a necessary condition for $\mathbf{u}(t)$ to be an optimal control in the unconstrained case is, as given by Equations 5.103, that the partial derivatives of $\mathscr{H}$ with respect to all the u_j are zero at every instant. However, in the present case where we have the $\mathbf{u}$ vector constrained to lie in a specified closed bounded region, the value of $\mathbf{u}$ satisfying this condition may lie outside the permissible region. In this case, the maximum principle simply replaces the conditions given by Equations 5.103 by the condition that $\mathbf{u}$ must at every instant take on such a value that, while remaining in the permissible closed bounded region, it makes the Hamiltonian $\mathscr{H}$ take on the largest[2] possible value that can be achieved by an admissible control at that instant.

---

[2] In view of the fact that Equations 6.9 are linear and homogeneous, if some vector function $\mathbf{q}(t)$ is a solution of Equations 6.9, $-\mathbf{q}(t)$ is also a solution. The value of $\mathscr{H}$ corresponding to one solution is the negative of the value corresponding to the other, and if it is a maximum in one case it is a minimum in the other. We can therefore consider either the maximization or the minimization of the Hamiltonian, and call the method we are using either the maximum principle or the minimum principle.

The maximum principle may be stated, in terms of the problem dealt with in this section, as follows: "If, for the system characterized by differential Equations 6.1, it is desired to transfer the system state from $\mathbf{x}^0$ at time t_0 to $\mathbf{x}^1$ at time t_1, in such a way as to minimize the value of the variable $x_0(t_1)$ defined by Equation 6.5, then the following conditions must be satisfied for optimal control. (1) There must exist a set of auxiliary variables $p_0, p_1, \ldots, p_n$, and a Hamiltonian $\mathscr{H}$ as defined by Equation 6.6, such that Equations 6.7 and 6.8 are satisfied at every instant in $[t_0, t_1]$. (2) The optimal control $\mathbf{u}^*(t)$ must be such that, at every instant in $[t_0, t_1]$, it makes the Hamiltonian $\mathscr{H}$ take on the maximum possible value that can be attained by any admissible control input under the conditions which exist at that instant. Note that this implies a 'global maximization' of $\mathscr{H}$ (maximization over the whole admissible region $\mathbf{U}$) instead of the local maximization implied by $\partial \mathscr{H} / \partial u_j = 0$."

As in the calculus of variations, we shall have to obtain some of the necessary boundary conditions using a transversality condition similar to that specified by Equation 5.104. If the endpoints $\mathbf{x}^0$ and $\mathbf{x}^1$ are fixed, as we have assumed, we have $2n$ boundary conditions specified for the $2n + 2$ first-order differential Equations 6.7 and 6.8. A further boundary condition is obtained by taking $x_0(t_0)$ to be zero as specified in Equation 6.5, and the remaining boundary condition needed is obtained from the transversality condition (Equation 5.104). As in Chapter 5 (see Equation 5.109, for example) this gives the value of $p_0(t_1)$ to be[3]

$$p_0(t_1) = -1 \tag{6.10}$$

From Equation 6.7 we see that the time derivative of p_0 is zero, so that p_0 is a constant and Equation 6.10 is satisfied at every instant during the optimal transition (compare Section 5.8).

FINAL TIME UNSPECIFIED

If the final time is not specified, the transversality condition, in the form given by Equation 5.104, specifies that the final value of $\mathscr{H}$ is zero. This item of information compensates for the information lost by not knowing the final time. As we shall see later, the value of $\mathscr{H}$ is in fact zero throughout the entire process in this case.

We shall now study in more detail a very commonly used performance criterion, namely that of minimum time, and examine several examples of systems which are controlled in such a way as to minimize the transit time.

---

[3] Because Equations 6.9 are linear and homogeneous, $p_0(t_1)$ can be taken to be any negative value and the other components of $\mathbf{p}$ will be scaled up or down to suit. If we are using the minimum principle, $p_0(t_1)$ is taken to be $+1$ (or other *positive* value).

6.3   THE MINIMUM-TIME CONTROL PROBLEM

FIXED ENDPOINTS

The minimum-time problem may be considered as a special case of the more general optimal-control problem considered in the previous section. If we suppose that it is desired to control the system characterized by Equation 6.1 so that the state is transferred from a specified point $\mathbf{x}^0$ at time t_0 to a specified point $\mathbf{x}^1$ in minimum time, we can state the performance criterion in the form of Equation 6.4 provided that the integrand is defined as

$$f_0(\mathbf{x}, \mathbf{u}) \equiv 1 \tag{6.11}$$

The Hamiltonian $\mathscr{H}$, as defined by Equation 6.6, therefore becomes

$$\mathscr{H} = p_0 + \sum_{i=1}^{n} p_i f_i(\mathbf{x}, \mathbf{u}) \tag{6.12}$$

In view of our remarks in the previous section, we can say that p_0 is constant and equal to -1. We can define a new Hamiltonian H by omitting the p_0 from Equation 6.12, and we obtain the relationship

$$H \triangleq \sum_{i=1}^{n} p_i f_i(\mathbf{x}, \mathbf{u}) \tag{6.13}$$

In view of Equations 6.7, 6.8, and 6.12, we can now say that

$$\frac{dp_i}{dt} = -\frac{\partial H}{\partial x_i} \qquad (i = 1, 2, \ldots, n) \tag{6.14}$$

$$\frac{\partial x_i}{dt} = \frac{\partial H}{\partial p_i} \qquad (i = 1, 2, \ldots, n) \tag{6.15}$$

We can therefore say that a necessary condition for the control input $\mathbf{u}$ to be a time-optimal control is that $\mathbf{u}$ must be chosen from the admissible region, at every instant of time during the process, in such a way that the Hamiltonian H achieves its maximum possible value. If the two endpoints $\mathbf{x}^0$ and $\mathbf{x}^1$ are prescribed, we have the $2n$ boundary conditions required for the complete solution of the $2n$ first-order differential Equations 6.14 and 6.15.[4] As before, the solution of the boundary-value problem may be quite difficult; we shall discuss this more fully in Chapter 8.

---

[4] Because the final time t_1 is free, the transversality condition tells us that the final value of H is unity (or, more generally, a positive value) in this instance. As we shall see later, the value of H is constant in this case.

The maximization of the Hamiltonian H or $\mathscr{H}$ can be interpreted geometrically. For example, the quantity H defined by Equation 6.13 can be interpreted as the scalar product of the vectors $\mathbf{p}$ and $\mathbf{f}$, and we can interpret the maximization of H as the maximization of the projection of the vector $\mathbf{f}$, which represents the velocity of the representative point $\mathbf{x}$, on the vector $\mathbf{p}$. Similarly, the maximization of $\mathscr{H}$ can be represented geometrically as the maximization of the velocity of the representative point $^0\mathbf{x}$ on the vector $^0\mathbf{p}$, where $^0\mathbf{x}$ represents the vector $x_0, x_1, \ldots, x_n$ and $^0\mathbf{p}$ the vector $p_0, p_1, \ldots, p_n$. We shall explore this geometric interpretation a little further in Chapter 7, when we discuss the similarities between the maximum principle and dynamic programming.

Let us now illustrate the use of the maximum principle in time-optimal control problems by considering a few simple examples.

A DOUBLE INTEGRATOR

Consider the time-optimal control of a double integrator, as shown in Fig. 6.3.

The values of x and its first derivative can be used as the two state variables for this system. Denoting these by x_1 and x_2, respectively, we can write the differential equations governing the behavior of the system as the following two first-order equations.

$$\frac{dx_1}{dt} = x_2$$

$$\frac{dx_2}{dt} = u$$

(6.16)

Suppose that it is desired to find the control input function $u(t)$ which will transfer the system state from a specified initial state $\mathbf{x}^0$ to a specified final state $\mathbf{x}^1$. Let us also assume that the input u is subject to a magnitude constraint defined by

$$|u| \leqslant M$$

(6.17)

The Hamiltonian H, as defined by Equation 6.13, has the following form in this case

$$H = p_1 x_2 + p_2 u$$

(6.18)

Fig. 6.3. A double integrator.

For a given set of values p_1, p_2, and x_2, the function H takes on its maximum value if u takes on one or other of its extreme values M or $-M$ (the former if p_2 is positive, the latter if p_2 is negative). We can express this mathematically by saying that the optimal value of $u(t)$, denoted by $u^*(t)$, is given by

$$u^*(t) = M \text{ sgn } [p_2(t)] \tag{6.19}$$

where sgn $[p_2(t)]$ is the *signum function* defined by

$$\text{sgn } [x] = \begin{cases} 1 & \text{for } x > 0 \\ -1 & \text{for } x < 0 \\ \text{undefined} & \text{for } x = 0 \end{cases} \tag{6.20}$$

The differential equations for p_1 and p_2 are derived in the manner of Equations 6.14, and are as follows:

$$\frac{dp_1}{dt} = 0$$
$$\frac{dp_2}{dt} = -p_1 \tag{6.21}$$

The four boundary conditions required for the complete solution of Equations 6.16 and 6.21 are provided by the two specified initial and two specified final values of the state variables x_1 and x_2. These equations, together with Equation 6.19 and the specified boundary conditions, allow the time-optimal control input $u^*(t)$ to be found.

It is very easy to find the *form* of the optimal control input u^* in this case. If we examine Equations 6.21, we see immediately that p_1 is a constant, which we may denote by the symbol a. The second equation of Equations 6.21 then shows p_2 to be linear in t. We have, therefore

$$\begin{aligned} p_1(t) &= a \\ p_2(t) &= -at + b \end{aligned} \tag{6.22}$$

where b is another constant. An examination of Equations 6.22 shows that, as t varies over any range whatever, the value of $p_2(t)$ changes sign not more than once. In view of Equation 6.19, therefore, we can immediately see that the optimal control input u^*, during the minimum-time transition from any specified initial state to any specified final state, takes on only the values M and $-M$, and changes sign not more than once during the transition.

In order to study the form of the optimal trajectories in a particular case, let us assume the following minor simplifications.

1. The final state $\mathbf{x}^1$ is the origin $(0, 0)$.
2. The value of M (the maximum allowable value of u) is unity. That is, u^* takes on only the values 1 and -1 during a time-optimal transition.

Let us study the state trajectories of this system under the influence of the input $u = +1$. From Equations 6.16 we see that

$$x_2 = t + c \tag{6.23}$$

and

$$x_1 = \frac{t^2}{2} + ct + d \tag{6.24}$$

where c and d are constants. From Equations 6.23 and 6.24 we see that

$$x_2{}^2 = t^2 + 2ct + c^2 = 2x_1 + e \tag{6.25}$$

where $e = c^2 - 2d$ is another constant. For different values of e, the relationship between x_1 and x_2 can be illustrated by the family of parabolas shown in Fig. 6.4. The arrows on the trajectories show the direction of increasing time t. If the representative point reaches the origin while $u = +1$, it must do so by following the trajectory AO in Fig. 6.4, as no other trajectory on the diagram passes through the origin.

Let us now study the state trajectories under the influence of an input $u = -1$. By similar reasoning to that in the previous case, we deduce that the relationship between x_1 and x_2 is of the form

$$x_2{}^2 = -2x_1 + f \tag{6.26}$$

where f is a constant. For different values of f, the relationship between x_1 and x_2 can be illustrated by the family of parabolas shown in Fig. 6.5. If the representative point reaches the origin while $u = -1$, it must do so by following the trajectory BO shown in Fig. 6.5, as no other trajectory on that diagram passes through the origin.

Recalling that the optimal input takes on only the values $+1$ and -1, and changes sign at most once, we see that, if the initial state is not on AO of

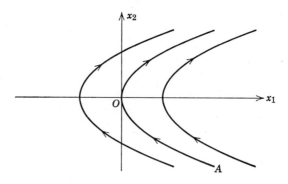

Fig. 6.4. State trajectories for $u = +1$.

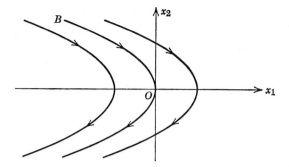

Fig. 6.5. State trajectories for $u = -1$.

Fig. 6.4 or BO of Fig. 6.5, the initial input must be such as to transfer the state to some point on one of these curves. When the representative point reaches one or other of these curves, the input must therefore switch from its maximum positive value to its maximum negative value, or vice versa. The family of time-optimal trajectories from arbitrary initial states to the origin of the state space can easily be seen to be as shown in Fig. 6.6. The curve AOB is formed by the combination of AO of Fig. 6.4 and BO of Fig. 6.5.

If the initial state point is above AOB in Fig. 6.6, the input u^* is -1, and this continues until the curve AO is reached, at which point u^* becomes $+1$ and the curve AO is followed to the origin. Below AOB the input u^* is $+1$, and this continues until the curve BO is reached, at which point u^* becomes -1 and the curve BO is followed to the origin. The curve AOB is therefore a switching curve, which divides the phase plane into two regions corresponding

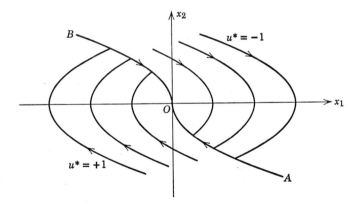

Fig. 6.6. Family of time-optimal trajectories for double integrator.

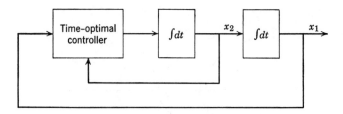

Fig. 6.7. Time-optimal controller operating on state variables.

to $u^* = +1$ and $u^* = -1$. A time-optimal controller, which can be represented as in the block diagram of Fig. 6.7, is required to choose u^* in accordance with the following logical rules:

$$\begin{aligned} u^* &= +1 && \text{if } \mathbf{x} \text{ is below } AOB \text{ or on } AO \\ u^* &= -1 && \text{if } \mathbf{x} \text{ is above } AOB \text{ or on } BO \end{aligned} \tag{6.27}$$

It is easy to see from Fig. 6.6 that it is possible to reach the origin from any initial state whatever with at most one sign change in the control input u^*. It should be noted that the optimal input at any instant is a function of the instantaneous state of the system.

A SECOND-ORDER LINEAR SYSTEM

Let us now consider another example of time-optimal control of a linear system. We shall take as our example the second-order linear system shown in Fig. 6.8, where we shall represent the state of the system by the variable x (called x_1) and its first derivative $\dot{x}$ (called x_2). Let us suppose that it is desired to transfer the system from some specified initial state to some specified final state in the shortest possible time, with the input $u(t)$ being subjected to the magnitude constraint (Equation 6.17) as before.

The differential equations governing the behavior of the system of Fig. 6.8 may be written in the form

$$\frac{dx_1}{dt} = x_2$$

$$\frac{dx_2}{dt} = -x_1 - \alpha x_2 + u \tag{6.28}$$

$$U(s) \longrightarrow \boxed{\frac{1}{s^2 + \alpha s + 1}} \longrightarrow X(s)$$

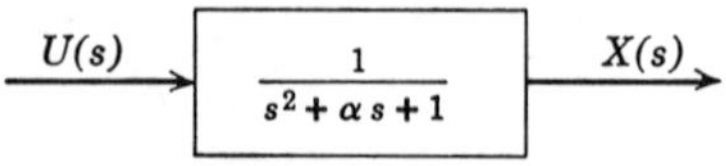

Fig. 6.8. A second-order linear system.

We can write the Hamiltonian H, as defined by Equation 6.13, in the form

$$H = p_1 x_2 + p_2(-x_1 - \alpha x_2 + u) \qquad (6.29)$$

From Equation 6.29 we see that the optimal value of u is given by

$$u^* = M \operatorname{sgn} [p_2] \qquad (6.30)$$

The differential equations governing the behavior of the p variables may be derived from Equation 6.14 in the form

$$\frac{dp_1}{dt} = p_2$$
$$\frac{dp_2}{dt} = -p_1 + \alpha p_2 \qquad (6.31)$$

Taken together, the two Equations 6.31 may be written in the form of a single differential equation in terms of p_2, as follows:

$$\frac{d^2 p_2}{dt^2} - \alpha \frac{dp_2}{dt} + p_2 = 0 \qquad (6.32)$$

The solution to Equation 6.32 may be written in the form

$$p_2 = e^{\alpha t/2}[Pe^{(\sqrt{\alpha^2 - 4})t/2} + Qe^{-(\sqrt{\alpha^2 - 4})t/2}] \qquad (6.33)$$

where P and Q are constants, which may be complex if the roots of the characteristic Equation 6.32 are complex.

If the roots of the characteristic equation corresponding to differential Equation 6.32 are real, which can easily be found to correspond to the case where the roots of the characteristic equation of the original system are real, it is easy to see by inspection of Equation 6.33 that $p_2(t)$ changes sign at most once during the course of an optimal transition. This means that u^* as given by Equation 6.30 has only one sign change, or two periods of constant input M or $-M$, during the course of a time-optimal transition from one state to another.

If the roots of the characteristic equation corresponding to differential Equation 6.32 are complex (this case corresponding to the case of complex roots of the original system characteristic equation), Equation 6.33 can be written in the form

$$p_2 = Ve^{\alpha t/2} \sin \left[\frac{(\sqrt{4 - \alpha^2})t}{2} + \phi \right] \qquad (6.34)$$

where V and ϕ are constants. Equation 6.34 shows that, as the time t changes, there is no limit to the number of changes of sign of p_2, and therefore of u^*, which may occur during an optimal transition. However, assuming that the transition is accomplished in a finite time, the number of sign changes of p_2, and therefore of u^*, is finite.

Let us illustrate the case of complex roots by an example. A fairly simple example is obtained by taking $\alpha = 0$, in which case the roots of the characteristic equation of the system are purely imaginary and the system is simply a linear oscillator. For simplicity, also, let us assume that the maximum allowable value of u is unity, meaning that the value of M in Equation 6.30 is unity, and let us assume also that the desired final state is the origin. Since $\alpha = 0$, we can write Equation 6.34 in the form

$$p_2 = V \sin(t + \phi) \qquad (6.35)$$

It is obvious that we can ensure that the value of V in Equation 6.35 is positive, because a reversal of the sign of V can be counteracted by changing the angle ϕ by π radians, and therefore we can write the expression for u^* in the form

$$u^* = \text{sgn}\,[\sin(t + \phi)] \qquad (6.36)$$

It is obvious from Equation 6.36 that u^* does not remain constant at one value for longer than π seconds. Depending on the value of ϕ, and the initial and final time instants t_0 and t_1, the first and last intervals of constant input may be less than π seconds, as shown in Fig. 6.9. All the periods of constant input except the first and last are exactly π seconds in duration.

In order to find the form of the optimal trajectories, let us consider the behavior of the system of Fig. 6.8 under the influence of each of the two possible inputs, $+1$ and -1.

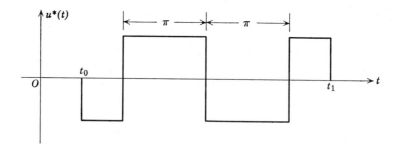

Fig. 6.9. A typical time-optimal control input for the system of Fig. 6.8, with imaginary roots.

With input $u = +1$, Equations 6.28 may be written as

$$\frac{dx_1}{dt} = x_2$$

$$\frac{dx_2}{dt} = -x_1 + 1 \tag{6.37}$$

Making the substitutions

$$y_1 = x_1 - 1$$
$$y_2 = x_2 \tag{6.38}$$

we can express Equations 6.37 in the form

$$\frac{dy_1}{dt} = y_2$$

$$\frac{dy_2}{dt} = -y_1 \tag{6.39}$$

Equations 6.39 are the differential equations corresponding to simple harmonic motion (similar to Equations 6.31 with $\alpha = 0$), and the solutions are of the form

$$y_1 = W \sin(t + \theta)$$
$$y_2 = W \cos(t + \theta) \tag{6.40}$$

where W and θ are constants. It is obvious from Equations 6.40 that y_1 and y_2 satisfy at every instant the equation

$$y_1^2 + y_2^2 = W^2 \tag{6.41}$$

The trajectories of the representative point in the $y_1 y_2$ phase plane are a family of concentric circles with common center at the origin. In view of the transformation described by Equation 6.38 the corresponding trajectories in the $x_1 x_2$ plane (the phase plane of the system we are considering) are a family of concentric circles with their common center at the point $(1, 0)$, as shown in Fig. 6.10. The arrows on the trajectories indicate the direction of increasing time. The time taken for the representative point to travel around a complete circle is 2π seconds in this case, regardless of the radius of the circle. From Equation 6.36 it can be seen that the maximum length of time which can elapse between sign changes of u^* is π seconds, so that any one circular trajectory will be followed for not more than half a revolution during a time-optimal transition. In view of Equation 6.36, when the representative point reaches the origin the input must be $+1$ or -1. If u^* is $+1$ during the period of constant input immediately prior to arrival at the origin, the representative point must follow part or all of the semicircle A_1O during that period.

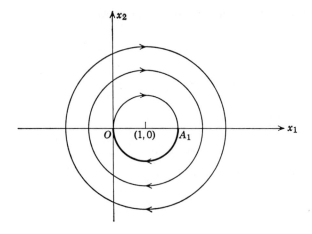

Fig. 6.10. Trajectories of system state for $u = +1$.

When the input to the system is -1, it is easy to show that the state trajectories in the x_1x_2 phase are concentric circles with their common center at $(-1, 0)$, as shown in Fig. 6.11. If the input u^* is -1 during the period of constant input immediately prior to arrival at the origin, the representative point must follow part or all of the semicircle B_1O during that period.

Let us now suppose that the time-optimal process consists of at least three periods of constant input, and that during the last period the input u^* is -1. The state point, during the penultimate period of constant input, must

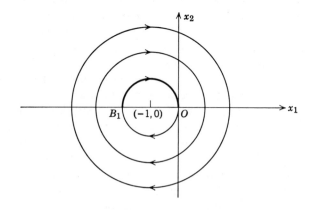

Fig. 6.11. Trajectories of system state for $u = -1$.

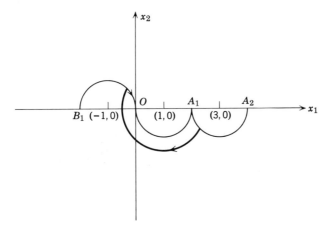

Fig. 6.12. A typical trajectory for the penultimate period.

therefore describe an exact semicircle, with center at $(+1, 0)$, which ends somewhere on the curve B_1O of Fig. 6.11. It is easy to see, by symmetry, that the start of such a semicircle must be on some point of the semicircle A_1A_2, with center at $(+3, 0)$ and unit radius, as shown in Fig. 6.12. Extending this argument, it is easy to show that a curve made up of semicircles of unit radius, in the form of $\cdots B_3B_2B_1OA_1A_2A_3 \cdots$ in Fig. 6.13, divides the phase plane into two regions such that u^* is $+1$ in one region and is -1 in the other. In other words, this curve is a "switching" curve because it shows when the input should be switched from one extreme to the other.

To be specific, the time-optimal controller should make the following logical choice of u^*:

$$\begin{aligned} u^* &= +1 & &\text{if } \mathbf{x} \text{ is below } \cdots B_4B_3B_2B_1OA_1A_2 \cdots \text{ or on } OA_1 \\ u^* &= -1 & &\text{if } \mathbf{x} \text{ is above } \cdots B_4B_3B_2B_1OA_1A_2 \cdots \text{ or on } B_1O \end{aligned} \qquad (6.42)$$

As before, the optimal input u^* is an instantaneous function of the state of the system. It is obvious from Fig. 6.13 that, for any finite initial state, the number of periods of constant input is finite. However, the number of switchings may be very large. We see that the transition from a two-period optimal transition process to one requiring an arbitrary number of periods occurs when the roots of the characteristic equation of the system become complex. We shall see later that, for an nth-order linear system whose characteristic equation has real roots, and with a simple magnitude constraint on the control variable, the time-optimal transition requires not more than n periods of constant input; if the roots are complex, this is no longer true.

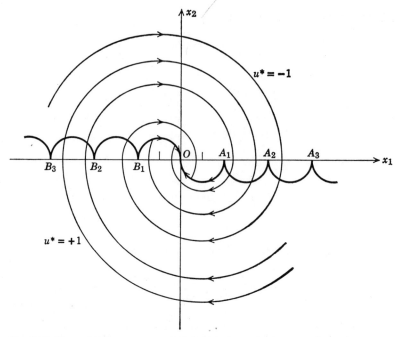

Fig. 6.13. The switching curve $\cdots B_3 B_2 B_1 O A_1 A_2 \cdots$ in the $x_1 x_2$ phase plane.

6.4   GENERAL CONSIDERATIONS IN MINIMUM-TIME CONTROL OF LINEAR SYSTEMS

The foregoing two problems may be considered as special cases of minimum-time control of linear systems. Suppose we have a general linear system whose differential equations are written in the vector-matrix form

$$\dot{\mathbf{x}} = \mathbf{A}\mathbf{x} + \mathbf{B}\mathbf{u} \qquad (6.43)$$

where, as in similar equations in Chapter 4, $\mathbf{A}$ is an $n \times n$ constant matrix, $\mathbf{B}$ is an $n \times r$ constant matrix, $\mathbf{x}$ is an n vector and $\mathbf{u}$ is an r vector. It is assumed that the control vector $\mathbf{u}$ is required to lie in a specified closed, bounded, convex region $\mathbf{U}$. Equation 6.43 may be written in the form

$$\dot{x}_i = \sum_{j=1}^{n} a_{ij}x_j + \sum_{k=1}^{r} b_{ik}u_k \qquad (i = 1, \ldots, n) \qquad (6.44)$$

The Hamiltonian H may be written as

$$H = \mathbf{p}\cdot\mathbf{A}\mathbf{x} + \mathbf{p}\cdot\mathbf{B}\mathbf{u} \qquad (6.45)$$

which may be written in the form

$$H = \sum_{i=1}^{n} \sum_{j=1}^{n} p_i a_{ij} x_j + \sum_{k=1}^{n} \sum_{l=1}^{r} p_k b_{kl} u_l \tag{6.46}$$

The differential equations governing the behavior of the p_i may be derived from Equation 6.46 to be

$$\frac{dp_j}{dt} = -\frac{\partial H}{\partial x_j} = -\sum_{i=1}^{n} a_{ij} p_i \qquad (j = 1, \ldots, n) \tag{6.47}$$

In vector-matrix form, Equations 6.47 may be written as

$$\frac{d\mathbf{p}}{dt} = -\mathbf{A}'\mathbf{p} \tag{6.48}$$

where $\mathbf{A}'$ is the transpose of the matrix $\mathbf{A}$. It will be recalled from Chapter 4 that Equation 6.48 is the adjoint equation corresponding to $\dot{\mathbf{x}} = \mathbf{A}\mathbf{x}$. The auxiliary variables p_i are sometimes referred to as the adjoint variables or co-state variables.

We see from Equation 6.45 that H reaches its maximum with respect to $\mathbf{u}$ when the second term on the right, $\mathbf{p} \cdot \mathbf{B}\mathbf{u}$, is maximum. As this term is a linear function of $\mathbf{u}$, and as the control vector $\mathbf{u}$ is required to lie in a closed, convex, bounded region $\mathbf{U}$, it is obvious that the maximum value of $\mathbf{p} \cdot \mathbf{B}\mathbf{u}$ will, unless this quantity is identically zero, take on its maximum value when $\mathbf{u}$ is on the boundary of the admissible region and cannot have its maximum at any interior point.

More specifically, it is shown in reference [2] that, if the admissible region $\mathbf{U}$ of the control vector is a closed, bounded, convex polyhedron, the time-optimal control vector $\mathbf{u}(t)$ for a linear system is piecewise constant, and all its values correspond to vertices of the polyhedron $\mathbf{U}$. It is also shown that the number of time intervals of constant $\mathbf{u}$ is finite. These results are based on the assumption that a condition called the *general position condition* [2] is satisfied. This condition may be stated approximately as follows: the system represented by Equation 6.43 must be controllable by an input vector $\mathbf{u}$ which, while it may take on any magnitude, is restricted in direction so that it lies in the direction of a vector $\mathbf{w}$ (or in the opposite direction) where $\mathbf{w}$ has the direction of any one of the edges of the polyhedron $\mathbf{U}$. For a more precise statement of this condition, reference [2] may be consulted.

Pontryagin *et al.* [2] also prove the very important fact that, for the general nth-order linear system of Equation 6.43, if the eigenvalues of $\mathbf{A}$ are all real, if the system is controllable by each component of the input vector $\mathbf{u}$ acting alone,[5] and if the admissible control region **U** is a parallelepiped of the form

$$M_i \leqslant u_i \leqslant N_i \qquad (i = 1, 2, \ldots, r) \tag{6.49}$$

then each control input u_i is piecewise constant, takes on only the values M_i and N_i, and has at most $n - 1$ switchings (n periods of constant value) during a time-optimal transition from one specified state to another.

The wording of the previous paragraph requires careful interpretation. It should be noted that, if each component of the control input vector can change $n - 1$ times, the vector itself can change more often than $n - 1$ times because there is no stipulation that the $n - 1$ changes of one component are synchronous with those of any other component. Problem 5 at the end of this chapter is intended to illustrate this point.

6.5   GEOMETRICAL INTERPRETATION OF THE TRANSVERSALITY CONDITION

When the right-hand endpoint of the state trajectory of the system is free, we introduce the transversality condition, as in the calculus of variations, to find all the boundary conditions which are required for the solution of the problem. In general, the transversality condition may be written in the form

$$\left[dx_0 - \mathcal{H} \, dt + \sum_{i=0}^{n} p_i \, dx_i \right]_1 = 0 \tag{6.50}$$

In all cases the value of x_0 at the right-hand endpoint is unspecified, because that value of x_0 is by definition equal to the functional which is required to be minimized. The value of p_0 is therefore equal to -1 at the right-hand endpoint, and because its derivative is always zero it is equal to -1 at every instant. Let us consider a few typical possible specifications for the right-hand endpoint of the trajectory, and see what the transversality condition (Equation 6.50) tells us about the boundary conditions.

1. *Right-hand endpoint completely specified.* If we assume that the final values $x_1^1, \ldots, x_n^1$ are all prescribed in advance, the transversality condition (Equation 6.50) tells us that the right-hand boundary values of $p_1, p_2, \ldots, p_n$ are completely free. If, in addition, the final time is specified, the final value of $\mathcal{H}$ is unspecified. If, on the other hand, the final time is free, the final value of $\mathcal{H}$ is zero.

---

[5] This condition is a special case of the general position condition [2], for the admissible control region **U** specified by Equations 6.49. A system which is controllable with respect to each component of the control input vector is called a *normal* system [1].

2. *Right-hand endpoint completely free.* In this case the final time must be fixed, as otherwise the control problem would be meaningless. The transversality condition tells us that in this case the right-hand boundary values of the p_i are given by

$$p_0 = -1$$
$$p_1 = p_2 = \cdots = p_n = 0 \qquad (6.51)$$

The meaning of Equation 6.51 can be interpreted geometrically as follows: as we have discussed in Section 6.3, optimal control requires the maximization of the projection of the velocity of the representative point on the vector $^0\mathbf{p}$ at every instant. At the final instant, Equation 6.51 shows that optimal control requires the minimum possible increase in x_0. At earlier instants, when the values of $p_1, \ldots, p_n$ are not zero, it is not the best policy to concentrate *only* on the slowest possible increase in x_0, because this short-term improvement would in general be outweighed by larger increases in x_0 later in the process. At the end of the process there is no future to consider, and no definite endpoint to be reached, and so we can concentrate only on minimizing the increase in x_0. This is a phenomenon with which we are familiar in our common experience. For example, an athlete attempting to cover a mile in minimum time will not run at top speed at the beginning of the race, because his early lead would soon be lost; at the end of the race, however, he will run as fast as he can.

3. *Right-hand endpoint partially free.* If some of the x_i coordinates at the right-hand endpoint are fixed, and the others are completely free, the transversality condition (Equation 6.50) shows us that the final values of the p_i corresponding to the fixed x_i will be free, while those corresponding to the free x_i will be zero, for $i = 1, \ldots, n$. More generally, it is possible for the right-hand endpoint to be constrained to lie on a prescribed surface or hypersurface in the state space, sometimes referred to as the "target set." For example, let us suppose that, in the three-dimensional space of the variables x_1, x_2, and x_3, the right-hand endpoint is constrained to lie on a given fixed smooth surface. The transversality condition specifies that (in addition to the conditions on x_0 and possibly on $\mathscr{H}$)[6] the following relationship must be satisfied at the right-hand endpoint

$$p_1 \, dx_1 + p_2 \, dx_2 + p_3 \, dx_3 = 0 \qquad (6.52)$$

---

[6] It is assumed for simplicity here that the final endpoint is *not* determined by a relationship of the form $\phi(t_1, \mathbf{x}^1) = 0$ (representing a hypersurface in the $t, x_1, \ldots, x_n$ space) but that it *is* represented by a relationship of the form $\psi(\mathbf{x}^1) = 0$ (representing a hypersurface in the $x_1, \ldots, x_n$ space) with the final time t_1 either completely free or completely fixed. This means that the two items $\mathscr{H} \, dt$ and $\sum_{i=0}^{n} p_i \, dx_i$ in the transversality condition (Equation 6.50) must be zero independently of one another.

where the dx_i are not independent, but indicate infinitesimal variations in the coordinates of the endpoint such that the point remains on the prescribed smooth surface. Equation 6.52 can be interpreted geometrically to mean that the right-hand endpoint x^1 must be in such a position on the specified surface that the final vector $p(t_1)$ must be orthogonal to the smooth surface at the point x^1. Similarly, if the initial point x^0 is to be on a smooth curve or a smooth surface, the initial vector $p(t_0)$ must be orthogonal to the curve or surface at x^0. For a system of higher order, where we may have the endpoints free to take any position on a smooth manifold,[7] analogous considerations apply; these are studied in detail in the book by Pontryagin et al. [2].

A SIMPLE EXAMPLE TO ILLUSTRATE THE TRANSVERSALITY CONDITION

To illustrate the condition described above, where the p vector is orthogonal to the surface or manifold on which the right-hand endpoint lies, let us consider the time-optimal control of the double integrator already studied in Section 6.3, with an input u subject to the magnitude constraint $|u| \leqslant M$. Suppose that we start from an arbitrary initial state, and suppose that the final state is to be anywhere on the straight line $x_2 = 0$. This condition corresponds to zero velocity, with an unspecified position. Direct application of the transversality condition (Equation 6.50) tells us that the final value of the coordinate p_1 is zero, because the final value of x_1 is free. Equations 6.16 and 6.22 still apply to this case, with the special result that $p_1(t) = 0$ and $p_2 = b$. This means that $p_2(t)$ does not change sign, so that the optimal input u^* does not change sign and takes on only the value $+M$ or the value $-M$ during an optimal process. It is easy to see that, if the initial state point is in the upper half plane, $u^* = -1$ (taking the value of M to be unity, as we did before), and vice versa, so that the time-optimal trajectories are of the form shown in Fig. 6.14.

In terms of orthogonality of the final p vector, we see that the direction of $p(t_1)$ is vertical. Furthermore, as we have established that optimal control requires maximization of the projection of the $\dot{x}$ vector in the direction of the p vector, we see that the final direction of the p vector is vertically downwards if x started in the upper half plane. Thus p_2 is a negative constant if x is in the upper half plane, and the value of u^* is negative as expected. This example is, of course, so simple that the result can be immediately found by intuition; more difficult examples are considered in the next section.

---

[7] A manifold in n-dimensional space is a space of $n - 1$ or fewer dimensions. For example, in three-dimensional space, a surface is a two-dimensional manifold, a curve is a one-dimensional manifold, and a point may be thought of as a manifold of zero dimension. More precise definitions of manifolds may be found in Pontryagin [2], and in books on vector spaces.

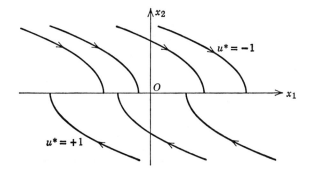

Fig. 6.14. Trajectories to reach zero velocity in minimum time.

6.6 FURTHER EXAMPLES ILLUSTRATING THE TRANSVERSALITY CONDITION

Let us now consider two more difficult examples to illustrate the transversality condition. In both cases we shall study the time-optimal control of a second-order linear system, and in both cases we shall assume that the system is to be controlled in such a way that the representative point in the x_1x_2 state space reaches any point on the circle with center at the origin and radius R, in minimum time. It is assumed that the initial state point is outside that circle. We shall study this problem for the double integrator and for the linear oscillator for which we have already studied the fixed-endpoint cases.

THE DOUBLE INTEGRATOR

We shall assume that all the conditions are the same as for the double-integrator problem studied in Section 6.3, except that the desired end state is to be any point on the circle whose equation is

$$x_1^2 + x_2^2 = R^2 \tag{6.53}$$

In other words, the system state is to be transferred, in minimum time, from a given initial point outside the circle (Equation 6.53) to some point on the circumference of the circle.

Equations 6.16 to 6.22 still apply as before, and we shall assume that the value of M in Equation 6.17 is unity, so that the input is constrained in such a way that $|u| \leq 1$. The state trajectories for $u = +1$ and $u = -1$ are again parabolas as derived in Section 6.3. However, because the desired final state is not the origin but the circumference of the circle (Equation 6.53), we know from our previous discussion of the transversality condition that, at the final

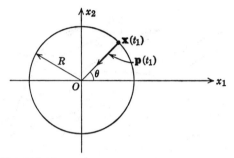

Fig. 6.15. Illustrating the transversality condition.

instant, the $\mathbf{p}$ vector must be orthogonal to the circumference of the circle at the final point $\mathbf{x}^1$. That is, referring to Fig. 6.15, if the final state is $\mathbf{x}^1$ as shown, the vector $\mathbf{p}(t_1)$, where t_1 is the time at which the state reaches $\mathbf{x}^1$, must be orthogonal to the circumference at that point. In other words, $\mathbf{p}(t_1)$ must be either radially outwards or radially inwards. As we have already established, optimal control involves the maximization of the projection of the $\dot{\mathbf{x}}$ velocity vector on the $\mathbf{p}$ vector, and as we wish to reach the circumference of the circle from outside we must take the inward direction of the $\mathbf{p}$ vector. The final value of the $\mathbf{p}$ vector, corresponding to the vector $\mathbf{x}^1$ represented in polar coordinates as $R\angle\theta$ in Fig. 6.15, therefore has the components

$$p_1(t_1) = -\cos\theta$$
$$p_2(t_1) = -\sin\theta \tag{6.54}$$

It will be recalled that the $\mathbf{p}$ vector can be multiplied by a positive constant if desired; in Equation 6.54 we have taken the simplest forms of the components.

Let us now consider values of θ between $0°$ and $180°$. For example, if θ is between $0°$ and $90°$, both components of Equation 6.54 have the same sign. We see from Equation 6.22 that, if p_2 changes sign, after its change of sign it has the opposite sign to p_1. This means that, if the final state is on the circle at an angle θ such that $0° < \theta < 90°$, p_2 did not change sign, and therefore u did not change sign, during the time-optimal process leading to that endpoint.

For values of θ between $90°$ and $180°$ the situation is much more complicated. Equations 6.54 show that in this case $p_1(t_1)$ and $p_2(t_1)$ have opposite signs, showing that p_2 changed sign at some time in the past (if the time-optimal process had been in operation long enough). We must therefore find out the time and state at which the sign change occurred. Now, because p_2 has the value $-\sin\theta$ at time t_1, and because it is changing at a rate equal to

p_1, the time which elapsed between the sign change and t_1 is equal in magnitude to $-\sin\theta/\cos\theta$ (which is obviously positive in this case).

The values of x_1 and x_2 at time t_1 are given by

$$x_1(t_1) = R\cos\theta$$
$$x_2(t_1) = R\sin\theta \tag{6.55}$$

If we now introduce a variable $\tau = t_1 - t$, we can write the system Equations 6.16 in the form

$$\frac{dx_1}{d\tau} = -x_2$$

$$\frac{dx_2}{d\tau} = -u \tag{6.56}$$

The variable τ represents an independent variable running backwards in time from t_1, and we can solve these equations for the period between t_1 and the earlier switching, which occurs at $\tau = -\tan\theta$. During that period the value of p_2 is negative, and therefore the value of u is equal to -1. Equations 6.56 are easily solved; we can first solve for x_2 and we obtain

$$x_2(\tau) = R\sin\theta + \tau \tag{6.57}$$

In particular, at the switching instant $\tau = -\tan\theta$, we have

$$x_2 = R\sin\theta - \tan\theta \tag{6.58}$$

We can find the value of $x_1(\tau)$ by integrating Equation 6.57, taking into account the boundary condition $x_1 = R\cos\theta$ at $\tau = 0$, and we obtain

$$x_1(\tau) = R\cos\theta - \tau R\sin\theta - \frac{\tau^2}{2} \tag{6.59}$$

For $\tau = -\tan\theta$, we find the value of x_1 at the switching instant to be

$$x_1 = \frac{R}{\cos\theta} - \frac{\tan^2\theta}{2} \tag{6.60}$$

Equations 6.60 and 6.58 give the x_1 and x_2 coordinates, respectively, of a point on the switching curve. This is enough information to plot the switching curve, and a sketch of the complete set of optimal trajectories is shown in Fig. 6.16. It should be noted that, in Fig. 6.16, the switching curve is not itself an optimal trajectory. The parabola BF and the switching curve CE meet at infinity. The values of $p_1(t_1)$ and $p_2(t_1)$ corresponding to the trajectory endpoint B are 0 and -1, respectively, which means that p_2 was constant throughout the whole process (or, if preferred, it means that a change of sign of p_2 occurred infinitely far back in the past).

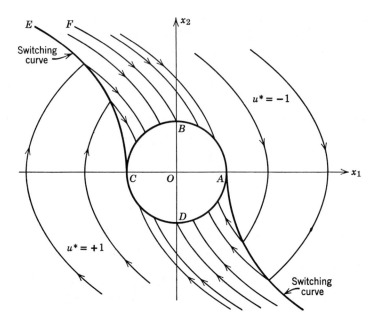

Fig. 6.16. Switching curves and time-optimal trajectories (not to scale).

It so happens that increasing the radius of the target circle may cause a change in the details of the solution of this particular problem. If the radius is made larger, the relative curvatures of the target circle and the trajectory parabolas may make the trajectories appear as in Fig. 6.17. In this case, in which a trajectory parabola is tangential to the circle at the point G, the circumference GA of the shaded sector is "shielded," and no point on that portion of the circumference can qualify as the earliest point reached on the circle, starting from a point outside the circle. If the initial state were P, for example, the trajectory must go to Q in order to reach the circle in minimum time. Similarly, no point on CH can qualify as the earliest point reached. The reader may wish to verify for himself, by simple analytic geometry, that Fig. 6.16 corresponds to $R \leqslant 1$, and Fig. 6.17 to $R > 1$, under the conditions of this particular problem.

THE LINEAR OSCILLATOR

Let us now consider the time-optimal control of the linear oscillator (the second-order system of Fig. 6.8, with $\alpha = 0$). We shall assume all the conditions of the problem are as specified when solving the corresponding

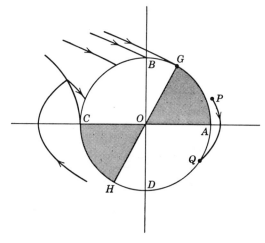

Fig. 6.17

problem in Section 6.3, except that it is desired to reach some point on the circumference of the circle whose equation is Equation 6.53, from a point outside that circle, instead of trying to reach the origin in minimum time. As before, the value of u is sgn $[p_2]$. The final $\mathbf{p}$ vector at time t_1 may again be found as we did in the double-integrator problem just described (see Fig. 6.15). Let us write the vector $\mathbf{p}(t_1)$ in this case in the form

$$\begin{aligned} p_1(t_1) &= -V \cos \theta \\ p_2(t_1) &= -V \sin \theta \end{aligned} \tag{6.61}$$

where V is chosen to correspond with the constant V appearing in Equation 6.35. Now, in order for $p_2(t_1)$ to be equal to $-V \sin \theta$ as in Equation 6.61, we must have

$$p_2(t_1) = V \sin (t_1 + \phi) = -V \sin \theta = V \sin (-\theta) \tag{6.62}$$

From Equation 6.62 we find the value of ϕ to be $-(t_1 + \theta)$, and hence we find $p_2(t)$ by substitution in Equation 6.35 to be

$$p_2(t) = V \sin (t - t_1 - \theta) \tag{6.63}$$

As before, the optimal control input u^* is given by Equation 6.30, which, on taking $M = 1$ and substituting in Equation 6.63, becomes

$$u^*(t) = \text{sgn} [\sin (t - t_1 - \theta)] \tag{6.64}$$

As before, the optimal control input takes on only its extreme values $+1$ and -1, and no period of constant input can be longer than π seconds. In fact, Equation 6.64 shows us that the length of the *last* period of constant input, before reaching the point $\mathbf{x} = R \angle \theta$, is $\pi - \theta$ seconds. (If we substitute

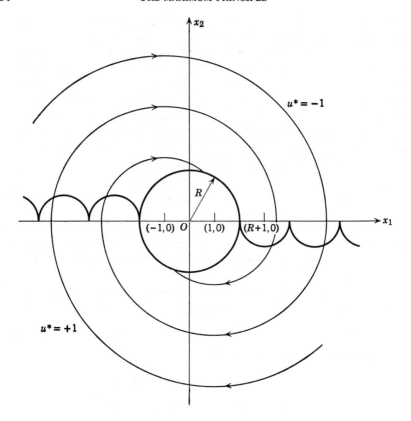

Fig. 6.18. Switching curves in the $x_1 x_2$ plane.

the value $\pi - \theta$ for $t_1 - t$, the sine in Equation 6.64 is zero.) The switching curves in the $x_1 x_2$ plane turn out to be as shown in Fig. 6.18; reference [2] may be consulted for fuller details of the method of obtaining these curves. The switching curves are made up of unit semicircles placed end to end as shown. Above the switching curves, $u^* = -1$ and the optimal trajectories are portions of circles with center at $(-1, 0)$; below, $u^* = +1$, and the optimal trajectories are portions of circles with center at $(+1, 0)$. Sample time-optimal trajectories are shown on the diagram.

6.7 MINIMUM-FUEL CONTROL

An important type of optimal control problem is the problem of transferring a system from a prescribed initial state to a desired final state in such a way as to minimize the fuel consumed. This type of problem has been studied in considerable detail by Athans and others [1, 3].

As an example of this type of optimal control problem, let us consider a double integrator of the form of Fig. 6.3, with behavior governed by the differential Equations 6.16, and with the control input u subject to the magnitude constraint described by Equation 6.17 as before. We shall assume the value of M in Equation 6.17 to be unity as before, for simplicity.

The rate of fuel consumption may be assumed to be proportional to the magnitude of the input forcing function or control variable u, so that the functional we wish to minimize is of the form

$$I = \int_{t_0}^{t_1} |u|\, dt \qquad (6.65)$$

Let us assume that we are required to transfer the system from a specified initial state to a specified final state, in such a way as to minimize the integral I of Equation 6.65. Let us assume for the present that the transit time $t_1 - t_0$ is unspecified.

Introducing, as before, an extra state variable x_0 to represent the value of the functional, the differential equation governing the behavior of x_0 is

$$\dot{x}_0 = |u| \qquad (6.66)$$

and the Hamiltonian $\mathscr{H}$ may be written as

$$\mathscr{H} = p_0|u| + p_1 x_2 + p_2 u \qquad (6.67)$$

The differential equations governing the behavior of the p_i are

$$\frac{dp_0}{dt} = 0$$

$$\frac{dp_1}{dt} = 0 \qquad (6.68)$$

$$\frac{dp_2}{dt} = -p_1$$

Hence p_0 and p_1 are constants (p_0 being equal to -1 as usual), and p_2 is of the form

$$p_2 = -c_1 t + c_2 \qquad (6.69)$$

where c_1 is the value of p_1. Equation 6.67 may be rewritten in the form

$$\mathscr{H} - p_1 x_2 = -|u| + p_2 u \qquad (6.70)$$

where the value of $p_0 = -1$ has been inserted. The choice of u to maximize $\mathscr{H}$ must also maximize the right side of Equation 6.70, because the term $p_1 x_2$

does not contain u explicitly. Inspection of the right side of Equation 6.70 shows us that the right side is maximized, subject to the constraint $|u| \leqslant 1$, if the value of u is as follows:

$$
\begin{aligned}
u &= 1 & \text{if } p_2 > 1 \\
u &= 0 & \text{if } |p_2| < 1 \\
u &= -1 & \text{if } p_2 < -1
\end{aligned}
\tag{6.71}
$$

Equation 6.69 shows that the value of p_2 varies linearly with time, so that a minimum-fuel optimal input u^* must be a sequence $-1, 0, +1$ or $1, 0, -1$ (or possibly a subsequence of one of these) as time goes on. A minimum-fuel trajectory in the $x_1 x_2$ state space might therefore be of the form $ABCO$ of Fig. 6.19, where we have assumed the final state to be the origin for simplicity. During the time interval during which $u = 0$, the system coasts with constant velocity, as represented by the horizontal trajectory BC.

Examination of the trajectory $ADEO$ of Fig. 6.19 shows that the fuel consumed is less than for trajectory $ABCO$, but that the time taken is longer. In $AFGO$ the fuel is still less, but the transit time still greater. The amount of fuel used in the transition from A to O can be made as small as desired by making the horizontal portion of the trajectory sufficiently close to AO. However, the time taken becomes very long, approaching infinity as the amount of fuel required approaches zero. A free-time specification of the minimum-fuel problem is therefore unrealistic because it does not allow the

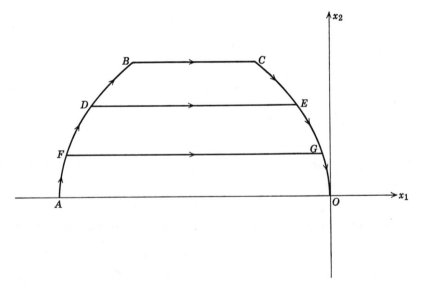

Fig. 6.19. Minimum-fuel trajectories.

optimal control input to be uniquely specified; in practice we may specify a fixed transit time or an upper bound on the allowable transit time. In this case we would use the trajectory, of the form of those in Fig. 6.19, which had its horizontal portion as low as possible without violating the transit-time constraint. Further discussion of this problem may be found in reference [3]. Another possible way of handling this problem is by studying the trade-off between fuel and time, as has been done by Nelson [4].

SUMMARY

This chapter has introduced the maximum principle, treating it as an extension of the classical calculus of variations. The proof of the maximum principle has not been attempted, nor have we attempted to deal with the more difficult problems which arise if the state variables are bounded or otherwise constrained. Other topics, such as the discrete maximum principle, singular controls, control of distributed-parameter systems, and the like, are suggested for further study. Many references for further study in various areas are given in a survey paper by Athans [5]. For further reading on the maximum principle in general, the reader is referred to the various books and articles listed below; in particular, references [1, 2] are recommended.

REFERENCES

[1] Athans, M., and P. L. Falb, *Optimal Control: An Introduction to the Theory and its Applications*, McGraw-Hill, New York, 1966.
[2] Pontryagin, L. S., V. G. Boltyanskii, R. V. Gamkrelidze, and E. F. Mishchenko. *The Mathematical Theory of Optimal Processes*, Interscience (Wiley), 1962.
[3] Athans, M., "Fuel Optimal Control of a Double Integral Plant with Response Time Constraints," *IEEE Transactions, Applications and Industry*, 83, 240–246 (1964).
[4] Nelson, W. L., "On the Use of Optimization Theory for Practical Control System Design," *IEEE Transactions on Automatic Control*, AC-9, 469–477 (1964).
[5] Athans, M., "The Status of Optimal Control Theory and Applications for Deterministic Systems," *IEEE Transactions on Automatic Control*, AC-11, 580–596 (1966).
[6] Kopp, R. E., "Pontryagin Maximum Principle," in *Optimization Techniques*, G. Leitmann, ed., Academic Press, New York, 1962, pp. 255–279.
[7] Rozonoer, L. I., "The L. S. Pontryagin Maximum Principle in the Theory of Optimal Systems, I, II, and III," *Automation and Remote Control*, 20, 1288–1302, 1405–1421, 1517–1532 (1959).
[8] Meditch, J. S., "The Pontryagin Maximum Principle and Some of its Applications," in *Advances in Control Systems*, Vol. 1, C. T. Leondes, ed., Academic Press, New York, 1964, pp. 55–74.

[9] Meditch, J. S., "An Introduction to the Pontryagin Maximum Principle," in *Modern Control Systems Theory*, C. T. Leondes, ed., McGraw-Hill, New York, 1965, pp. 285–318.

PROBLEMS

1. Solve Problem 1(a) of Chapter 5, for the case where the control input is subject to the magnitude constraint $|u| \leqslant 1 \cdot 1$.
2. Solve Problem 5 of Chapter 5, for the case where the control input is subject to the magnitude constraint $|u| \leqslant 1$.
3. For the system shown in Fig. 6.20, find the form of the control input $u(t)$,

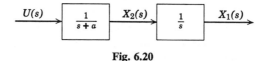

Fig. 6.20

such that the system is transferred from a given initial state to the origin in minimum time, with the control input subject to the magnitude constraint $|u| \leqslant 1$. Sketch the optimal trajectories in the phase plane.
4. For the system shown in Fig. 6.21, write the differential equations in matrix form. Find the form of the optimal control input $\mathbf{u}(t)$ which transfers the

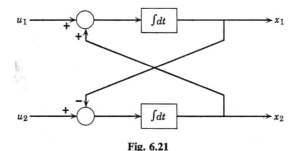

Fig. 6.21

system state from a given initial state to the origin in minimum time, for each of the following constraint conditions

(a) $|u_1| \leqslant 1, |u_2| \leqslant 1$
(b) $|u_1| + |u_2| \leqslant 1$
(c) $u_1^2 + u_2^2 \leqslant 1$

Sketch the switching curves for cases (a) and (b), and the time-optimal trajectories for all three cases.

5. For the system shown in Fig. 6.22, write the differential equations in matrix form, and find the form of the control input vector **u** which transfers the system

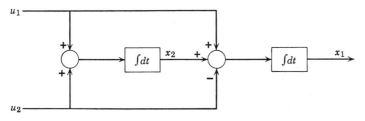

Fig. 6.22

from an arbitrary initial state to the origin in minimum time, subject to the constraint $|u_1| \leq 1$, $|u_2| \leq 1$.

Show the switching curves on the phase plane, and sketch a set of optimal trajectories.

6. (a) For the double integrator shown in Fig. 6.23, the control input u is limited by the magnitude constraint $|u| \leq 1$. It is required to transfer the system

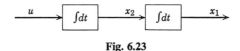

Fig. 6.23

state from a point outside the square shown in Fig. 6.24a, to any point on the boundary of the square, in minimum time. Find the appropriate

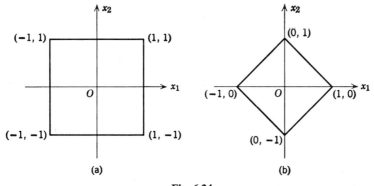

(a)   (b)

Fig. 6.24

switching curve or curves in the state plane, and sketch typical trajectories for various initial states.

(b) Repeat the above problem, using the square of Fig. 6.24b as the target set.

7. In the circuit shown in Fig. 6.25, the input variables are the voltages u_1 and u_2, each resistance is 1 megohm, and each capacitance is 1 microfarad.

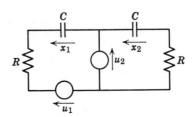

Fig. 6.25

(a) Write the state differential equations of the system in the form $\dot{\mathbf{x}} = \mathbf{A}\mathbf{x} + \mathbf{B}\mathbf{u}$, where the state variables x_1 and x_2 are the capacitor voltages as shown in Fig. 6.25.

(b) Is the system controllable?

(c) Is the system controllable (i) with u_1 acting alone, with $u_2 = 0$? (ii) with u_2 acting alone, with $u_1 = 0$?

(d) Consider the time-optimal control of this system, subject to the constraints $|u_1| \leqslant 1$, $|u_2| \leqslant 1$. Show that it is not always necessary for both inputs to take on their extreme values in order to achieve a specified state transition in minimum time. Consider, for example, the transition from the state $(1, 0)$ to the origin.

7

Dynamic Programming

7.1 MULTISTAGE DECISION PROCESSES

The optimization method known as dynamic programming was developed by Bellman [1, 2, 3], and arose out of the study of multistage decision processes. Multistage decision processes arise in situations where decisions are to be made at discrete times during the course of some transaction, in which the outcome of the transaction is a function of all the decisions. Examples of multistage decision processes are the sequences of decisions involved in playing chess, card games such as bridge, and various other games.

In the context of control systems, we can consider the sequence of inputs to be applied to a sampled-data system to be the result of a sequence of decisions in the manner of a multistage decision process. In the terminology of dynamic programming, a set of rules for making the decisions throughout a particular process is called a *policy*. A policy which results in optimal control is called an optimal policy.

Fundamental to the theory of dynamic programming is the principle of optimality, which may be stated as follows. An optimal policy has the property that, whatever the initial state and the initial decision may be, the remaining decisions must constitute an optimal policy with respect to the state resulting from the first decision. In terms of state transitions of a control system, we may express the principle of optimality in the following way. Given a system initially in state $\mathbf{x}^0$, and given that an N-stage optimal process advances by successive transitions to specified states $\mathbf{x}^1, \mathbf{x}^2, \ldots, \mathbf{x}^N$, that part of the set of transitions from any intermediate state $\mathbf{x}^k$ onwards is the same as the $(N - k)$-stage optimal process starting from state $\mathbf{x}^k$.

A word of caution concerning the application of the principle of optimality may be appropriate. The principle does *not* say, as it is sometimes misquoted, that *any* part of an optimal process is an optimal process. While this may be true in many cases, such as the time-optimal control problem, it is not true in general; in general, it is the *last* part of an optimal process which is itself

171

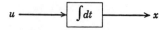

Fig. 7.1. A simple integrator.

an optimal process. The following simple example will make this clear. Suppose we have a simple integrator as shown in Fig. 7.1, in which the input u remains constant over one-second intervals. If we suppose also that the output can be observed only at discrete instants of time exactly 1 second apart, we can describe the behavior of this system by the difference equation

$$x(k + 1) = x(k) + u(k) \tag{7.1}$$

Now suppose that we wish to control the system throughout a two-stage process, starting from an initial state $x(0) = -0.8$, in such a way that the quantity $|x(2)|$ is maximized [where $x(2)$ represents the value of x at the end of the two-stage process], subject to the constraint that the control input $u(k)$ can only take on the value $+1$ or the value 0, for every value of k. It is obvious that the optimal two-stage process results from the following choice of inputs

$$u(0) = +1, \qquad u(1) = +1 \tag{7.2}$$

giving the following state transitions

$$x(1) = +0.2, \qquad x(2) = +1.2 \tag{7.3}$$

By the principle of optimality, if we start from $x(1) = 0.2$ and follow a one-stage process, the choice of input is $u(1) = +1$, causing a transition to $x(2) = +1.2$. However, if we start from $x(0) = -0.8$ and follow a one-stage process in such a way as to maximize $|x(1)|$, the best choice of input in the presence of the constraint is $u(0) = 0$, leading to the state $x(1) = -0.8$. This is not the same input which forms part of the optimum two-stage sequence of inputs.

7.2   USE OF THE PRINCIPLE OF OPTIMALITY

Let us consider a simple process of subdividing a straight line into a finite number of parts, in such a way as to optimize some payoff function, and treat this problem as a multistage decision process in order to illustrate the use of the principle of optimality. Suppose, for example, that we are given a straight line of length l, and that it is desired to subdivide it into N parts in such a way that the summation

$$\sum_{n=1}^{N} nx_n^2 \tag{7.4}$$

is minimized. The quantities x_n are the lengths of the separate subdivisions, and must satisfy the requirements

$$\sum_{n=1}^{N} x_n = l \tag{7.5}$$

$$x_n \geqslant 0, \qquad \text{for all } n$$

This subdivision may be considered as a multistage decision process by supposing that we start with the line of length l, decide one subdivision length in an optimum way, then decide another subdivision length, and so on. It should be emphasized at the outset that dynamic programming is not the easiest way to solve this problem; it is used here to illustrate the method.

Let us start by defining a quantity $S_N(l)$ as follows:

$$S_N(l) \triangleq \text{minimum possible value of summation 7.4,} \atop \text{with the } x_n \text{ subject to constraints 7.5} \tag{7.6}$$

Quantities defined in this way play a very important part in dynamic programming, and we shall encounter them frequently in this chapter.

Having defined the quantity $S_N(l)$ as shown above, the next step is to solve the problem for $N = 1$. This is a trivial problem, and the result is

$$S_1(l) = l^2 \tag{7.7}$$

for

$$x_1 = l \tag{7.8}$$

We can interpret l as a variable here; Equation 7.7 gives the optimum value $S_1(l)$ for any positive value of l. Having found the result $S_1(l)$, we can use this to find the result for $S_2(l)$. The quantity $S_2(l)$ can be written in the form

$$S_2(l) = \min_{x_2} [2x_2^2 + S_1(l - x_2)] \tag{7.9}$$

Equation 7.9 uses the principle of optimality, and may be interpreted as follows. The best possible subdivisions for the two-stage process are such that, after one subdivision (x_2) has been chosen, the remainder of the straight line (of length $l - x_2$) is then subdivided in the optimum way for a one-stage process. Substituting Equation 7.7 in Equation 7.9, we obtain

$$S_2(l) = \min_{x_2} [2x_2^2 + (l - x_2)^2] \tag{7.10}$$

We can easily find, by simple calculus, the value of x_2 which minimizes the expression in the square brackets in Equation 7.10, and we find

$$S_2(l) = \frac{2l^2}{3} \tag{7.11}$$

for

$$x_2 = \frac{l}{3} \qquad (7.12)$$

We can now proceed to the three-stage process, and write the value of $S_3(l)$ as

$$S_3(l) = \min_{x_3} [3x_3{}^2 + S_2(l - x_3)] \qquad (7.13)$$

Equation 7.13 also uses the principle of optimality in the sense that, after one subdivision (x_3) has been chosen, the remainder of the line $(l - x_3)$ is sub-divided in the optimum way for a two-stage process. Substituting Equation 7.11 in Equation 7.13, we obtain

$$S_3(l) = \min_{x_3} [3x_3{}^2 + \tfrac{2}{3}(l - x_3)^2] \qquad (7.14)$$

By simple calculus we find that

$$S_3(l) = \frac{6l^2}{11} \qquad (7.15)$$

for

$$x_3 = \frac{2l}{11} \qquad (7.16)$$

This process may be continued indefinitely, and $S_N(l)$ may be written as

$$S_N(l) = \min_{x_N} [Nx_N{}^2 + S_{N-1}(l - x_N)] \qquad (7.17)$$

Let us now solve the problem completely for $N = 3$. Suppose, for example, that $l = 11$. We have, from Equation 7.16, $x_3 = 2$, leaving a remainder of 9 to be divided into two parts. Equation 7.12 shows that x_2 must be equal to 9/3, leaving a remainder of 6 for x_1.

Let us check this result by simple calculus. We have a problem with constraints, which can easily be handled by introducing a Lagrange multiplier λ. We therefore consider the minimization of the function

$$F = \sum_{n=1}^{3} nx_n{}^2 + \lambda \sum_{n=1}^{3} x_n \qquad (7.18)$$

Taking partial derivatives, we obtain

$$\frac{\partial F}{\partial x_1} = 2x_1 + \lambda \qquad (7.19)$$

$$\frac{\partial F}{\partial x_2} = 4x_2 + \lambda \qquad (7.20)$$

$$\frac{\partial F}{\partial x_3} = 6x_3 + \lambda \qquad (7.21)$$

Setting all these partial derivatives to zero, we find that

$$x_1 = 2x_2 = 3x_3 \tag{7.22}$$

Equation 7.22, together with the constraint $\sum_{n=1}^{3} x_n = 11$, gives the same result as that found by dynamic programming.

The above example has illustrated the use of the principle of optimality in a simple optimization problem. Let us now consider its use in a control problem. We shall begin with a discrete-time problem although, as we shall see, dynamic programming can be used to obtain the solution of continuous-time problems by allowing the interval between successive decisions to become arbitrarily small.

7.3 A DISCRETE-TIME SYSTEM

Let us consider, for example, a sampled-data system as discussed in Section 4.12. Equation 4.174, for example, can be written in the more general form

$$\mathbf{x}(k + 1) = \mathbf{g}[\mathbf{x}(k), \mathbf{u}(k)] \tag{7.23}$$

The sampling period T has been dropped from the arguments for simplicity, but its presence is still understood, and Equation 7.23 is still intended to represent a relationship involving time as the independent variable. The state $\mathbf{x}(k)$ should be interpreted as the system state at $t = kT$, and $\mathbf{u}(k)$ as the input vector at time $t = kT$. As the vector $\mathbf{u}$ is assumed to remain constant during each sampling period, the notation $\mathbf{u}(k)$ should therefore be interpreted as the value of the input vector $\mathbf{u}$ at any time t during the interval $kT \leqslant t < (k + 1)T$. The form of Equation 7.23 includes the case of nonlinear systems, but we shall assume that the vector function $\mathbf{g}$ is a time-invariant function of the arguments $\mathbf{x}$ and $\mathbf{u}$.

Let us now suppose that, associated with the state transition described by Equation 7.23, a certain "cost" or "penalty" is incurred. To be more specific, let us assume that the cost or penalty during the interval from kT to $(k + 1)T$ is a definite time-invariant scalar function of the state $\mathbf{x}(k)$ and the input $\mathbf{u}(k)$. Mathematically, this may be expressed as

$$\text{Cost} = c[\mathbf{x}(k), \mathbf{u}(k)] \tag{7.24}$$

A problem in optimal control might therefore be expressed in the following terms. Given an initial state $\mathbf{x}^0$, choose a sequence of N control inputs $\mathbf{u}(0), \mathbf{u}(1), \ldots, \mathbf{u}(N - 1)$ in such a way as to minimize the accumulated cost, expressed by the summation

$$C = \sum_{i=0}^{N-1} c[\mathbf{x}(i), \mathbf{u}(i)] \tag{7.25}$$

For the present, let us assume that the final state $\mathbf{x}(N)$ is not specified in advance, but that the total number of stages N is specified.

The method of dynamic programming is to start by assuming that we have only one stage to go to reach the end of the process, that is, that we are initially dealing with a one-stage process so that $N = 1$. Then, for an arbitrary state $\mathbf{x}(0)$ at the start of the one-stage process, there is a definite value of $\mathbf{u}(0)$ which will incur the minimum cost. If this minimum cost is defined by the symbol S_1 (where the subscript 1 refers to the one-stage process), the value of S_1 is given by

$$S_1(\mathbf{x}) = \min_{\mathbf{u}} \{c[\mathbf{x}, \mathbf{u}]\} \qquad (7.26)$$

The right side of Equation 7.26 represents the minimum possible value of $c[\mathbf{x}, \mathbf{u}]$, taken over all admissible controls $\mathbf{u}$ (that is, all those controls which satisfy whatever constraints may apply to the particular problem), for an arbitrary initial state $\mathbf{x}$. The right side of Equation 7.26 is therefore a function of $\mathbf{x}$ only.

In some cases the optimum input $\mathbf{u}$ for a simple one-stage process can be obtained by differentiation of the quantity inside the braces of Equation 7.26. In other cases it can be obtained (at least in theory) by scanning the admissible region of $\mathbf{u}$ until the minimum is found. If the input is constrained in some way, it often makes the problem easier because there is a smaller range of values to investigate. Methods of finding a maximum or minimum of a function defined in a limited interval are described in Chapter 8. In any event, we can suppose the optimum input to be found for all initial states $\mathbf{x}$, so that the one-stage process is completely solved and $S_1(\mathbf{x})$ is known for all $\mathbf{x}$.

Now let us suppose that, armed with complete knowledge of the one-stage process, we study the two-stage process where $N = 2$. If we start from an arbitrary initial state $\mathbf{x}$, the minimum possible total cost for the two stages, which we denote by $S_2(\mathbf{x})$, can be written as

$$S_2(\mathbf{x}) = \min_{\mathbf{u}(0), \mathbf{u}(1)} \{c[\mathbf{x}, \mathbf{u}(0)] + c[\mathbf{x}(1), \mathbf{u}(1)]\} \qquad (7.27)$$

where $\mathbf{u}(0)$ and $\mathbf{u}(1)$ are the first and second control inputs, respectively. But we know that $\mathbf{x}(1)$ is given by

$$\mathbf{x}(1) = \mathbf{g}[\mathbf{x}, \mathbf{u}(0)] \qquad (7.28)$$

Therefore, Equation 7.27 may be written in the form

$$S_2(\mathbf{x}) = \min_{\mathbf{u}(0)} \left\{ c[\mathbf{x}, \mathbf{u}(0)] + \min_{\mathbf{u}(1)} \{c[\mathbf{g}[\mathbf{x}, \mathbf{u}(0)], \mathbf{u}(1)]\} \right\} \qquad (7.29)$$

where we have also shifted the minimizing operation over $\mathbf{u}(1)$ to a new position, valid because the first term in the outer braces is independent of

$\mathbf{u}(1)$. In other words, we have invoked the principle of optimality by saying that, whichever $\mathbf{u}(0)$ is chosen, the optimal policy to be followed after making that choice is to minimize the quantity

$$c[\mathbf{g}[\mathbf{x}, \mathbf{u}(0)], \mathbf{u}(1)] \qquad (7.30)$$

over all admissible control inputs $\mathbf{u}(1)$. The classical approach would be to perform the direct minimization shown in Equation 7.27 over the variables $\mathbf{u}(0)$ and $\mathbf{u}(1)$, possibly by partial differentiation with respect to all the components of those vectors.

The minimum value of expression 7.30, over all admissible $\mathbf{u}(1)$, is a function of $\mathbf{u}(0)$ and $\mathbf{x}$ only. Furthermore, after choosing a value of $\mathbf{u}(0)$ we then obtain a one-stage process whose optimal solution has already been found for all initial states $\mathbf{x}$. We can represent the minimum value of expression 7.30 by the expression

$$\min_{\mathbf{u}(1)} \{c[\mathbf{g}[\mathbf{x}, \mathbf{u}(0)], \mathbf{u}(1)]\} = S_1(\mathbf{g}[\mathbf{x}, \mathbf{u}(0)]) \qquad (7.31)$$

where $\mathbf{g}[\mathbf{x}, \mathbf{u}(0)]$ is the new state resulting from the first transition. Substituting Equation 7.31 in Equation 7.29, we obtain

$$S_2(\mathbf{x}) = \min_{\mathbf{u}(0)} \{c[\mathbf{x}, \mathbf{u}(0)] + S_1(\mathbf{g}[\mathbf{x}, \mathbf{u}(0)])\} \qquad (7.32)$$

Expression 7.32, after performing the minimization, is a function of $\mathbf{x}$ only, because S_1 has already been found as a function of $\mathbf{x}$.

If we have a two-stage process, therefore, we first find $S_1(\mathbf{x})$ for all $\mathbf{x}$, and then find the value of $\mathbf{u}(0)$ which minimizes the expression in braces in Equation 7.32, for the specified initial value $\mathbf{x}$. We can then find the state $\mathbf{x}(1)$ after the first transition, and treat this as the initial state for the remaining one-stage process whose solution is completely known. This is repeated for a range of values of $\mathbf{x}$, so that we obtain $S_2(\mathbf{x})$ as a function of $\mathbf{x}$.

If we wish to solve a three-stage process, we first find $S_2(\mathbf{x})$ for an appropriate range of values of $\mathbf{x}$, as described above. Having done this, we see that $S_3(\mathbf{x})$, the minimum possible cost for a three-stage process, starting from the initial state $\mathbf{x}$, is given by

$$S_3(\mathbf{x}) = \min_{\mathbf{u}} \{c[\mathbf{x}, \mathbf{u}] + S_2(\mathbf{g}[\mathbf{x}, \mathbf{u}])\} \qquad (7.33)$$

where $\mathbf{u}$ represents $\mathbf{u}(0)$ for the three-stage process, and where we have dropped the argument of $\mathbf{u}$ for simplicity.

Proceeding in this way, we obtain a recurrence relationship for the N-stage process as follows:

$$S_N(\mathbf{x}) = \min_{\mathbf{u}} \{c[\mathbf{x}, \mathbf{u}] + S_{N-1}(\mathbf{g}[\mathbf{x}, \mathbf{u}])\} \qquad (7.34)$$

where $S_N(\mathbf{x})$ is the minimum total cost incurred in the N-stage process, starting from an initial state $\mathbf{x}$.

In the foregoing development, we have assumed that the final state was unspecified. If the final state is specified in advance it merely means that, in the one-stage process which ends the N-stage process, we must choose $\mathbf{u}$ so as to give the correct final state if it is possible to do so. This usually means that the value of $\mathbf{u}$ for the one-stage process which ends the N-stage process is uniquely specified as a function of the penultimate state. In other words, in such cases it is not necessary to perform a minimization operation to find $S_1(\mathbf{x})$. The remainder of the derivation of the recurrence relationship, however, proceeds exactly as before.

If the optimal control is defined in terms of the maximization of a profit or return rather than the minimization of a penalty or cost, the foregoing results are all valid, with "min" replaced by "max" in all cases.

DISCRETE-TIME, BINARY-INPUT SYSTEM

Let us now consider a very simple example of a discrete-time process, to illustrate the above developments. We shall use once again the very simple system whose behavior is governed by the difference Equation 7.1, and we shall suppose, as before, that the input $u(k)$ can take on only the value $+1$ or the value 0, for all k. As we shall see, restrictions of this type make the problem simpler when using dynamic programming, whereas in the calculus of variations the imposition of constraints usually makes the problem much more difficult.

The problem may be stated as follows. Find the sequence of control inputs $u(0)$ to $u(3)$ which transfers the system state x from $x(0) = -2$ to $x(4) = 0$ in such a way as to minimize the quantity[1]

$$C = \sum_{k=0}^{3} c[x(k), u(k)] = \sum_{k=0}^{3} |3x(k) + 2| \tag{7.35}$$

With the restrictions we have imposed, there is a finite number of paths in the k, x plane from the point $(0, -2)$ to the point $(4, 0)$. These paths are shown in Fig. 7.2, where the discrete points representing all possible $x(k)$ throughout the process are represented by circles, and all possible transitions between them are represented by the straight lines with directional arrows; the significance of the numbers appearing inside the circles and beside the transition lines will now be explained.

---

[1] This quantity is not intended to illustrate some subtle criterion of excellence, but is contrived for the present example in order to obtain an optimum input sequence which is not completely obvious at first sight.

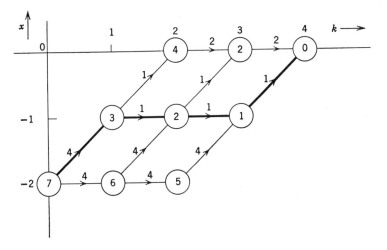

Fig. 7.2. Graph of all state transitions of 4-stage process.

For every possible transition, the number beside the arrowed line shows the cost associated with the corresponding transition; as shown by Equation 7.35 each cost is a function only of the state x before making the transition. The numbers in the circles correspond to the values of $S_i(x)$, the minimum total cost for the i-stage process starting from an initial state x. The method of finding these numbers is as follows.

At $k = 3$, where we have a one-stage process remaining, there is only one possible route from each starting point to the specified endpoint. Therefore, no minimization is required, and the values of $S_1(x)$ are given by

$$S_1(0) = 2$$
$$S_1(-1) = 1 \tag{7.36}$$

Having solved the one-stage process completely, we proceed to the two-stage process starting at $k = 2$. The starting point of this process is at $x = 0, -1$, or -2. If we start from $x = 0$ or $x = -2$ we have only one possible route available to us, and $S_2(0)$ and $S_2(-2)$ are found by adding the costs of the two transitions for the appropriate route. For the initial state $x = -1$, we have two choices of initial transition. Mathematically, we can express $S_2(-1)$ in the following form

$$S_2(-1) = \min_{u} [1 + S_1(-1 + u)] \tag{7.37}$$

The minimization in Equation 7.37 merely represents the comparison of two values, and it is easy to see that the minimum is obtained by making u, the initial input for the two-stage process starting at $x = -1$, zero, giving a value of 2 for $S_2(-1)$. We can therefore list the values of $S_2(x)$ as follows

$$S_2(0) = 4$$
$$S_2(-1) = 2 \tag{7.38}$$
$$S_2(-2) = 5$$

We can now proceed backwards to the three-stage process starting at $k = 1$, and we obtain by simple minimizations

$$S_3(-1) = 3$$
$$S_3(-2) = 6 \tag{7.39}$$

Finally we obtain, for the four-stage process starting at $k = 0$, the result

$$S_4(-2) = 7 \tag{7.40}$$

We now have enough information to find the optimal path, not only from $(0, -2)$ in the kx plane, but also from any of the points denoted by circles in Fig. 7.2, to the point $(4, 0)$. The optimal path from $(0, -2)$ to $(4, 0)$ is shown by the heavy line in Fig. 7.2. The method of finding the optimal path, having computed all the appropriate values of $S_i(x)$ for all the possible points along the various routes, may be simply stated as follows. The optimal path must be such that the difference between the encircled numbers at the two ends of any elementary part of the path is equal to the cost incurred in traversing that elementary portion of the path. For example, starting from $(0, -2)$ in the kx plane, at which the encircled number is 7, if we proceed to $(1, -1)$ the difference between the two encircled numbers is $7 - 3 = 4$, and this is equal to the cost incurred in going from $(0, -2)$ to $(1, -1)$. The required equality is not satisfied for the two ends of the horizontal path from $(0, -2)$ to $(1, -2)$, because $7 - 6 \neq 4$, and therefore this is not a portion of the optimal path from $(0, -2)$.

We can state the above requirement mathematically as follows: "The equation

$$S_i(x_1) - S_{i-1}(x_2) = \text{cost incurred in the transition from } x_1 \text{ to } x_2 \tag{7.41}$$

must be satisfied along an optimal path." It should be emphasized that i is the number of stages to go until the end of the process, and in terms of the k coordinate of the graph of Fig. 7.2 we can write $i = 4 - k$. Now, if we use the symbol $S(k, x)$ to represent the minimum cost incurred in going from the point (k, x) in Fig. 7.2 to the end of the process [for example, $S(2, -2) = 5$], we can write Equation 7.41 in the form

$$\Delta S = S(k + 1, x_2) - S(k, x_1) = -(\text{cost incurred in the transition}$$
$$\text{from } x_1 \text{ to } x_2) \tag{7.42}$$

where ΔS represents the change in S as we advance one step in the process. Equation 7.42 must therefore be satisfied for all transitions along an optimal path. A little thought will make the meaning of Equation 7.42 quite obvious. If we start at any initial state and continue along an optimal path, and if we evaluate for any point on the path the sum of the cost already incurred and the cost yet to be incurred, this sum must remain constant as we move along the optimal path.

DISCRETE-TIME SYSTEM WITH UNCONSTRAINED INPUT

Let us now consider a discrete-time system in which the input is allowed to take on any real value, with the restriction as before that the input remains constant throughout the sampling period. Let us use once again as our example the simple integrator of Fig. 7.1, but let us introduce a sampling period of T seconds instead of 1 second. In this case, the equation relating the output x to the input u is the difference equation

$$x[(k + 1)T] = x(kT) + Tu(kT) \tag{7.43}$$

where the input $u(t)$ is assumed to remain constant in the interval of time $kT \leqslant t < (k + 1)T$, and the notation $u(kT)$ represents this constant value of the input. Let us suppose that the cost incurred in a sampling period is given by

$$c[x(kT), u(kT)] = [x^2(kT) + u^2(kT)]T \tag{7.44}$$

Equations 7.43 and 7.44 correspond to Equations 7.23 and 7.24, respectively. Now suppose that we wish to transfer the system state from $x(0) = x^0$ to $x(NT) = 0$ in such a way as to minimize the total cost C defined by Equation 7.25. The procedure is as follows.

Consider first the one-stage process ($N = 1$). In this case we have only one possible value of input u during the one interval; if the starting state is x, then $u(0)$ must be equal to $-x/T$ in order to make $x(T)$ equal to zero. Therefore, we obtain the following expressions for $S_1(x)$ and the corresponding control input

$$S_1(x) = \left(x^2 + \frac{x^2}{T^2}\right)T = x^2\left(T + \frac{1}{T}\right)$$

$$u_1{}^0(x) = -\frac{1}{T}x \tag{7.45}$$

where the notation $u_1{}^0(x)$ represents the zeroth input of the one-stage process starting from state x. Knowing $S_1(x)$, we can find $S_2(x)$ from the following expression, which is analogous to Equation 7.32

$$S_2(x) = \min_u \left[(x^2 + u^2)T + (x + Tu)^2\left(T + \frac{1}{T}\right)\right] \tag{7.46}$$

where $x + Tu$ is, by Equation 7.43, the state at time T resulting from the application of the input u at time $t = 0$. We can find the minimum of the expression in brackets in Equation 7.46 by differentiating with respect to u, by which we obtain the optimum value of u during the first interval of the two-stage process to be

$$u_2^{\,0}(x) = \frac{-x(1 + T^2)}{T(2 + T^2)} \tag{7.47}$$

Substituting Equation 7.47 in Equation 7.46 we obtain the expression for $S_2(x)$ to be

$$S_2(x) = \frac{T^3 + 3T^2 + 1}{T^3 + 2T}\, x^2 \tag{7.48}$$

At this point, let us consider the special case $T = 1$. We can write the following relationships

$$u_1^{\,0}(x) = -x \qquad S_1(x) = 2x^2 \tag{7.49}$$

$$u_2^{\,0}(x) = -\tfrac{2}{3}x \qquad S_2(x) = \tfrac{5}{3}x^2 \tag{7.50}$$

It can be observed from the above expressions that each item involves the ratio of two numbers from the Fibonacci sequence, which is a sequence of numbers $F(n)$ such that

$$F(n + 1) = F(n) + F(n - 1) \tag{7.51}$$

with $F(0) = 0$, $F(1) = 1$ (see Section 4.12). The first few numbers of the sequence are

$$
\begin{array}{c|cccccc}
n & 0 & 1 & 2 & 3 & 4 & 5 \\
F(n) & 0 & 1 & 1 & 2 & 3 & 5
\end{array}
$$

For this problem, with $T = 1$ and with a fixed endpoint at $x = 0$, the values of the initial input and the minimum of the cost function can be expressed in the form

$$u_N^{\,0}(x) = -\frac{F(2N - 1)}{F(2N)}\, x \tag{7.52}$$

$$S_N(x) = \frac{F(2N + 1)}{F(2N)}\, x^2 \tag{7.53}$$

It is obvious that expressions 7.49 and 7.50 correspond with the above results, and it can easily be proved by mathematical induction that Equations 7.52 and 7.53 are valid for higher values of N. For the same problem with a free endpoint (an unspecified final state, which means that the control input during the last sampling period is zero) the appropriate relationships are

$$u_N{}^0(x) = -\frac{F(2N - 2)}{F(2N - 1)} x \qquad (7.54)$$

$$S_N(x) = \frac{F(2N)}{F(2N - 1)} x^2 \qquad (7.55)$$

It can also be shown that, for the same problem with a T-second sampling period, the relationships are similar except that Lucas functions must be used instead of the Fibonacci sequence. A particular type of Lucas function may be defined by the relationship

$$L(n + 1) = TL(n) + L(n - 1) \qquad (7.56)$$

with $L(0) = 0$, $L(1) = 1/T$ (where T is the sampling period). The Fibonacci sequence is a particular case of this Lucas function. The values of $L(n)$ can be found directly from the difference Equation 7.56, by finding each item from the previous two, or they can be found from the expression

$$L(n) = \frac{\gamma_1{}^n - \gamma_2{}^n}{T(\gamma_1 - \gamma_2)} \qquad (7.57)$$

where γ_1 and γ_2 are the roots of

$$\gamma^2 - T\gamma - 1 = 0 \qquad (7.58)$$

Using the Lucas functions defined by Equation 7.56 the values of the initial input and the minimum of the cost function, for the system with the T-second sampling period, are given by the following expressions.

1. Fixed endpoint $x = 0$

$$u_N{}^0(x) = -\frac{L(2N - 1)}{L(2N)} x \qquad (7.59)$$

$$S_N(x) = \frac{L(2N + 1)}{L(2N)} x^2 \qquad (7.60)$$

These are analogous to Equations 7.52 and 7.53 for the 1-second case.

2. Free endpoint

$$u_N{}^0(x) = -\frac{L(2N - 2)}{L(2N - 1)} x \qquad (7.61)$$

$$S_N(x) = \frac{L(2N)}{L(2N - 1)} x^2 \qquad (7.62)$$

These are analogous to Equations 7.54 and 7.55 for the 1-second case.

TABLE 7.1

n	$L(n)$
0	0
1	2
2	1
3	2.5
4	2.25
5	3.625
6	4.0625
7	5.65625
8	6.890625
9	9.1015625
10	11.44140625
11	14.822265625

The above results are easily proved by mathematical induction; these proofs are left to the reader.

Let us consider a specific numerical example for the purpose of illustration. Suppose $N = 5$, $T = 0.5$, and that the final endpoint is to be at $x = 0$. Equations 7.59 and 7.60 show that the Lucas function must be evaluated up to $L(11)$, and the sequence can be written as in Table 7.1. From Table 7.1 we can construct a table of $S_N(x)$ and $u_N{}^0(x)$ as shown in Table 7.2 (correct to three decimal places).

Now let us suppose that we wish to start from an initial state $x^0 = 1$, and find the optimum piecewise-constant input $u(0), u(T), \ldots, u(4T)$ which changes the value of x from $x(0) = 1$ to $x(5T) = 0$ in such a way as to

TABLE 7.2   VALUES OF $S_N(x)$ AND INITIAL INPUT $u_N{}^0(x)$ FOR AN N-STAGE PROCESS STARTING FROM STATE x, WITH $T = 0.5$ AND $x(NT) = 0$ (CORRECT TO THREE DECIMAL PLACES)

N	$S_N(x)$	$u_N{}^0(x)$
1	$2.500x^2$	$-2.000x$
2	$1.611x^2$	$-1.111x$
3	$1.392x^2$	$-0.892x$
4	$1.321x^2$	$-0.821x$
5	$1.295x^2$	$-0.795x$

TABLE 7.3   THE OPTIMAL SET OF CONTROL INPUTS AND STATE TRANSITIONS FOR
THE FIVE-STAGE PROCESS

k	$x(kT)$	$u(kT)$	$x[(k + 1)T]$ $= x(kT) + \frac{1}{2}u(kT)$
0	1	$-0.795 \times 1 = -0.795$	0.6025
1	0.6025	$-0.821 \times 0.6025 = -0.495$	0.3550
2	0.3550	$-0.894 \times 0.3550 = -0.317$	0.1965
3	0.1965	$-1.111 \times 0.1965 = -0.218$	0.0875
4	0.0875	$-2.000 \times 0.0875 = -0.175$	0

minimize the total cost incurred. Using the values given in Table 7.2, we find
the set of inputs to be as shown in Table 7.3.

Table 7.2 is used to derive Table 7.3 as follows. Starting from $x(0) = 1$, we
read off the optimum initial value of u for the five-stage process from line 5
of Table 7.2 to be -0.795×1. This causes a transition, specified by Equation
7.43 with $T = 0.5$, to $x = 0.6025$. Using this as the initial state for a four-
stage process, we find the optimum initial input for the four-stage process
from line 4 of Table 7.2 to be -0.821×0.6025. This is therefore the input
during the second period of the five-stage process. Continuing in this way, we
derive the optimal sequence of inputs $u(kT)$ given in Table 7.3.

The piecewise-continuous control input u, as tabulated in Table 7.3, is
plotted on the graph on Fig. 7.3. On the same graph is plotted the optimum
continuous control input for a simple integrator, which transfers the system
state x from 1 to 0 in a time of 2.5 seconds, in such a way as to minimize the
integral

$$I = \int_0^{2.5} (x^2 + u^2)\, dt \qquad (7.63)$$

The integral (Equation 7.63) is the same as the limit, as T approaches zero
while maintaining $NT = 2.5$, of the summation of N elementary cost functions of the form of Equation 7.44. The problem of minimizing the integral
(Equation 7.63) was solved in Chapter 5, the optimal input being given by
Equation 5.34. In terms of the data of the present problem, the optimum
continuous control input is given by

$$u(t) = -\left[\frac{e^t + e^5 e^{-t}}{e^5 - 1}\right]$$
$$= -0.00678e^t - 1.00678e^{-t} \quad \text{for} \quad 0 \leqslant t \leqslant 2.5 \quad (7.64)$$

The graph in Fig. 7.3 shows that the piecewise-continuous control input is a
reasonable approximation to the continuous input. If we used finer subdivisions of the total time period, by making the number N of stages of the

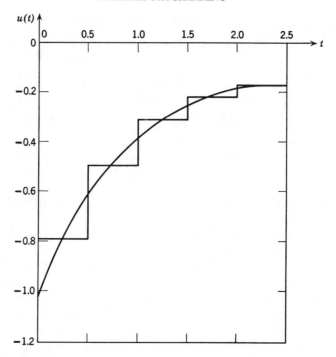

Fig. 7.3. Continuous and piecewise-continuous optimal inputs to simple integrator.

process larger, we would expect to approach the continuous control input of Fig. 7.3 more closely.

We have used Tables 7.2 and 7.3 to derive the optimal control sequence for this problem. While this derivation from a set of tabulated values (which might, in a more complicated problem, be stored in the memory of a digital computer) is an illustration of the kind of procedure often used in dynamic-programming calculations, there is an easier way of deriving the optimal control sequence in this case. Let us extend expression 7.59 to find the second input of the N-stage process starting at state x. After applying the initial input $u_N{}^0(x^0)$ given by Equation 7.59, we find the state $x(t)$ after one sampling period to be

$$x(T) = x^0 - \frac{TL(2N - 1)}{L(2N)} x^0 \qquad (7.65)$$

In view of the properties of the Lucas function, as defined by Equation 7.56, Equation 7.65 can be written as

$$x(T) = \frac{L(2N - 2)}{L(2N)} x^0 \qquad (7.66)$$

The next input $u_N{}^1(x^0)$ can be written as if it were the initial input of an $(N - 1)$-stage process starting at $x(T)$, which is

$$u_N{}^1(x^0) = -\frac{L(2N - 3)}{L(2N)} x^0 \qquad (7.67)$$

Proceeding in this way, the optimum sequence of control inputs can be expressed in the form

$$u_N{}^i(x^0) = -\frac{L(2N - 2i - 1)}{L(2N)} x^0 \qquad \text{for} \qquad i = 0, 1, \ldots, N - 1 \quad (7.68)$$

In view of the fact that Equation 7.68 represents a sequence of odd-order Lucas numbers, all divided by a constant $L(2N)$, we can see a further similarity between the discrete and continuous cases. In view of expression 7.57, the sequence of odd-order Lucas numbers can be observed to be the sum of an increasing geometric progression (with ratio of each term to the preceding term greater than unity) and a decreasing one of the same sign. This is because $\gamma_1 = -1/\gamma_2$, which can be deduced from Equation 7.58. The corresponding continuous input (Equation 5.34) is the sum of an exponentially increasing function and an exponentially decreasing one (if the final state is to be zero, Equation 5.33 shows that A and B have opposite signs, so that Equation 5.34 represents the sum of two terms which have the same sign).

7.4 CONTINUOUS VERSION OF DYNAMIC PROGRAMMING

In order to illustrate the continuous version of dynamic programming, let us consider a fundamental problem of the calculus of variations, as described in Chapter 5. To be specific, let us study the problem of finding the curve $y(x)$, joining two fixed points A and B in the xy plane as shown in Fig. 7.4, such that the functional I given by Equation 7.69 takes on a minimum value.

$$I = \int_{x_0, y_0}^{x_1, y_1} f(x, y, y') \, dx \qquad (7.69)$$

The dynamic-programming solution of a problem of this type has been described by Bellman and Dreyfus [3, 4].

The procedure is to assume that the right-hand endpoint is fixed at B, but that the left-hand endpoint is arbitrary. Suppose, for example, we start from an arbitrary point C, whose coordinates are x and y, to the left of B. For curves joining C to B, there is some definite minimum achievable value of the functional specified by

$$I(x, y) = \int_{x, y}^{x_1, y_1} f(x, y, y') \, dx \qquad (7.70)$$

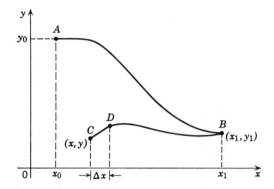

Fig. 7.4. Graph illustrating the continuous version of dynamic programming.

The minimum possible value of the functional (Equation 7.70) for the specified right-hand endpoint B, is a function of x and y, the coordinates of the left-hand endpoint. Let us denote this minimum achievable value by the symbol $S(x, y)$. This symbolism is analogous to $S(k, x)$ introduced in the previous section.

Let us now suppose that, starting at the arbitrary point C, we begin by following a straight line of arbitrary slope y' throughout a short interval Δx, to reach a point D as shown in Fig. 7.4, and thereafter follow an optimal path from D to B.

If we evaluate the functional (Equation 7.70) corresponding to the path CDB obtained as described above, we obtain a definite result. If we vary the ordinate of the point D, by varying the slope y' in the interval Δx, the value of the corresponding functional varies. For some position of D, corresponding to some value of slope y' in the interval Δx, a minimum of the functional is achieved. Then, provided the interval Δx is small, we can say that the path in question is approximately the same as the optimal curve from C to B and approaches it as Δx approaches zero.

For the position of the point D which gives a minimum of the functional (Equation 7.70), the value of the functional is $S(x, y)$, assuming that Δx is very small. If we consider the point D, we see that the minimum value of the integral of the form of Equation 7.70 from D to B, is $S(x + \Delta x, y + y' \Delta x)$. As we follow the optimal curve from D to B, we can therefore express the function $S(x, y)$ in the form

$$S(x, y) = \min_{y'} [f \Delta x + S(x + \Delta x, y + y' \Delta x)] \qquad (7.71)$$

where we assume that Δx is very small so that terms in $(\Delta x)^2$ and higher powers may be neglected. This equation is analogous to Equation 7.34 for the discrete case.

Assuming that $S(x, y)$ is a smooth function, we can express Equation 7.71 in the form

$$S(x, y) = \min_{y'} \left[f \, \Delta x + S(x, y) + \frac{\partial S}{\partial x} \, \Delta x + \frac{\partial S}{\partial y} \, y' \, \Delta x \right] \qquad (7.72)$$

where we have once again neglected terms in $(\Delta x)^2$ and higher powers. Equation 7.72 can now be expressed in the form

$$\min_{y'} \left(f + \frac{\partial S}{\partial x} + y' \frac{\partial S}{\partial y} \right) = 0 \qquad (7.73)$$

In view of the minimization with respect to y', we can say that the quantity in the parentheses of Equation 7.73 satisfies the following two conditions simultaneously: (1) the quantity in parentheses is zero; and (2) its derivative with respect to y' is zero. Expressing these mathematically, we obtain the equations

$$f + \frac{\partial S}{\partial x} + y' \frac{\partial S}{\partial y} = 0 \qquad (7.74)$$

$$\frac{\partial f}{\partial y'} + \frac{\partial S}{\partial y} = 0 \qquad (7.75)$$

Differentiating Equation 7.75 with respect to x, and Equation 7.74 partially with respect to y, we obtain, respectively,

$$\frac{d}{dx} \left(\frac{\partial f}{\partial y'} \right) + \frac{\partial^2 S}{\partial y^2} \frac{dy}{dx} + \frac{\partial^2 S}{\partial y \, \partial x} = 0 \qquad (7.76)$$

$$\frac{\partial f}{\partial y} + \frac{\partial f}{\partial y'} \frac{\partial y'}{\partial y} + \frac{\partial^2 S}{\partial x \, \partial y} + y' \frac{\partial^2 S}{\partial y^2} + \frac{\partial y'}{\partial y} \frac{\partial S}{\partial y} = 0 \qquad (7.77)$$

Substituting Equation 7.75 in Equation 7.77, we obtain

$$\frac{\partial f}{\partial y} - \frac{\partial S}{\partial y} \frac{\partial y'}{\partial y} + \frac{\partial^2 S}{\partial x \, \partial y} + y' \frac{\partial^2 S}{\partial y^2} + \frac{\partial y'}{\partial y} \frac{\partial S}{\partial y} = 0 \qquad (7.78)$$

Subtracting Equation 7.78 from Equation 7.76, and noting that the second and fifth terms of Equation 7.78 cancel, we obtain

$$\frac{d}{dx} \left(\frac{\partial f}{\partial y'} \right) - \frac{\partial f}{\partial y} = 0 \qquad (7.79)$$

Equation 7.79 is the same as the Euler-Lagrange Equation 5.11. This shows that we can use dynamic programming to derive the Euler-Lagrange equations which feature so prominently in the calculus of variations.

7.5   A CONTINUOUS CONTROL PROBLEM

Let us now consider the control of a simple linear system with a quadratic performance index. Suppose we have a simple first-order linear system with one state variable x, and one input u, with $\dot{x}$ a definite function of x and u. If we consider the minimization of an integral of the form

$$I = \int_{t_0}^{t_1} f(x, \dot{x}, t)\, dt \qquad (7.80)$$

we can write the conditions for minimization of the integral, by analogy with Equation 7.73, as

$$\min_{u} \left(f + \frac{\partial S}{\partial t} + \dot{x}\frac{\partial S}{\partial x} \right) = 0 \qquad (7.81)$$

where we can consider minimization with respect to u instead of $\dot{x}$, as $\dot{x}$ is a definite function of u for any particular state x. The function S is now a function $S(t, x)$ and has the same significance as before, namely, the minimum value of an integral of the form of Equation 7.80 achievable by starting from time t and state x.

Let us now suppose that the right-hand endpoint is completely free, and that the differential equation of the system is of the form

$$\dot{x} = ax + bu \qquad (7.82)$$

Suppose that the performance index is of the form

$$I = \int_{t_0}^{t_1} (gx^2 + hu^2)\, dt \qquad (7.83)$$

where g and h are positive real numbers, and it is assumed that t_0 and t_1 are both specified in advance. We shall assume for the present that t_1 is finite.

Let us assume that $S(t, x)$ is of the form[2]

$$S(t, x) = K(t)x^2 \qquad (7.84)$$

The form of the function S, for the previous results derived for the discrete system (see Equations 7.53 and 7.55, for example), makes this assumption appear reasonable for a quadratic performance index.

Substituting the known and assumed relationships in Equations 7.82, 7.83, and 7.84 into Equation 7.81, we obtain

$$\min_{u} [gx^2 + hu^2 + \dot{K}x^2 + (ax + bu)(2Kx)] = 0 \qquad (7.85)$$

---

[2] A more general form would be $S(t, x) = K_0(t) + K_1(t)x + K_2(t)x^2$. If the final endpoint is unspecified or zero, K_0 and K_1 are found to be zero.

Differentiating the expression in square brackets in Equation 7.85 partially with respect to u, and setting to zero, we obtain

$$2hu + 2Kbx = 0 \tag{7.86}$$

From Equation 7.86, we find the optimum control input u^* to be

$$u^* = -\frac{bK}{h} x \tag{7.87}$$

Equation 7.87 gives the instantaneous value of u^*, the optimal control input, in terms of the state x. If K is known, this would allow us to connect a (possibly time-varying) feedback loop to give u^* as a function of x. It may be noted that, in the foregoing developments, a, b, g, and h may all be functions of time.

Substituting the value of u^* given by Equation 7.87 into Equation 7.85 we obtain, after some simplification

$$\left(g + \frac{K^2 b^2}{h} + \dot{K} + 2aK - \frac{2b^2 K^2}{h}\right)x^2 = 0 \tag{7.88}$$

Equation 7.88 is satisfied, for all values of x, if the quantity inside the parentheses is zero. This gives the following differential equation for K:

$$\dot{K} = -g - 2aK + \frac{b^2 K^2}{h} \tag{7.89}$$

This differential equation is of the type known as the Riccati equation [5, 6]. In order to obtain the complete solution of this equation we need one boundary condition. The boundary condition to be used here is $K(t_1) = 0$. The reason for this is that, for a free-endpoint problem ending at time t_1, the function $S(t_1, x)$ must be zero for all x because it represents the minimum cost incurred in a process of zero time duration. It should be noted, however, that this would not be true if the final endpoint were not completely free. We shall deal with the fixed-endpoint case later.

If desired, the Riccati equation can be written in terms of a variable τ, defined by $\tau \triangleq t_1 - t$, as follows

$$\frac{dK}{d\tau} = g + 2aK - \frac{b^2 K^2}{h} \tag{7.90}$$

$$K(0) = 0 \tag{7.91}$$

Let us now consider a simple example to illustrate the use of the Riccati equation in the solution of an optimal control problem. We shall use as our example the system studied in Section 5.3, the simple integrator with a quadratic performance criterion. The system equation is as follows

$$\dot{x} = u \tag{7.92}$$

The quantity to be minimized is

$$I = \int_{t_0}^{t_1} (x^2 + u^2)\, dt \tag{7.93}$$

In terms of the quantities used in the above derivation, the data of the problem are as follows:

$$\begin{aligned} a &= 0 \\ b &= 1 \\ g &= 1 \\ h &= 1 \end{aligned} \tag{7.94}$$

We suppose the endpoint to be completely free, and assume the optimal control input is of the form

$$u^* = -Kx \tag{7.95}$$

The Riccati equation for K may be written as

$$\dot{K} = K^2 - 1 \tag{7.96}$$

with boundary condition $K(t_1) = 0$. This equation can be solved analytically in this case, for example, by the method of separation of variables, and the solution can be written in the form

$$K = -\tanh (t - t_1) \tag{7.97}$$

Substituting Equation 7.97 in Equation 7.95, and writing $\dot{x}$ for u, we obtain the following differential equation for x:

$$\dot{x} = x \tanh (t - t_1) \tag{7.98}$$

Equation 7.98 can also be solved by separation of variables, and the solution may be written in the form

$$x = R \cosh (t - t_1) \tag{7.99}$$

The optimal control input u^* can be written in the form

$$u^* = R \sinh (t - t_1) \tag{7.100}$$

It can easily be shown that these equations for x and u^* correspond to those found for the same problem in Section 5.3 (Equations 5.33 and 5.34). It is suggested that the reader verify that $Ae^t + Be^{-t}$ can be written in the form $R \cosh (t + S)$ if A and B have the same sign, and in the form $R \sinh (t + S)$ if A and B have opposite signs (where A, B, R, and S are real). If the right-hand endpoint is completely free, the final value $u^*(t_1)$ is zero, and A and B of Equation 5.34 must have the same sign.

EXTENSION TO THE FIXED-ENDPOINT CASE

The extension of this method to the fixed-endpoint case is not quite so simple. It will be recalled that we were able to take $S(t_1, x)$ to be zero for all x because the right-hand endpoint was free; if it is not free we are not able to assign a boundary value to K directly. The procedure we shall adopt is to assume the right-hand endpoint to be free, but to add to the cost function a penalty term which is large if the desired output is not reached. By making this penalty sufficiently large, the specified endpoint can be approached as closely as desired.

Let us assume that the specified state, to be reached at time t_1, is $x^1 = 0$. We shall redefine the performance index to include a term proportional to the square of the actual value of $x(t_1)$, so that the quantity to be minimized is expressed in the form

$$J = \int_{t_0}^{t_1} (gx^2 + hu^2)\, dt + px^2(t_1) \tag{7.101}$$

where p is a positive constant. Let us define $S_p(t, x)$ to be the minimum value of J achieved, starting from time t and state x, finishing at time t_1, with the final state free. Let us assume that $S_p(t, x)$ can be written in the form $K_p(t)x^2$. Equations 7.85 to 7.89 follow as before, but the boundary value $K_p(t_1)$ is now p instead of being zero. By taking p large, we can approach the exact solution of the fixed-endpoint problem. Let us illustrate this by studying the same problem, the simple integrator with the performance index given by Equation 7.93, but taking the desired end state to be $x^1 = 0$.

The solution of the Riccati Equation 7.89, with the new boundary condition $K_p(t_1) = p$, can be written in the form

$$K_p = -\coth\left(t - t_1 - \coth^{-1} p\right) \tag{7.102}$$

If we now allow p to become infinite, which means an infinitely large penalty imposed for missing the state $x = 0$ at time t_1, the value of K_p becomes

$$K_p = -\coth\left(t - t_1\right) \tag{7.103}$$

Substituting Equation 7.103 in Equation 7.95, and writing $\dot{x}$ for u, we obtain the following differential equation for x.

$$\dot{x} = x \coth\left(t - t_1\right) \tag{7.104}$$

Equation 7.104 can be solved by separation of variables, and the solution can be written in the form

$$x = R \sinh\left(t - t_1\right) \tag{7.105}$$

where R is a constant. The optimal control input can be written in the form

$$u^* = R \cosh\left(t - t_1\right) \tag{7.106}$$

These can also be shown to be the same as the results derived using the calculus variations in Chapter 5. It should be noted that, if the desired final state is some value other than $x^1 = 0$, the penalty term is of the form $p(x - x^1)^2$, and the value of $S_p(t, x)$ must be expressed in the more general form

$$S_p(t, x) = K_0(t) + K_1(t)x + K_2(t)x^2 \qquad (7.107)$$

INFINITE FINAL TIME

We have assumed throughout the preceding portions of this section that the final time t_1 is finite. Let us now consider a process of infinite duration.

Let us assume that the system and performance index are both time-invariant, in the sense that the parameters a, b, g, and h of Equations 7.82 and 7.83 are all constant. In this case it is reasonably obvious that, at any finite time t, the function $S(t, x)$ is independent of time t and is dependent only on the state x.[3] This is analogous to the result, for the corresponding discrete-time case, that the value of $S_N(x)$ approaches a constant multiplied by x^2 as N approaches infinity. This can be shown by examining Equation 7.53 or Equation 7.55, and recalling that the ratio of two successive Fibonacci numbers $F(n + 1)/F(n)$ approaches a definite limit as n approaches infinity, as shown in Chapter 4.

For the infinite-time process with constant parameters, therefore, we can assume that the value of K in Equations 7.84 and 7.87 is constant. This means that u is at any instant directly proportional to the instantaneous value of the state variable x, and that a feedback path with a constant gain parameter K can be used. The value of K can be found by setting the time derivative of K to zero in Equation 7.89 and solving the resulting algebraic equation. Analogous results can be obtained for the discrete-time case; these can be obtained by allowing N to approach infinity in Equation 7.52 or Equation 7.54.

THE MATRIX RICCATI EQUATION

The foregoing method of solving an optimal control problem in a linear system with a quadratic performance index can be extended to higher-order systems. Consider, for example, the system characterized by the vector-matrix differential equation

$$\dot{\mathbf{x}} = \mathbf{Ax} + \mathbf{Bu} \qquad (7.108)$$

---

[3] We shall assume the final state to be either free or zero in this case. Any different requirement will give an infinite value of performance index unless the value of g in Equation 7.83 is zero.

with the performance index

$$I = \int_{t_0}^{t_1} (\mathbf{x}'\mathbf{G}\mathbf{x} + \mathbf{u}'\mathbf{H}\mathbf{u}) \, dt \qquad (7.109)$$

where $\mathbf{x}'$ = transpose of $\mathbf{x}$, $\mathbf{u}'$ = transpose of $\mathbf{u}$, and $\mathbf{G}$ and $\mathbf{H}$ are symmetric positive-definite matrices.[4] If we define a quantity $S(t, \mathbf{x})$, to represent the minimum cost achievable by starting from state $\mathbf{x}$ at time t, the conditions for optimum control are obtained by generalizing Equation 7.81 to the case of n state variables and a vector control input as follows:

$$\min_{\mathbf{u}} \left(f_0 + \frac{\partial S}{\partial t} + \dot{\mathbf{x}} \cdot \frac{\partial S}{\partial \mathbf{x}} \right) = 0 \qquad (7.110)$$

where f_0 is the integrand appearing in the performance-criterion integral (Equation 7.109), and $\partial S/\partial \mathbf{x}$ represents the vector **grad** S with components $\partial S/\partial x_1, \ldots, \partial S/\partial x_n$.

Let us assume that $S(t, \mathbf{x})$ is of the form

$$S(t, \mathbf{x}) = \mathbf{x}'\mathbf{K}(t)\mathbf{x} \qquad (7.111)$$

where $\mathbf{K}$ is a matrix, which may be assumed to be symmetric without loss of generality. It is assumed that the endpoint is completely free. By following a procedure similar to that for the scalar case (but taking care to keep all matrix products in the correct order), we obtain [7] a matrix Riccati equation of the form

$$\dot{\mathbf{K}} = -\mathbf{G} - \mathbf{A}'\mathbf{K} - \mathbf{K}\mathbf{A} + \mathbf{K}\mathbf{B}\mathbf{H}^{-1}\mathbf{B}'\mathbf{K} \qquad (7.112)$$

The boundary condition for the free-endpoint case is

$$\mathbf{K}(t_1) = \mathbf{0} \qquad (7.113)$$

In general the matrix Riccati equation must be solved numerically to find the matrix $\mathbf{K}(t)$. It is helpful to remember that it is a symmetric matrix, so that only $\frac{1}{2}n(n + 1)$ elements are to be found instead of n^2. Having found $\mathbf{K}(t)$, the optimal control input $\mathbf{u}^*$ can be found [7] from the equation

$$\mathbf{u}^* = -\mathbf{H}^{-1}\mathbf{B}'\mathbf{K}\mathbf{x} \qquad (7.114)$$

If Equation 7.108 represents a controllable time-invariant system, if the matrices $\mathbf{G}$ and $\mathbf{H}$ in Equation 7.109 are constant and positive definite, and if the final time t_1 is infinite, the matrix $\mathbf{K}$ is constant and is the solution of the matrix algebraic equation obtained by setting the left side of Equation

---

[4] A positive-definite matrix is a square matrix $\mathbf{G}$ such that $\mathbf{x}'\mathbf{G}\mathbf{x}$ (which is a scalar quantity) is positive for all real $\mathbf{x}$ except for the null vector whose components are all zero.

7.112 equal to the null matrix [13]. For a more detailed discussion of optimal control problems involving linear systems with quadratic performance criteria, the reader is referred to reference [13].

STOCHASTIC OPTIMAL CONTROL PROBLEMS

In linear systems with quadratic error criteria and subjected to Gaussian inputs, the optimal control is obtained by using an optimal estimator and a deterministic optimal controller [14]. In other words, the estimation and control problems are separable, and the controller acts on the optimal estimates as if they were the true values of the variables. The state variables might be estimated, for example, by a Kalman filter (see Chapter 3). Both the optimal estimation problem and the optimal control problem require the solution of a differential equation of the matrix Riccati type. If these are to be solved by a digital computer, as will usually be the case in practice, the same computer program can be used for both computations [7]. This is a consequence of the duality relationship between the optimal estimation problem and the noise-free regulator problem, which has been pointed out by Kalman [15].

7.6 DYNAMIC PROGRAMMING AND THE MAXIMUM PRINCIPLE

Let us now investigate the relationship that exists between dynamic programming and the maximum principle. We shall do this by considering the scalar function $S(t, \mathbf{x})$ which occurs in the formulation of the dynamic-programming problem, and by showing that the gradient vector of this function is closely related to the adjoint vector or auxiliary vector which is used in the maximum principle.

Suppose we have a fixed-time fixed-endpoint problem, in a system characterized by the differential equations

$$\dot{x}_i = f_i(\mathbf{x}, \mathbf{u}) \qquad (i = 1, \ldots, n) \tag{7.115}$$

The system is to be controlled in such a way as to minimize the integral

$$I = \int_{t_0}^{t_1} f_0(\mathbf{x}, \mathbf{u}) \, dt \tag{7.116}$$

By imagining the initial time and state to be free, we define a scalar function $S(t, \mathbf{x})$ that represents the minimum value of an integral of the form of Equation 7.116 that can be achieved, if the initial time is t and the state at that time is $\mathbf{x}$.

Let us now introduce a variable x_0, as we have done before in Chapters 5 and 6, characterized by the differential equation

$$\dot{x}_0 = f_0(\mathbf{x}, \mathbf{u}) \tag{7.117}$$

If we start from a specified initial value of x_0 at time t_0, the change in x_0 from t_0 to t_1 represents the value of the integral I in Equation 7.116. If we suppose that the initial value of x_0 can be chosen to be any desired value, it is possible to define a new function $\mathscr{S}$ in the following way

$$\mathscr{S}(x_0, \mathbf{x}, t) \overset{\Delta}{=} S(t, \mathbf{x}) + x_0 \tag{7.118}$$

In this definition, $\mathscr{S}(x_0, \mathbf{x}, t)$ represents the minimum value of $x_0(t_1)$ that it is possible to achieve by starting at time t, state $\mathbf{x}$, and a given initial value of x_0.

If we consider the behavior of the function $\mathscr{S}$, in the light of the principle of optimality, we see that $\mathscr{S}$ remains constant as we move along an optimal trajectory. In other words, the function $S(t, \mathbf{x})$ decreases at the same rate as x_0 increases, as we move along an optimal trajectory. We can show by contradiction that this is true. Suppose, for example, that we move from an initial state $\mathbf{x}$, value of x_0, and time t, to a new state $\mathbf{x}^A$ at time t^A, with x_0 changing to x_0^A. If $S(t^A, \mathbf{x}^A) + x_0^A$ is less than $S(t, \mathbf{x}) + x_0$, then $S(t, \mathbf{x})$ could not have been the minimum cost achievable from state $\mathbf{x}$ at time t; if $S(t^A, \mathbf{x}^A) + x_0^A$ is greater than $S(t, \mathbf{x}) + x_0$, then the trajectory followed between t and t^A was not optimal because the system cannot now achieve as good a result as was originally available to it.

The function $\mathscr{S}$ is a scalar function of the $n + 2$ variables $x_0, x_1, \ldots, x_n, t$. Let us now introduce an extra state variable x_{n+1} to represent the time t, as we did in Section 4.14. The differential equation characterizing this state variable is

$$\dot{x}_{n+1} = 1 \tag{7.119}$$

We can now consider the scalar function $\mathscr{S}(x_0, x_1, \ldots, x_{n+1})$ to be defined in the $(n + 2)$-dimensional space of the variables $x_0, x_1, \ldots, x_{n+1}$. Accordingly, if the function $\mathscr{S}$ is smooth, we can consider the gradient of $\mathscr{S}$ at any point in the space as a vector with components $g_0, g_1, \ldots, g_n, g_{n+1}$, where

$$g_i \overset{\Delta}{=} \frac{\partial \mathscr{S}}{\partial x_i} \qquad (i = 0, 1, \ldots, n + 1) \tag{7.120}$$

Now, if $\mathscr{S}$ remains constant despite the fact that the state point is moving along an optimal trajectory, the direction of motion of the state point must be orthogonal to the gradient of $\mathscr{S}$. This means that

$$\sum_{j=0}^{n+1} g_j f_j = 0 \tag{7.121}$$

where $f_{n+1} = 1$, as in Equation 7.119. Differentiating Equation 7.121 partially with respect to x_i, we obtain

$$\sum_{j=0}^{n+1} \frac{\partial^2 \mathscr{S}}{\partial x_i\, \partial x_j} f_j + \sum_{j=0}^{n+1} \frac{\partial \mathscr{S}}{\partial x_j} \frac{\partial f_j}{\partial x_i} = 0 \qquad (7.122)$$

Consider the time derivative of the ith component of the gradient of $\mathscr{S}$, given by

$$\frac{dg_i}{dt} = \frac{d}{dt}\left(\frac{\partial \mathscr{S}}{\partial x_i}\right) = \sum_{j=0}^{n+1} \frac{\partial}{\partial x_j}\left(\frac{\partial \mathscr{S}}{\partial x_i}\right) \frac{dx_j}{dt}$$

$$= \sum_{j=0}^{n+1} \frac{\partial^2 \mathscr{S}}{\partial x_j\, \partial x_i} \frac{dx_j}{dt} \qquad (7.123)$$

Provided that the first partial derivatives $\partial \mathscr{S}/\partial x_i$ are continuous, the second partial derivatives in Equations 7.122 and 7.123 are equal [8]; substituting Equation 7.122 in Equation 7.123, we obtain

$$\dot{g}_i = -\sum_{j=0}^{n+1} g_j \frac{\partial f_j}{\partial x_i} \qquad (7.124)$$

Let us define a quantity $\tilde{\mathscr{H}}(\mathbf{g}, \mathbf{x}, \mathbf{u})$ or $\mathscr{H}(\mathbf{p}, \mathbf{x}, \mathbf{u})$ as

$$\tilde{\mathscr{H}} \overset{\Delta}{=} -\sum_{j=0}^{n+1} g_j f_j(\mathbf{x}, \mathbf{u}) = \sum_{j=0}^{n+1} p_j f_j(\mathbf{x}, \mathbf{u}) \qquad (7.125)$$

where the variables p_j are here defined to be

$$p_j \overset{\Delta}{=} -g_j \qquad (j = 0, 1, \ldots, n+1) \qquad (7.126)$$

The partial derivative of $\mathscr{H}(\mathbf{p}, \mathbf{x}, \mathbf{u})$ with respect to x_i is

$$\frac{\partial \tilde{\mathscr{H}}}{\partial x_i} = \sum_{j=0}^{n+1} p_j \frac{\partial f_j}{\partial x_i} \qquad (7.127)$$

This means that the time derivative of p_i can be written (see Equation 7.124) in the form

$$\dot{p}_i = -\frac{\partial \tilde{\mathscr{H}}}{\partial x_i} \qquad (i = 0, 1, \ldots, n+1) \qquad (7.128)$$

Also, we can say that

$$\frac{dx_i}{dt} = \frac{\partial \tilde{\mathscr{H}}}{\partial p_i} \qquad (i = 0, 1, \ldots, n+1) \qquad (7.129)$$

The last two equations are the same as Equations 6.7 and 6.8, relating the state variables and auxiliary variables in the maximum principle, except that they are in terms of $n + 2$ state variables instead of $n + 1$. The notation $\tilde{\mathscr{H}}$ is used to represent the summation of $n + 2$ terms as shown in Equation 7.125.

It still remains to be shown that **u** is to be chosen in such a way as to maximize the Hamiltonian. An inspection of Equation 7.110 shows that the quantity inside the parentheses is the same as $-\tilde{\mathscr{H}}$ as defined in Equation 7.125. Because of the definition of $\mathscr{S}$, in Equation 7.118, the partial derivative $\partial \mathscr{S}/\partial x_0$ is unity and the first term of $\tilde{\mathscr{H}}$ is $-f_0$. The components of the n-dimensional vector **grad** S are the same as the corresponding components of **grad** $\mathscr{S}$, and the partial derivative $\partial S/\partial t$ is the same as $\partial \mathscr{S}/\partial x_{n+1}$.[5] The quantity $-\tilde{\mathscr{H}}$ is to be minimized for optimal control, and this is obviously the same as requiring $\tilde{\mathscr{H}}$ to be maximized for optimal control. This is almost the same as the condition given by the maximum principle, except in that case we maximized $\mathscr{H}$. Consider the difference between $\tilde{\mathscr{H}}$ and $\mathscr{H}$, the term $p_{n+1}f_{n+1}$. The time derivative of p_{n+1} is given by

$$\dot{p}_{n+1} = \frac{-\partial \tilde{\mathscr{H}}}{\partial x_{n+1}} \tag{7.130}$$

As x_{n+1} represents time t, we can say that the derivative $\dot{p}_{n+1}$ is zero unless one of the functions $f_0, f_1, \ldots, f_n$ is an explicit function of time. Therefore p_{n+1} is a constant, and as $f_{n+1} = 1$, the difference between $\tilde{\mathscr{H}}$ and $\mathscr{H}$ is a constant and maximization of one implies maximization of the other. This shows that, in the determinate system we have considered, the maximum principle and dynamic programming are equivalent.

We can now add one further comment to the discussion of the geometric interpretation of the maximum principle, which is included in Chapter 6. The maximum principle can now be interpreted as follows:

1. It is necessary to choose the control input which maximizes the projection of the velocity vector ${}^0\mathbf{f}_{n+1}$ in the direction of the vector ${}^0\mathbf{p}_{n+1}$ (where the vectors ${}^0\mathbf{f}_{n+1}$ and ${}^0\mathbf{p}_{n+1}$ refer to the vectors with components $f_0, f_1, \ldots, f_{n+1}$ and $p_0, p_1, \ldots, p_{n+1}$).
2. The maximum value of this projection is equal to zero.

It may be helpful to summarize some of the foregoing information in the following way.

---

[5] It will be recalled that S is a function of $x_1, \ldots, x_n$ and t, while $\mathscr{S}$ is a function of $x_0, x_1, \ldots, x_n, x_{n+1}$.

1. In all determinate systems, autonomous or nonautonomous, the maximum value of $\tilde{\mathcal{H}}$ is constant along an optimal trajectory, and is equal to zero.[6]

2. In all determinate systems in which the f_i ($i = 0, 1, \ldots, n$) are not explicit functions of time, the maximum value of $\mathcal{H}$ is constant along an optimal trajectory. If the end time is completely free, the maximum value of $\mathcal{H}$ is zero by the transversality condition.

3. In all minimum-time problems in autonomous determinate systems, the maximum value of H is constant along an optimal trajectory.

We have seen that the maximum value of $\tilde{\mathcal{H}}$ is equal to zero. We can write $\tilde{\mathcal{H}}$ in the form $\mathcal{H} + p_{n+1}$, and this leads to the equation

$$\mathcal{H} - \frac{\partial S}{\partial t} = 0 \tag{7.131}$$

Equation 7.131 is a form of the Hamilton-Jacobi equation [3, 4, 9, 10], which arises frequently in the theory of mechanics and in optimal control theory. In mechanics, the Hamiltonian equations of motion and the Hamilton-Jacobi partial differential equation are alternative methods of characterizing the behavior of a system. In optimal control theory, the maximum principle is analogous to the Hamiltonian representation, whereas dynamic programming is analogous to the Hamilton-Jacobi representation. For a full treatment of these two characterizations of the behavior of mechanical systems, the reader is recommended to refer to Lanczos [9].

SUMMARY

In this chapter we have studied the principle of optimality and its use in obtaining solutions of optimization problems by dynamic programming. We have seen that the method of dynamic programming is, at least in the determinate systems we have considered, very closely related to the maximum principle and the calculus of variations.

For further study of dynamic programming, including a discussion of computational methods, the book by Nemhauser [11] is recommended. Other useful references are [1, 2, 3, 12].

---

[6] It is always possible to introduce the extra variables x_{n+1} and p_{n+1}, although it is not always necessary to do so.

REFERENCES

[1] Bellman, R., *Dynamic Programming*, Princeton University Press, Princeton, 1957.
[2] Bellman, R., *Adaptive Control Processes: A Guided Tour*, Princeton University Press, Princeton, 1961.
[3] Bellman, R. E., and S. E. Dreyfus, *Applied Dynamic Programming*, Princeton University Press, Princeton, 1962.
[4] Dreyfus, S. E., "Dynamic Programming and the Calculus of Variations," *J. Math. An. Appl.*, 1, 228–239 (1960).
[5] James, G., and R. C. James, eds., *Mathematics Dictionary*, Van Nostrand, Princeton, 1959.
[6] Piaggio, H. T. H., *Differential Equations*, G. Bell & Sons, London, 1952.
[7] Noton, A. R. M., *Introduction to Variational Methods in Control Engineering*, Pergamon Press, Oxford, 1965.
[8] Pipes, L. A., *Applied Mathematics for Engineers and Physicists*, 2nd ed., McGraw-Hill, New York, 1958.
[9] Lanczos, C., *The Variational Principles of Mechanics*, 2nd ed., University of Toronto Press, Toronto, 1962.
[10] Tou, J. T., *Modern Control Theory*, McGraw-Hill, New York, 1964.
[11] Nemhauser, G. L., *Introduction to Dynamic Programming*, Wiley, New York, 1966.
[12] Hadley, G., *Nonlinear and Dynamic Programming*, Addison-Wesley, Reading, Mass., 1964.
[13] Athans, M., and P. L. Falb, *Optimal Control: An Introduction to the Theory and its Applications*, McGraw-Hill, New York, 1966.
[14] Lee, R. C. K., *Optimal Estimation, Identification, and Control*, Research Monograph No. 28, M.I.T. Press, Cambridge, Mass., 1964.
[15] Kalman, R. E., "A New Approach to Linear Filtering and Prediction Problems," *ASME Trans.*, Series D (*J. Basic Eng.*), 82, 35–45 (1960).

PROBLEMS

1. (a) Use dynamic programming to find the sequence of values x_1 to x_4 which (i) maximizes, and (ii) minimizes the summation

$$\sum_{i=1}^{4} ix_i \tag{7.132}$$

where the x_i are all nonnegative real numbers such that

$$\sum_{i=1}^{4} x_i^2 = c^2 \tag{7.133}$$

where c is a constant.

(b) Use dynamic programming to find the sequence of values x_1 to x_4 which (i) maximizes, and (ii) minimizes the summation

$$\sum_{i=1}^{4} ix_i^2 \tag{7.134}$$

where the x_i are all nonnegative real numbers such that

$$\sum_{i=1}^{4} x_i = c \qquad (7.135)$$

where c is a constant.

2. A system is characterized by the difference equation

$$x(k + 1) = \tfrac{1}{2}x(k) + u(k) \qquad (7.136)$$

If the initial state $x(0)$ is zero, find the input sequence $u(0)$ to $u(3)$ which, subject to the constraint

$$\sum_{i=0}^{3} [u(i)]^2 \leqslant c^2 \qquad (7.137)$$

(where c is a constant), gives the maximum possible value of $x(4)$.

3. Suppose that it is desired to weigh objects having weights which are all integral multiples of a basic unit, using a balance with two equal arms and the smallest possible number of weights. Assume that weights can be placed in both pans of the balance if desired.

(a) Derive a recurrence relationship for the following.
  (i) S_N, the largest number of units of weight which can be fully covered by N weights.
  (ii) W_N, the largest single weight in the optimum set of N weights.

(b) If four weights are to be used, what sizes should they be, and what is the maximum range of weights which can be covered?

4. (a) Use dynamic programming to obtain an approximate solution to Problem 1(a) of Chapter 5, using a sampled-data representation of the system, of the form

$$x[(n + 1)T] = x(nT) + Tu(nT) \qquad (7.138)$$

(assuming u is constant during each sampling period), and a performance criterion of the form

$$J = \sum_{n=0}^{N-1} [u^2(nT) + x^2(nT)]T \qquad (7.139)$$

where $NT = 1$. Choose N to be some small value, for example 3, and compare the results with the result of Problem 1(a) of Chapter 5 by plotting graphs of the control input for the two cases.

If desired, the problem may be repeated for higher values of N, using a digital computer.

(b) Repeat the above with appropriate changes to find an approximate solution to Problem 1(b) of Chapter 5.

5. Use dynamic programming to obtain approximate solutions to Problems 2(a) and 2(b) of Chapter 5, by using a sampled-data representation of the form

$$x[(n + 1)T] = e^{-T}x(nT) + (1 - e^{-T})u(nT) \qquad (7.140)$$

and a performance criterion of the same form as Equation 7.139, with $NT = 1$ as before.

6. (a) For the system governed by the difference Equation 7.138 choose $T = 1$ second and use dynamic programming to find the sequence of control inputs which controls the system, starting from an arbitrary state x, in such a way as to minimize the performance criterion given by Equation 7.139, for $N = 1, 2, 3, 4$, with $x(NT)$ free in each case. Observe that the minimum value of the performance criterion is directly proportional to x^2 in each case.

(b) Investigate the behavior of the system as N approaches infinity by assuming that

$$\lim_{N \to \infty} S_N(x) = ax^2 \qquad (7.141)$$

and using the recurrence relationship

$$S_N(x) = \min_u [(u^2 + x^2)T + S_N(x + Tu)] \qquad (7.142)$$

Find the value of a, and the corresponding value of u, and compare with the results of part (a).

(c) Repeat part (b), taking the value of T to be 0.1 seconds, and compare the value of a and the value of u with the appropriate results in Problem 1(c) of Chapter 5.

7. Consider the system shown in Fig. 7.5. It is required to find an unconstrained optimum control input $u(t)$, for t such that $0 \leqslant t \leqslant 1$, so that the performance index

$$I = \int_0^1 (u^2 + x^2) \, dt \qquad (7.143)$$

is minimized. The initial state is $x^0 = 1$, and the final state at $t = 1$ is completely free.

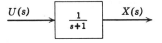

Fig. 7.5

Derive $u(t)$ and $x(t)$ by solving the appropriate Riccati equation, and show that the result is the same as that obtained in Problem 2(b) of Chapter 5.

8

Computational Methods of Optimization

The foregoing chapters of this book have attempted to provide an introduction to several theoretical methods of optimization. In order to help the student to develop an overall understanding of the field, problems with simple analytical solutions have been emphasized. Unfortunately, however, the practical solution of a real optimization problem may require numerical computation from start to finish. Because of this, a great deal of research work has been and is being done to develop efficient methods of computation of solutions of problems in optimal control.

The computation of solutions of optimization problems in complex systems is an art which must be learned by practice. A great deal has been learned about this subject, but a great deal still remains to be learned. Because of the wide range of methods which have been developed and are likely to be developed in the near future, we shall not attempt to cover the field of computational methods in detail, but shall study only a few of the basic principles of computational optimization. The reader who wishes to pursue the subject further will find much useful information in the highly readable books by Wilde [1] and Rosenbrock and Storey [2].

8.1 DERIVATION OF AN OPTIMUM SEARCH PROCEDURE

Let us begin our study of computational methods of optimization by considering the problem of finding the maximum value of a function which is defined at a discrete set of points. It is assumed that the analytic form of the function is not known, but that we must evaluate the function at various points and compare these values in order to find the maximum.

Let us suppose, for example, that we are given a function of x, which is defined only at the integral values of x from 1 to k, inclusive, as shown in Fig. 8.1. It is desired to find the maximum value of the function $y(x)$.

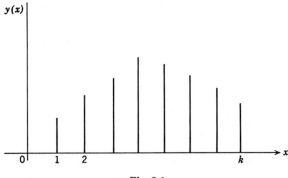

Fig. 8.1

Let us suppose that the function is *unimodal* [1]. This means that it has a single peak at a unique point in the range from $x = 1$ to $x = k$, and that we can say that, if two values of x are chosen on the same side of the peak, the value of $y(x)$ corresponding to the value of x nearer the peak is the larger of the two values. Furthermore, if the values of $y(x)$ corresponding to two values of x are equal, the peak must lie between those two values of x. A unimodal function is illustrated in Fig. 8.1.

Let us suppose that it is desired to find the value of x which gives the largest value of y, by computing the values of y for different values of x and comparing the magnitudes. We wish to find a method of choosing the values of x at which to evaluate y, so as to obtain the value of y with as few evaluations as possible. In other words, not only do we wish to find the maximum or optimum value of y, we also wish to optimize the method of finding it.[1] While it is obviously possible that a lucky chance could give the maximum with as few as three[2] evaluations, we wish to find the method of search which, using as few function evaluations as possible, *guarantees* the finding of the peak uniquely.

It is easy to see that we cannot improve our information on the location of the peak by evaluating one value of y; we must evaluate $y(x)$ for two values of x and compare them. For example, if we compute the values of $y(i)$ and

---

[1] Whether a minimum number of evaluations is in fact the optimum method of search depends on the practical situation. Suppose, for example, that each function evaluation requires an experiment which lasts a week, and that k of these experiments can be performed simultaneously without cost. The optimal result would then be to evaluate all k values simultaneously. The case we are considering in this section corresponds to a situation in which there is only one piece of apparatus (or computer) available to evaluate y, so that the evaluations must be performed *sequentially* rather than simultaneously.

[2] Even two evaluations might be sufficient, if the maximum occurs at the end of the range of values (that is, at $x = 1$ or $x = k$ in this example).

$y(j)$, where i and j are integral values of x as shown in Fig. 8.2, with $j > i$, we can say that:

1. If $y(i) > y(j)$, the peak is at an integral value p such that $1 \leqslant p < j$.
2. If $y(j) > y(i)$, the peak is at an integer value q such that $i < q \leqslant k$.
3. If $y(i) = y(j)$, the peak is at an integer value r such that $i < r < j$.

These statements follow from the definition of unimodality. Let us now use the word "remainder" to refer to the set of points still to be searched at any given stage of the process. That is, the remainder is the smallest set of points in which the maximum value is known to lie. After computing the values $y(i)$ and $y(j)$ as in Fig. 8.2, the remainder has been reduced from the original set of k points to a set of $j - 1$ points (possibility 1), or a set of $k - i$ points (possibility 2). Possibility 3 gives a remainder smaller than either of the previous two; this possibility may be considered improbable (and a lucky chance), and we shall assume that this favorable outcome does not occur.

As we do not know in advance whether i or j will give the larger value, the biggest reduction in the number of values to be explored would be obtained by taking i and j as close as possible to the center of the original set of values. For example, if $k = 10$, and if we started by evaluating $y(x)$ at $x = 5$ and $x = 6$, the set of points still to be searched would be five in number. No greater reduction in the remainder could be obtained by any other pair of evaluations (except by chance).

Our problem is not, however, to choose a pair of values which gives the largest initial reduction in the remainder. As has been pointed out before, the fastest start in a race may not be the best strategy to adopt. Our problem is to specify an overall strategy which will allow us to find the peak uniquely, using the smallest possible number of evaluations. This problem can be

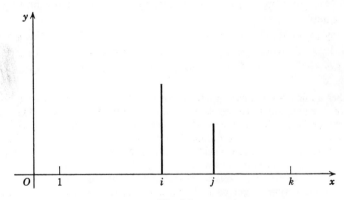

Fig. 8.2

studied by a dynamic-programming approach using the principle of optimality [1, 3, 4, 5]. The method will now be described.

Let us find, for any number n of function evaluations, the maximum number of function values (the maximum value of k in Fig. 8.1) such that the n evaluations will allow us to find the maximum of a unimodal function uniquely. Let us define the quantity S_n to mean this maximum number of function values. Our procedure will be to derive a recurrence relationship which will give S_{n+1} when $S_1, \ldots, S_n$ are known.

Let us therefore start with S_1. S_1 is, by definition, the maximum value of k in Fig. 8.1 such that the maximum value of a unimodal function defined at k values can be found uniquely. It is obvious that $S_1 = 1$. For $n = 2$, the value of S_n is equal to 2. While it is true that it *might* be possible to find the maximum value of a function defined at three points by using two evaluations, we cannot guarantee to find the maximum of a function defined at any more than two points by two function evaluations.

Let us now consider S_3. Consider the function defined at the four values of x shown in Fig. 8.3. We see that, if we evaluate $y(2)$ and $y(3)$, and if $y(3) > y(2)$, the maximum must occur at $x = 3$ or at $x = 4$. [The values $y(1)$ and $y(4)$ in Fig. 8.3 are not necessarily zero; the diagram represents the information known after evaluating $y(2)$ and $y(3)$.] If $y(2) > y(3)$, the maximum must occur at $x = 1$ or $x = 2$. The maximum can therefore be found uniquely by making three evaluations. We can easily see that it is not possible to guarantee the finding of the maximum of a function defined at five points by using only three evaluations, and therefore $S_3 = 4$. We also see that, after making the first pair of evaluations, the remainder is equal to S_2. Let us now proceed to higher values of n, in order to find the recurrence relationship.

Consider $n = 4$. The above developments suggest that, after making the first pair of function evaluations, we should have reduced the remainder to S_3; furthermore, one of the first two evaluations should appear in this set of S_3 points at the optimum location for one of the first pair of function

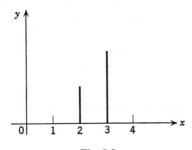

Fig. 8.3

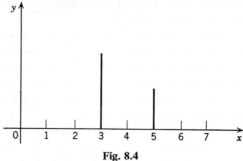

Fig. 8.4

evaluations required for the search of this set of S_3 points. This is made clear in Fig. 8.4, where the function is defined at the seven points $x = 1$ to $x = 7$.

If, after evaluating $y(3)$ and $y(5)$ in Fig. 8.4, we find that $y(3) > y(5)$, we must still search the set of points $x = 1$ to $x = 4$. This can be done in an optimal way by next evaluating $y(2)$, the value $y(3)$ having already been found. We see that, as the principle of optimality would lead us to expect, after the first pair of evaluations the remainder has been reduced to S_3, and that one of the first two evaluations is at an optimum location for the next part of the search.

We see that the remainder (the set of points still to be searched) is always the set of points between the lower of the first two function values and the more remote end of the original set of points.[3] For example, in Fig. 8.4, the set of points still to be searched is $x = 1$ to $x = 4$. If $y(5)$ had been greater than $y(3)$, the set of points still to be searched would have been $x = 4$ to $x = 7$. Both sets of points are equal in number to S_3.

If we consider the set of four points $x = 1$ to $x = 4$ in Fig. 8.4, ignoring the set $x = 5$ to $x = 7$ that we assume to have been eliminated by the first two evaluations if $x(3) > x(5)$, we see that the number of points between $x = 3$ and the remote end of the remaining *four-point* set (that is, the number of points to the left of $x = 3$) is S_2. This follows by a reasoning process similar to that used above, in which we found that, after the first two function evaluations of the n allowed, the remainder is S_{n-1} (or, after the first two of the $n - 1$ allowed, the remainder is S_{n-2}).

Using the symmetry of the set of points in Fig. 8.4, we can say that the number of points to the right of $x = 5$ is S_2, while that to the left of $x = 5$ is S_3. We find that

$$S_4 = S_3 + S_2 + 1 \tag{8.1}$$

---

[3] This is true because the first two function evaluations are symmetrically placed, so that the higher value is always between the lower value and the more remote end of the original set.

In general, we can say that

$$S_n = S_{n-1} + S_{n-2} + 1 \qquad (8.2)$$

The significance of S_n can be seen in Fig. 8.5, where the points marked $\times$ indicate the first two function evaluations. The first two function evaluations are symmetrically disposed, in such a way that after making the first pair of evaluations the remainder is S_{n-1}; furthermore, the higher of the two function values is already placed at the optimal location in the set of points still to be searched (the remainder). The third evaluation is placed in such a way that it, and the higher of the two original evaluations, is symmetrically placed within the set of S_{n-1} points still to be searched; this means that each of the two points has S_{n-2} points between itself and the remote end of the set of S_{n-1} points being searched.

Equation 8.2 is a difference equation, which can be solved provided that two initial conditions are known. We have already found that

$$S_1 = 1, \qquad S_2 = 2 \qquad (8.3)$$

so that the solution of Equation 8.2 can be written as a sequence as follows:

n	1	2	3	4	5	6	$\cdots$
S_n	1	2	4	7	12	20	$\cdots$

Any value of S_n can be found by adding 1 to the sum of the previous two values.

If it is desired to search for the maximum of a function defined at a number of points which is not one of the values of S_n (for example, 8), we could do it by adding a suitable number of "dummy points" to make the total equal to the next higher value of S_n (in this case, we would add 4 to 8 to give 12). The values of y corresponding to the dummy points would be taken to be very small, and the search would proceed in a similar way.

The numbers S_n defined by difference Equation 8.2 with initial conditions given by Equation 8.3 are, as might be expected, closely related to the

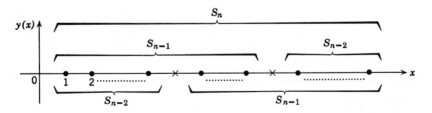

Fig. 8.5

Fibonacci numbers which we have discussed in Chapters 4 and 7. To be specific, the value of S_n can be expressed in the form

$$S_n = F(n + 2) - 1 \qquad (8.4)$$

where $F(n)$ is the Fibonacci number defined by Equations 4.178 and 4.179 or Equation 7.51. It can easily be shown by mathematical induction that

$$\sum_{i=0}^{n} F(i) = F(n + 2) - 1 \qquad (8.5)$$

We can therefore express the value of S_n, if desired, in the form

$$S_n = \sum_{i=0}^{n} F(i) \qquad (8.6)$$

Maximum value of a unimodal function defined along a line

Now let us consider another closely related problem. Suppose that we wish to find the value of x which gives the maximum value of a unimodal function $y(x)$, where x can take on a continuous range of values. For example, suppose we have a function $y(x)$ defined for all x such that $0 \leqslant x \leqslant k + 1$, and suppose that we wish to find the value of x in that range which makes $y(x)$ a maximum, *with an error of not more than one unit in the value of x*. This is, in fact, the same problem as the one discussed above, because the maximum value of $y(x)$ at the points $x = 1, \ldots, k$ gives the maximum value of $y(x)$ in the interval $[0, k + 1]$ with an error in x of not more than one unit. If we define R_n as the maximum range of values of x that can be explored in n evaluations, to find the peak value of $y(x)$ with not more than one unit error in the value of x, the value of R_n will be one more than the value of S_n found in the preceding section. We shall have $R_1 = 2$, $R_2 = 3$, and in general

$$R_n = S_n + 1 = F(n + 2) \qquad (8.7)$$

This means that, if a unimodal function is defined over a certain interval of length L, along the axis of the independent variable, it is possible to make n evaluations of the function in such a way as to be able to specify that the maximum value of the function is within a specified interval of length $2L/F(n + 2)$ along the axis of the independent variable [a maximum error in the position of the maximum of $\pm L/F(n + 2)$].[4]

---

[4] This situation has been idealized by ignoring the problem of distinguishing between values of the function when two values of the independent variable are very close together. The reader should refer to Wilde [1] to find out how to take this problem into account.

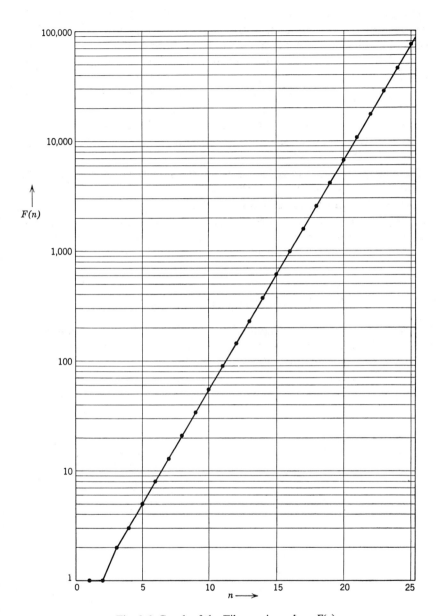

Fig. 8.6. Graph of the Fibonacci numbers $F(n)$.

The Fibonacci numbers, for n greater than about 4, can be represented very accurately by a geometric progression (see Equation 4.187 and the logarithmic plot in Fig. 8.6). We see that, if the maximum is to be located within an interval which is 1 percent of the original interval, n should be taken as 11 because $F_{n+2} = F_{13} > 200$. To place the maximum within an interval of 0.1 percent of the original interval, only 16 evaluations would be needed [$F(18) = 2584$].[5] Also, we see from Equation 8.4 that, for a unimodal function defined at 1500 discrete points, we can find the maximum uniquely by using only 15 evaluations, or 1 percent of the total number of values [$F(17) = 1597$].

The method of search described in this section could be used, for example, in finding the optimum value of the scalar control input u for a system at each stage of a dynamic-programming problem, or at each stage of a problem involving the maximum principle, by searching over the admissible range of values of the control input. The method could also be incorporated into a method of search for the maximum of a function of several variables.

8.2   NEWTON-RAPHSON METHOD OF MAXIMIZATION

Suppose now that we are required to find the maximum of a continuous differentiable function. We can now use information about the derivative of the function to help in the location of the minimum. For example, in Fig. 8.7, if we evaluate the derivative at a given point and find it to be positive, we know that there is a maximum to the right, and vice versa. By stepping to

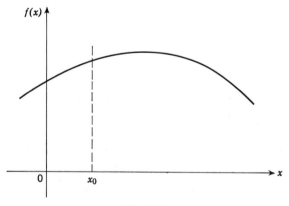

Fig. 8.7

---

[5] A table of Fibonacci numbers, from $F(0)$ to $F(385)$, can be found in reference [6].

another value of x, in the direction indicated, we may approach the peak more closely. A serious problem is to decide the size of step to take in the indicated direction; if steps are too small it will take too long to reach the peak, and if they are too large we may diverge from the peak instead of approaching it. One possibility is to use the Newton-Raphson method, which is similar to the method of the same name for finding the zeros of a function [7]. This method involves finding the first and second derivatives of the function, at a given point x_0, fitting a second-order equation to the function, and finding the position of the peak of the second-order function. Mathematically, we can consider the function $f(x)$ to be represented by a Taylor series as follows:

$$f(x) = f(x_0) + f'(x_0)(x - x_0) + \tfrac{1}{2}f''(x_0)(x - x_0)^2 + \cdots \qquad (8.8)$$

The condition for $f(x)$ to have a maximum at $x = x_1$ is that the derivative $f'(x)$ is zero at $x = x_1$. Differentiating Equation 8.8 with respect to x, we have

$$f'(x) = f'(x_0) + f''(x_0)(x - x_0) + \cdots \qquad (8.9)$$

Setting Equation 8.9 to zero and neglecting second- and higher-order terms in $(x - x_0)$, we obtain the relationship for the step size or for the new value of x, namely, x_1:

$$x_1 = x_0 - \frac{f'(x_0)}{f''(x_0)} \qquad (8.10)$$

If the function $f(x)$ is in fact a function of the second degree, this method will, in theory, give the exact maximum or minimum in one step. It may not do so in practice, even if the analytic forms of the derivatives are known, because of numerical round-off errors. Also, if the analytical forms of the derivatives are not known, further errors will arise in estimating these derivatives from numerical data. The method does, however, provide an iterative method of approaching the maximum value of a function.[6]

8.3 METHODS WHICH DO NOT INVOLVE DERIVATIVES

If the derivatives of the function with which we are dealing are not known as explicit functions, these derivatives may have to be estimated by evaluating the function at closely spaced points. Several methods have been derived for

---

[6] If there are several local maxima, the method may converge to one of them, which may not be the "global" optimum value. This is a serious problem and it is very difficult to guarantee that any given method will find the global optimum.

using these function evaluations directly in the maximization process, without having to go through the intermediate step of computing the derivatives. A well-known example is that described by Rosenbrock [8]. The method proceeds as follows.

We evaluate the function for any value of x, and then take a step of length δ to a new value of x. If this step is successful (giving a lower value of y if we are seeking a minimum, or a higher if we are seeking a maximum), we take a new step $\alpha\delta$ from the point so reached, where α is positive and greater than unity, and proceed in this manner. If a step is a failure (giving a higher value of y if we are seeking a minimum, or vice versa), we retract that step and take a step $\beta\zeta$ in the direction opposite to the unsuccessful step, where ζ is the length of the unsuccessful step and β is a positive constant less than unity. Proceeding in this way we converge to the maximum or minimum as required. A step which does not change the magnitude of the function should be considered to be successful; the reason for no change may be that the step size is too small for the numerical computation procedure to detect a difference in the two values and a longer step is desirable.

Rosenbrock describes the application of his method to the maximization of a function of several variables. Let us now study some of the general problems of optimizing a function of several independent variables.

8.4 EXTENSION TO MORE THAN ONE INDEPENDENT VARIABLE

If the function to be maximized is a function of several independent variables, the computational problem becomes much more serious. Let us now make a brief study of some of the basic ideas involved in the solution of such problems, but without investigating thoroughly all the problems which may arise.

Most of the basic ideas involved can be illustrated by limiting ourselves to the case of two independent variables, in order to use simple geometrical interpretations of the optimization process. Suppose, for example, that the value of a scalar function of two variables can be represented by contour lines such as those shown in Fig. 8.8. We wish to find the maximum value of the function by a computational method which allows us to start at an arbitrary value $\mathbf{x}^0$, and move to values of $\mathbf{x}$ giving higher and higher values of the function until the maximum is reached. The process of achieving this result is often called hill-climbing, because of the obvious analogy between climbing to the top of a hill and finding the peak value of a function.

One possible method of computing the coordinates of the optimum would be to start from the origin, find the maximum value of the function along

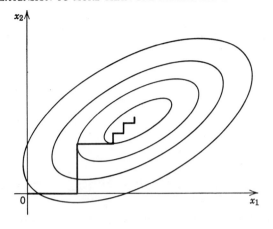

Fig. 8.8

the x_1 axis (possibly by a Fibonacci-type search or by Newton-Raphson iteration), move along a line parallel to the x_2 axis until a maximum is reached, then move along a line parallel to the x_1 axis until a maximum is reached, and so on. The path to the peak might be of the form shown in Fig. 8.8. Unfortunately this simple method, while it might work well in many cases, is not efficient or reliable enough for general use. For example, Fig. 8.9a shows a contour map which would make the method very inefficient because of the many short steps taken, and Fig. 8.9b shows a contour configuration which would make the method fail because the point P is a maximum in both the coordinate directions but is not the peak.

GRADIENT METHODS OF OPTIMIZATION

The maximization process can usually be more efficiently performed by evaluating the gradient vector of the function $f(\mathbf{x})$ at an arbitrary initial point $\mathbf{x}^0$, and then moving from $\mathbf{x}^0$ along the positive direction of the gradient vector. Mathematically, we can express this procedure in the form

$$\mathbf{x}^1 = \mathbf{x}^0 + k \operatorname{\mathbf{grad}} f \qquad (8.11)$$

where k is a scalar constant. Having reached $\mathbf{x}^1$ a new gradient is computed, and a new point $\mathbf{x}^2$ is found by moving along the gradient vector from $\mathbf{x}^1$, and so on. The value of the constant k must be chosen in such a way as to avoid the difficulties of slow convergence on the one hand and instability on the other. One possible method is to move along the direction of the computed gradient vector until a maximum is reached, and then move along the

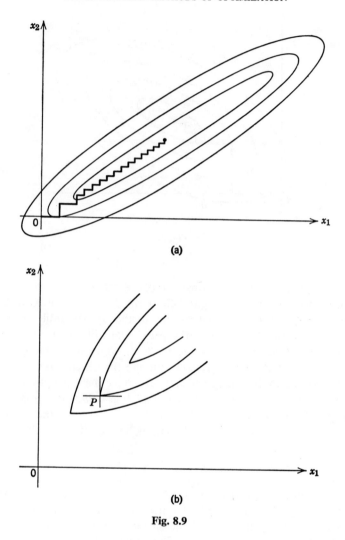

(a)

(b)

Fig. 8.9

new gradient direction. The path to the peak might be of the form shown in Fig. 8.10. It will be noted that the successive gradient directions are orthogonal to each other in this case.

Generalized newton-raphson method

If we can evaluate all first-order and second-order partial derivatives of $f(\mathbf{x})$ at a particular point $\mathbf{x}^0$, we can fit a second-order surface to the local $f(\mathbf{x})$ surface. The maximum of this second-order surface can be taken as the next

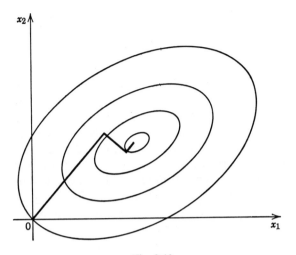

Fig. 8.10

point $\mathbf{x}^1$ in the recurrence relationship, and $\mathbf{x}^1$ will theoretically give the exact maximum point if the surface is in fact describable by a second-degree equation. The method is described in more detail by Rosenbrock and Storey [2].

8.5 HILL-CLIMBING METHODS OF SOLUTION OF EQUATIONS

Hill-climbing methods may be used to compute the solutions of simultaneous equations. For example, suppose we have a set of n equations in n unknowns as follows:

$$\begin{aligned}
f_1(x_1, \ldots, x_n) &= 0 \\
f_2(x_1, \ldots, x_n) &= 0 \\
&\vdots \\
f_n(x_1, \ldots, x_n) &= 0
\end{aligned} \tag{8.12}$$

If the solution of these equations is a set of real values of $x_1, \ldots, x_n$, we can compute the solution by forming the function F defined in terms of the functions of Equations 8.12 by the equation

$$F \triangleq f_1{}^2 + f_2{}^2 + f_3{}^2 + \cdots + f_n{}^2 \tag{8.13}$$

and by hill-climbing to find the minimum value of F (which should be zero).

Hill-climbing methods can also be used in the numerical solution of two-point boundary-value problems. Suppose, for example, we have a system with two state variables x_1 and x_2, whose derivatives are given by the vector differential equation

$$\dot{\mathbf{x}} = \mathbf{f}(\mathbf{x}, \mathbf{u}) \tag{8.14}$$

and suppose that the input vector $\mathbf{u}$ is known throughout a fixed time interval between an initial time t_0 and a final time t_1. In order to find the complete solution of Equation 8.14, we need to know two boundary values. If $x_1(t_0)$ and $x_2(t_0)$ are both known, Equation 8.14 may be integrated numerically by a digital computer, using the well-known methods available for the numerical solution of differential equations, to determine the behavior of the two variables x_1 and x_2 during the interval. However, it is possible that one of the boundary values may be known at the initial instant t_0, and one at the final instant t_1, in which case we could proceed in the following way. Suppose it is known that the initial value of x_1 and the final value of x_2 are to be $x_1{}^0$ and $x_2{}^1$, respectively, we can assume a value of $x_2(t_0)$, integrate the equations to t_1, and compare the value of $x_2(t_1)$ so achieved to the required value $x_2{}^1$. If we compute the quantity

$$F = [x_2{}^1 - x_2(t_1)]^2 \tag{8.15}$$

as a function of the starting point $x_2(t_0)$, we can seek for a minimum of F by varying $x_2(t_0)$ in accordance with one of the methods we have already described, such as the Newton-Raphson method. Having found the value which gives a minimum of F (which should be zero) we know the complete solution of the original differential equation, satisfying the specified two-point boundary conditions. If we can obtain an analytical solution of Equation 8.14, it is of course possible to use the two known boundary values to evaluate the unknown constants of the solution directly; a numerical method of the type described here will, however, be more usual when we are dealing with higher-order systems, particularly if the system differential equations are nonlinear.

More detailed information on the numerical solution of two-point boundary-value problems is given by Merriam [9] and by Kenneth and McGill [10].

8.6   COMPUTATIONAL OPTIMIZATION USING THE MAXIMUM PRINCIPLE

Let us now describe a possible method of solution of an optimal control problem involving the maximum principle. It should be stated at the outset that, even in this simple example in which there is only one control input, the computations are likely to be extremely lengthy and time-consuming in the form described here.

Suppose that we wish to solve an optimal control problem for the following system:

$$\dot{x}_i = f_i(\mathbf{x}, u) \qquad (i = 1, \ldots, n) \tag{8.16}$$

where $\mathbf{x}$ is an n vector of state variables, and u is a scalar control input. Suppose that the problem is to find the control input $u(t)$ which transfers the system state from a specified state $\mathbf{x}^0$ to a specified state $\mathbf{x}^1$ in a fixed time, and in so doing minimizes the functional defined by

$$I = \int_{t_0}^{t_1} f_0(\mathbf{x}, u)\, dt \tag{8.17}$$

As we have done in Chapter 6, we introduce a new state variable x_0 to represent the value of the accumulated performance criterion, and form the Hamiltonian $\mathscr{H}$ defined by

$$\mathscr{H} = p_0 f_0 + p_1 f_1 + \cdots + p_n f_n \tag{8.18}$$

We know from the work of Chapters 5 and 6 that

$$\frac{dp_i}{dt} = -\frac{\partial \mathscr{H}}{\partial x_i} \qquad (i = 0, 1, \ldots, n) \tag{8.19}$$

As before, we know the value of p_0 at the end of the process to be -1, but we do not know the boundary values of the other p_i variables. We have a total of $2n + 2$ first-order differential equations, namely, the n Equations 8.16, the $n + 1$ Equations 8.19, and the equation $\dot{x}_0 = f_0(\mathbf{x}, u)$. We know $2n + 2$ boundary values [the n initial and n final values of the x_i $(i = 1, \ldots, n)$, the final value of p_0, and the initial value of x_0 which we take to be zero].

We could use a similar procedure to that described in Section 8.5, namely, assume a set of initial values for $p_1, p_2, \ldots, p_n$, and integrate the equations numerically. However, we do not know the value of the control input u, except that u must maximize $\mathscr{H}$ for optimal control. A possible procedure for the solution of the problem is as follows:

1. Choose a set of initial values of $p_1, \ldots, p_n$ at time t_0.
2. Find the value of u which makes $\mathscr{H}$ take on its maximum value. This could be done by the search procedure described in Section 8.1 if u is limited by a simple magnitude constraint.
3. Proceed with one step in the integration process, using a suitable numerical procedure, and find the values of $x_0, x_1, \ldots, x_n, p_0, p_1, \ldots, p_n$ at the end of the step.
4. Repeat step 2 using a new set of values of the x_i and the p_i, to find the new value of u. Repeat step 3, taking one more step of the numerical integration process.

5. Repeat the maximization and numerical integration processes 2 and 3 until we reach the final time t_1. At this point we evaluate a function F_1, defined by

$$F_1 \triangleq \sum_{i=1}^{n} [x_i^1 - x_i(t_1)]^2 \tag{8.20}$$

where x_i^1 is the desired final value of x_i, and $x_i(t_1)$ is the value reached by the numerical integration process. The function F_1 is a measure of the discrepancy between the actual final state and the desired final state.

6. We now start again from step 1, choosing a new set of values of the p_i and repeating all the foregoing steps until we reach a new value of F_1. We proceed to hill-climb,[7] using the n initial values of the p_i as the independent variables (the initial value of p_0 being known to be -1), until we reach a minimum of F_1, which should be almost zero (an exact zero may not be obtained in practice because of round-off errors).

Obviously, the performance of the procedures described in steps 1 to 6 requires an enormous amount of computation, particularly if we have a high-order system. If we had several inputs, step 2 would be much more difficult because we would have to maximize a function of the r variables $u_1, u_2, \ldots, u_r$. Even with a high-speed digital computer, such computations would not be feasible except for relatively low-order systems with only one or two inputs. However, the process is rather simpler if we know that Equations 8.16 and 8.17 are linear in u and that u has a simple magnitude constraint. In such a case $\mathcal{H}$ reaches its maximum at one extreme value of u or the other, so that the maximization in step 2 is much simpler. If there are several control inputs, if the equations analogous to Equations 8.16 and 8.17 are linear in $\mathbf{u}$, and if the permissible region of $\mathbf{u}$ is a polyhedron, the analogous problem in step 2 would be to investigate the value of $\mathcal{H}$ at the vertices of the polyhedron.

8.7   DIRECT COMPUTATION OF AN OPTIMAL CONTROL INPUT

Optimization methods can be divided into direct and indirect methods [10]. The direct methods are those in which a sequence of solutions is obtained, each one better than the previous one; the process of hill-climbing is an example of a direct method. Indirect methods are those in which we find a solution which satisfies the necessary conditions for an extreme value, using

---

[7] The procedure is still referred to as hill-climbing, even if the extreme being sought is a minimum instead of a maximum.

calculus of variations, the maximum principle, or some similar method. This section is devoted to a direct method of computation of an optimal control input for a simple system.

The procedure will be to start with an arbitrarily chosen control input $u(t)$, compute a correction to $u(t)$ which gives an improvement, and proceed to compute further corrections until the control input converges to the optimal function. The adjoint equations, which we met in Chapter 4, are used to help find the correction to be made to the nonoptimal control input [11].

Let us consider the problem of controlling the linear system characterized by the differential equation

$$\dot{\mathbf{x}}(t) = \mathbf{A}(t)\mathbf{x}(t) + \mathbf{b}(t)u(t) \tag{8.21}$$

where $\mathbf{x}$ is a vector with n components, $\mathbf{A}$ is an $n \times n$ matrix, $\mathbf{b}$ is a vector with n components, and u is a scalar. Suppose that the system is in state $\mathbf{x}^0$ at time t_0, that the final time t_1 is specified, and that the final state $\mathbf{x}(t_1)$ is completely free. It is required to find the control input $u(t)$, during the time interval $[t_0, t_1]$, which makes a specified scalar function $F(\mathbf{x})$ take on its maximum value at time t_1.

Suppose we choose as a first approximation an arbitrary control input function $u^0(t)$ throughout the interval $[t_0, t_1]$, giving a definite value $\mathbf{x}(t_1)$ and a corresponding value of the scalar function F. We wish to find an incremental control input $\Delta u(t)$ throughout the interval, so that by using the input $u^0(t) + \Delta u(t)$ the value of F is increased.

The extra input $\Delta u(t)$ causes the value of $\mathbf{x}$ at time t to change by an amount $\Delta \mathbf{x}(t)$. The differential equation relating $\Delta \mathbf{x}$ to Δu is

$$\frac{d}{dt}(\Delta \mathbf{x}) = \mathbf{A}(t)\,\Delta \mathbf{x}(t) + \mathbf{b}(t)\,\Delta u(t) \tag{8.22}$$

From Equation 8.22, we obtain the value of $\Delta \mathbf{x}(t_1)$ to be

$$\Delta \mathbf{x}(t_1) = \int_{t_0}^{t_1} \mathbf{\Phi}(t_1, \tau)\mathbf{b}(\tau)\,\Delta u(\tau)\,d\tau \tag{8.23}$$

where $\mathbf{\Phi}(t_1, \tau)$ is the transition matrix of the system.

Let us now consider the gradient of the scalar function F, at the point $\mathbf{x}(t_1)$ reached by applying the input $u^0(t)$ during the interval $[t_0, t_1]$. The gradient of F is the vector with components $\partial F/\partial x_1, \ldots, \partial F/\partial x_n$. Call this vector $\mathbf{g}$. Having chosen the input $u^0(t)$, and having computed $\mathbf{x}(t_1)$, the vector $\mathbf{g}$ can be found. The change in F, when the final value of the state vector changes from $\mathbf{x}(t_1)$ to $\mathbf{x}(t_1) + \Delta \mathbf{x}(t_1)$, can be approximately expressed as

$$\Delta F = \mathbf{g} \cdot \Delta \mathbf{x}(t_1) \tag{8.24}$$

Substituting Equation 8.23 in Equation 8.24, we obtain

$$\Delta F = \mathbf{g} \cdot \int_{t_0}^{t_1} \Phi(t_1, \tau)\mathbf{b}(\tau) \, \Delta u(\tau) \, d\tau \qquad (8.25)$$

Expression 8.25 can be written in the form

$$\Delta F = \int_{t_0}^{t_1} \mathbf{g} \cdot \Phi(t_1, \tau)\mathbf{b}(\tau) \, \Delta u(\tau) \, d\tau \qquad (8.26)$$

Expressing the scalar product in terms of transposed vector quantities, we obtain the expression

$$\Delta F = \int_{t_0}^{t_1} \mathbf{b}'(\tau)\Phi'(t_1, \tau)\mathbf{g} \, \Delta u(\tau) \, d\tau \qquad (8.27)$$

Consider now the quantity $\Phi'(t_1, \tau)\mathbf{g}$. This can be written in the form

$$\Phi'(t_1, \tau)\mathbf{g} = \Psi(\tau, t_1)\mathbf{g} \qquad (8.28)$$

where Ψ is the transition matrix of the adjoint system (see Chapter 4). The quantity $\Psi(\tau, t_1)\mathbf{g}$ can therefore be viewed as the solution of the adjoint differential equation

$$\dot{\mathbf{y}}(t) = -\mathbf{A}'(t)\mathbf{y}(t) \qquad (8.29)$$

solved backwards in time from time t_1, with boundary condition $\mathbf{y}(t_1) = \mathbf{g}$. This solution can be computed, because the gradient vector $\mathbf{g}$ is known. Calling the solution $\mathbf{p}(t)$, we have

$$\Delta F = \int_{t_0}^{t_1} \mathbf{b}'(\tau)\mathbf{p}(\tau) \, \Delta u(\tau) \, d\tau \qquad (8.30)$$

Equation 8.30 allows ΔF to be computed, based on the known data of the problem, for a small incremental control input $\Delta u(t)$ throughout the interval $[t_0, t_1]$.

In order to keep $\Delta u(t)$ small we might, for example, impose the requirement

$$\int_{t_0}^{t_1} [\Delta u(t)]^2 \, dt = \epsilon \qquad (8.31)$$

where ϵ is a specified small number. In order to maximize ΔF for a given ϵ, we must maximize the quantity

$$\frac{\Delta F}{\epsilon} = \frac{\int_{t_0}^{t_1} \mathbf{b}'(\tau)\mathbf{p}(\tau) \, \Delta u(\tau) \, d\tau}{\int_{t_0}^{t_1} [\Delta u(\tau)]^2 \, d\tau} \qquad (8.32)$$

The numerator of the right side of Equation 8.32 may be interpreted as the scalar product of the function $\mathbf{b}'\mathbf{p}$ with the function Δu[18], and the denominator as the scalar product of Δu and itself. By Schwarz's inequality [18], this ratio will be a maximum, subject to the constraint (Equation 8.31) on Δu, when the function Δu is of the form

$$\Delta u(\tau) = k\mathbf{b}'(\tau)\mathbf{p}(\tau) \tag{8.33}$$

where k is a positive scalar constant, whose magnitude is chosen in such a way as to satisfy the requirement given by Equation 8.31. The incremental control input $\Delta u(t)$ can therefore be computed, and the optimal control input can be found by iteration of this process. A more general and rigorous description of this method of computation is described by Zadeh and Desoer [11].

If we consider the adjoint variables $p_1, \ldots, p_n$, or the adjoint vector $\mathbf{p}$ (see Equation 8.30), we see that these are characterized by the same differential equations as the auxiliary or adjoint variables encountered in the maximum principle or the Hamiltonian form of the calculus of variations. We can write the Hamiltonian H in the form

$$H = \mathbf{p}'(\mathbf{Ax} + \mathbf{b}u) \tag{8.34}$$

The H form is used here, rather than the $\mathscr{H}$ form (see Chapter 5), because the performance index is defined in terms of the final state, so that the problem is already in the Mayer form and there is no need to introduce an extra state variable x_0. From Equation 8.34 the partial derivative $\partial H/\partial u$ is given by

$$\frac{\partial H}{\partial u} = \mathbf{p}'\mathbf{b} = \mathbf{b}'\mathbf{p} \tag{8.35}$$

In an unconstrained problem of the type we are considering, the partial derivative $\partial H/\partial u$ must be zero for optimal control. Therefore, if $\partial H/\partial u$ is not zero, a better control input can be found, and the derivative can be used to guide us to a better control input. We see, by comparing Equations 8.35 and 8.33, that the incremental control input Δu can be found from the expression

$$\Delta u(t) = u_0(t) + k\frac{\partial H}{\partial u} \tag{8.36}$$

This result is derived directly by Rosenbrock and Storey [2], based on the work of Kelley [12, 13] and Bryson and Denham [14].

8.8 ANALOGUE-COMPUTER SOLUTION OF AN OPTIMAL CONTROL PROBLEM

An interesting method of using an analogue computer to find the optimal trajectories for a system has been described by Brennan and Roberts [15]. The following is an outline of the method.

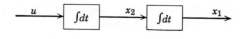

Fig. 8.11

Consider the double integrator shown in Fig. 8.11, for which the differential equations may be written as

$$\dot{x}_1 = x_2$$
$$\dot{x}_2 = u \tag{8.37}$$

Let us assume that the input u is subject to the magnitude constraint

$$|u| \leqslant 1 \tag{8.38}$$

Suppose that we wish to control the system, starting from a specified initial state $\mathbf{x}^0$, in such a way as to minimize the functional

$$I = \int_{t_0}^{\infty} x_1{}^2 \, dt \tag{8.39}$$

where the right-hand endpoint is free. As before, we introduce an extra state variable x_0 to represent the accumulated value of the functional; the differential equation for x_0 is

$$\dot{x}_0 = x_1{}^2 \tag{8.40}$$

We would expect that, as u is linear wherever it appears in the equations, the optimal control input u^* takes on only the values $+1$ and -1. This can be shown by using the maximum principle, defining the Hamiltonian $\mathscr{H}$ by

$$\mathscr{H} = p_0 x_1{}^2 + p_1 x_2 + p_2 u \tag{8.41}$$

As before, we derive the differential equations of the p_i as follows:

$$\dot{p}_0 = -\frac{\partial \mathscr{H}}{\partial x_0} = 0$$

$$\dot{p}_1 = -\frac{\partial \mathscr{H}}{\partial x_1} = -2p_0 x_1 \tag{8.42}$$

$$\dot{p}_2 = -\frac{\partial \mathscr{H}}{\partial x_2} = -p_1$$

For maximum $\mathscr{H}$, we see from Equation 8.41 that u is given by

$$u = \text{sgn} \, [p_2] \tag{8.43}$$

Since the final endpoint x^1 has not been specifically prescribed, we can write the boundary values of the p_i as follows:

$$
\begin{aligned}
p_0(\infty) &= -1\\
p_1(\infty) &= 0\\
p_2(\infty) &= 0
\end{aligned}
\tag{8.44}
$$

We know from Equations 8.42 and 8.44 that p_0 is constant at -1, as is normally the case. Substituting this value and the value of u from Equation 8.43 in the differential equations for $\mathbf{x}$ and $\mathbf{p}$, we obtain

$$
\begin{aligned}
\dot{x}_1 &= x_2\\
\dot{x}_2 &= \operatorname{sgn}[p_2]\\
\dot{p}_1 &= 2x_1\\
\dot{p}_2 &= -p_1
\end{aligned}
\tag{8.45}
$$

For which the boundary conditions are

$$
\begin{aligned}
x_1(t_0) &= x_1{}^0\\
x_2(t_0) &= x_2{}^0\\
p_1(\infty) &= 0\\
p_2(\infty) &= 0
\end{aligned}
\tag{8.46}
$$

Supposing we wish to compute backwards in time from the final state, we can use the equations derived from Equations 8.45 by substituting τ for $-t$ as follows:

$$
\frac{dx_1}{d\tau} = -x_2
$$

$$
\frac{dx_2}{d\tau} = -\operatorname{sgn}[p_2]
$$

$$
\frac{dp_1}{d\tau} = -2x_1
\tag{8.47}
$$

$$
\frac{dp_2}{d\tau} = +p_1
$$

Although the final state was not actually specified, it is obvious that the final values of x_1 and x_2 will both be zero. Taking these, and the final values of p_1 and p_2 from Equation 8.44, to be the initial state of the reverse-time process, we find the boundary values for differential Equations 8.47 to be

$$
\begin{aligned}
x_1(0) &= 0\\
x_2(0) &= 0\\
p_1(0) &= 0\\
p_2(0) &= 0
\end{aligned}
\tag{8.48}
$$

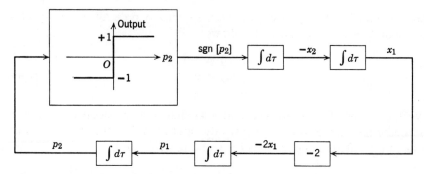

Fig. 8.12. Block-diagram simulation of Equations 8.47.

Equations 8.47 can be simulated on an analogue computer using the block diagram shown in Fig. 8.12, where it is assumed for simplicity that no sign changes occur in the integrating blocks.

It can easily be observed that the system shown in Fig. 8.12 is unstable. Although the boundary conditions (Equation 8.48) indicate a trivial solution, if there is any noise in an amplifier of the analogue computer the system will diverge from its state of unstable equilibrium. If we plot x_1 and x_2 on a phase

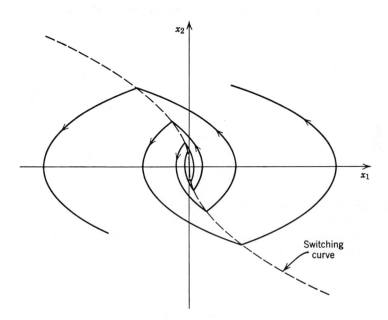

Fig. 8.13. Unstable trajectories of the system of Fig. 8.12 (not to scale).

plane as τ increases (which can be done in practice using an oscilloscope or an $x - y$ plotter), we trace out an optimal trajectory for the original system, but in the reverse direction, as shown in Fig. 8.13 (in which the arrow indicates the direction of increasing τ). If we reset the computer to the null state and release it again, another such trajectory is traced out.[8] By repetition of this procedure, we can trace out a family of optimal trajectories, as shown in Fig. 8.13. After obtaining a reasonably large family of trajectories in this way, it becomes an easy matter to sketch the switching curve as shown in Fig. 8.13. In this particular example the switching curve is known from analytical results to be given by

$$x_1 + 0.445x_2|x_2| = 0 \qquad (8.49)$$

This provides a check of the method in this simple case.

SUMMARY

This chapter has described some of the principles of computational methods of optimization. It should be stressed that no attempt has been made to give a comprehensive treatment of the many methods available; for more detailed information, the reader is referred to the books by Wilde [1], Rosenbrock and Storey [2], Leitmann [16], Merriam [9], and Balakrishnan and Neustadt [17].

REFERENCES

[1] Wilde, D. J., *Optimum Seeking Methods*, Prentice-Hall, Englewood Cliffs, N.J., 1964.
[2] Rosenbrock, H. H., and C. Storey, *Computational Techniques for Chemical Engineers*, Pergamon Press, Oxford, 1966.
[3] Nemhauser, G. L., *Introduction to Dynamic Programming*, Wiley, New York, 1966.
[4] Bellman, R., *Dynamic Programming*, Princeton University Press, Princeton, 1957.
[5] Bellman, R. E., and S. E. Dreyfus, *Applied Dynamic Programming*, Princeton University Press, Princeton, 1962.

---

[8] While in the original system an infinitely large number of switchings is required to reach the origin [19], the number of switchings would be finite if the desired end state were merely required to be within a certain specified distance of the origin. Therefore, if the state of the analogue computer were transferred from the null state to some neighboring state by noise, the computer would trace out a backward-time trajectory with a finite number of switchings. Alternatively, a set of trajectories could be traced out more systematically by choosing, as initial states for the backward-time system, various points on the circumference of a very small circle centered at the origin of the x_1x_2 plane.

[6] Jarden, D., *Recurring Sequences*, 2nd ed., Riveon Lematematika, Jerusalem, Israel, 1966.

[7] Booth, A. D., *Numerical Methods*, 2nd ed., Butterworth, London, 1957.

[8] Rosenbrock, H. H., "An Automatic Method for Finding the Greatest or Least Value of a Function," *Computer Journal*, 3, 175–184 (1960).

[9] Merriam, C. W., *Optimization Theory and the Design of Feedback Control Systems*, McGraw-Hill, New York, 1964.

[10] Kenneth, P., and R. McGill, "Two-Point Boundary-Value-Problem Techniques," in *Advances in Control Systems*, Vol. 3, C. T. Leondes, ed., Academic Press, New York, 1966, pp. 69–109.

[11] Zadeh, L. A., and C. A. Desoer, *Linear System Theory: The State Space Approach*, McGraw-Hill, New York, 1963.

[12] Kelley, H. J., "Gradient Theory of Optimal Flight Paths," *Am. Rocket Soc. J.*, 30, 947–954 (1960).

[13] Kelley, H. J., "Method of Gradients," in *Optimization Techniques*, F. Leitmann, ed., 1962. (Reference [16].)

[14] Bryson, A. E., and W. F. Denham, "A Steepest-Ascent Method for Solving Optimum Programming Problems," *Trans. ASME, Ser. E (J. Appl. Mech.)*, 29, 247–257 (1962).

[15] Brennan, P. J., and A. P. Roberts, "Use of an Analogue Computer in the Application of Pontryagin's Maximum Principle to the Design of Control Systems with Optimum Transient Response," *J. Electron. Control*, 12, 345–352 (1962).

[16] Leitmann, G., ed., *Optimization Techniques; With Applications to Aerospace Systems*, Academic Press, New York, 1962.

[17] Balakrishnan, A. V., and L. W. Neustadt, eds., *Computing Methods in Optimization Problems*, Academic Press, New York and London, 1964.

[18] Smith, L. P., *Mathematical Methods for Scientists and Engineers*, Dover Pub., New York, 1953.

[19] Fuller, A. T., "Relay Control Systems Optimized for Various Performance Criteria," in *Automation and Remote Control*, Vol. I (Proceedings of the First International Conference of I.F.A.C., Moscow, 1960), Butterworth, London, 1961, pp. 510–519.

Bibliography

The following is a list of books (in English) on optimal control and related topics.

Aris, R., *The Optimal Design of Chemical Reactors: A Study in Dynamic Programming*, Academic Press, New York, 1961.

Aris, R., *Discrete Dynamic Programming*, Blaisdell, New York, 1963.

Athans, M., and P. L. Falb, *Optimal Control; An Introduction to the Theory and Its Applications*, McGraw-Hill, New York, 1966.

Balakrishnan, A. V., and L. W. Neustadt, eds., *Computing Methods in Optimization Problems*, Academic Press, New York and London, 1964.

Bellman, R., *Dynamic Programming*, Princeton University Press, Princeton, 1957.

Bellman, R., *Adaptive Control Processes: A Guided Tour*, Princeton University Press, Princeton, 1961.

Bellman, R., ed., *Mathematical Optimization Techniques*, University of California Press, Berkeley, 1963.

Bellman, R. E., and S. E. Dreyfus, *Applied Dynamic Programming*, Princeton University Press, Princeton, 1962.

Bliss, G. A., *Lectures on the Calculus of Variations*, University of Chicago Press, Chicago, 1946.

Bolza, O., *Lectures on the Calculus of Variations*, Dover Pub., New York, 1960. (Paperback.)

Bucy, R. S., & P. D. Joseph, *Filtering for Stochastic Processes with Applications to Guidance*, Wiley, New York.

Chang, S. S. L., *Synthesis of Optimum Control Systems*, McGraw-Hill, New York, 1961.

DeRusso, P. M., R. J. Roy, and C. M. Close, *State Variables for Engineers*, Wiley, New York, 1965.

Dorf, R. C., *Time-Domain Analysis and Design of Control Systems*, Addison-Wesley, Reading, Mass., 1965.

Dreyfus, S., *Dynamic Programming and the Calculus of Variations*, Academic Press, New York, 1965.

Duffin, R. J., E. L. Peterson, and C. Zener, *Geometric Programming—Theory and Application*, Wiley, New York, 1967.

Eveleigh, V. W., *Adaptive Control and Optimization Techniques*, McGraw-Hill, New York, 1967.

Fan, L. T., *The Continuous Maximum Principle*, Wiley, New York, 1966.

Fan, L. T., and C. S. Wang, *The Discrete Maximum Principle: A Study of Multistage Systems Optimization*, Wiley, New York, 1964.

Fel'dbaum, A. A., *Optimal Control Systems*, Academic Press, New York, 1966.

Flügge-Lotz, I, *Discontinuous and Optimal Control*, McGraw-Hill, New York, 1968.

Gelfand, I. M., and S. V. Fomin, *Calculus of Variations*, Prentice-Hall, Englewood Cliffs, N.J., 1963.

Gupta, S. C., *Transform and State Variable Methods in Linear Systems*, Wiley, New York, 1966.

Hadley, G., *Nonlinear and Dynamic Programming*, Addison-Wesley, Reading, Mass., 1964.

Halfman, R. L., *Dynamics. Volume II. Systems, Variational Methods, and Relativity*, Addison-Wesley, Reading, Mass., 1962.

Hestenes, M. R., *Calculus of Variations and Optimal Control Theory*, Wiley, New York, 1966.

Howard, R. A., *Dynamic Programming and Markov Processes*, Technology Press of M.I.T. and Wiley, New York, 1960.

Jacobs, O. L. R., *An Introduction to Dynamic Programming: The Theory of Multistage Decision Processes*, Chapman and Hall, London, 1967.

Karreman, H. F. *Stochastic Optimization and Control*, Wiley, New York.

Kipiniak, W., *Dynamic Optimization and Control—A Variational Approach*, Technology Press of M.I.T. and Wiley, New York, 1961.

Lanczos, C., *The Variational Principles of Mechanics*, 2nd ed., University of Toronto Press, Toronto, 1962.

Laning, J. H., and R. H. Battin, *Random Processes in Automatic Control*, McGraw-Hill, New York, 1956.

Lapidus, L., and R. Luus, *Optimal Control of Engineering Processes*, Blaisdell, Waltham, Mass., 1967.

Lavi, A., and T. P. Vogl, eds., *Recent Advances in Optimization Techniques*, Wiley, New York, 1966.

Lee, E. B., and L. Markus, *Foundations of Optimal Control Theory*, Wiley, New York, 1967.

Lee, T. H., G. Adams & W. M. Gaines, *Computer Process Control: Modeling and Optimization*, Wiley, New York.

Leitmann, G., ed., *Optimization Techniques; With Applications to Aerospace Systems*, Academic Press, New York, 1962.

Leitmann, G., *An Introduction to Optimal Control*, McGraw-Hill, New York, 1966.

Leondes, C. T., ed., *Advances in Control Systems: Theory and Applications*, Academic Press, New York, Vol. 1, 1964, Vol. 2, 1965, Vol. 3, 1966.

Leondes, C. T., ed., *Modern Control Systems Theory*, McGraw-Hill, New York, 1965.

Luenberger, D. G., *Optimization in Linear Spaces*, Wiley, New York, 1969.

MacFarlane, A. G. J., *Engineering Systems Analysis*, Harrap, London, and Addison-Wesley, Reading, Mass., 1964.

Merriam, C. W., *Optimization Theory and the Design of Feedback Control Systems*, McGraw-Hill, New York, 1964.

Nahi, N. E., *Estimation Theory and its Applications*, Wiley, New York, 1969

Nemhauser, G. L., *Introduction to Dynamic Programming*, Wiley, New York, 1966.

Newton, G. C., L. A. Gould, and J. F. Kaiser, *Analytical Design of Linear Feedback Controls*, Wiley, New York, 1957.

Noton, A. R. M., *Introduction to Variational Methods in Control Engineering*, Pergamon Press, New York, 1965.

Ogata, K., *State Space Analysis of Control Systems*, Prentice-Hall, Englewood Cliffs, N.J., 1967.

Oldenburger, R., *Optimal Control*, Holt, Rinehart, and Winston, New York, 1966.

Papoulis, A., *Probability, Random Variables, and Stochastic Processes*, McGraw-Hill, New York, 1965.

Peschon, J., ed., *Disciplines and Techniques of Systems Control*, Blaisdell, New York, 1965.

Peterson, E. L., *Statistical Analysis and Optimization of Systems*, Wiley, New York, 1961.

Pierre, D. A., *Optimization Theory and Its Applications*, Wiley, New York, 1969.

Pontryagin, L. S., V. G. Boltyanskii, R. V. Gamkrelidze, and E. F. Mishchenko, *The Mathematical Theory of Optimal Processes*, Interscience (Wiley), New York, 1962.

Porter, W. A., *Modern Foundations of Systems Engineering*, Macmillan, New York, 1966.

Rosenbrock, H. H., and C. Storey, *Computational Techniques for Chemical Engineers*, Pergamon, Oxford, 1966.

Sage, A. P., *Optimum Systems Control*, Prentice-Hall, Englewood Cliffs, N.J., 1968.

Schultz, D. G., and J. L. Melsa, *State Functions and Linear Control Systems*, McGraw-Hill, New York, 1967.

Schwarz, R. J., and B. Friedland, *Linear Systems*, McGraw-Hill, New York, 1965.

Solodovnikov, V. V., *Introduction to the Statistical Dynamics of Automatic Control Systems*, Dover Pub., New York, 1960.

Timothy, L. K., and B. E. Bona, *State Space Analysis: An Introduction*, McGraw-Hill, New York, 1968.

Tou, J. T., *Optimum Design of Digital Control Systems*, Academic Press, New York, 1963.

Tou, J. T., *Modern Control Theory*, McGraw-Hill, New York, 1964.

Weinstock, R., *Calculus of Variations with Applications to Physics and Engineering*, McGraw-Hill, New York, 1952.

Westcott, J. H., ed., *An Exposition of Adaptive Control*, Pergamon Press, Oxford, 1962.

Wiener, N., *Extrapolation, Interpolation, and Smoothing of Stationary Time Series*. Pub. jointly by the Technology Press of M.I.T. and John Wiley, New York, 1949.

Wilde, D. J., *Optimum Seeking Methods*, Prentice-Hall, Englewood Cliffs, N.J., 1964.

Wilde, D. J., and C. S. Beightler, *Foundations of Optimization*, Prentice-Hall, Englewood Cliffs, N.J., 1967.

Yaglom, A. M., *An Introduction to the Theory of Stationary Random Functions*, Prentice-Hall, Englewood Cliffs, N.J., 1962.

Zadeh, L. A. and C. A. Desoer, *Linear System Theory: The State Space Approach*, McGraw-Hill, New York, 1963.

APPENDIX A

Parseval's Theorem

Suppose that we wish to find the value of the integral

$$I = \int_{-\infty}^{\infty} x(t)y(t)\, dt \tag{A.1}$$

where $x(t)$ and $y(t)$ are both Laplace transformable. We can write $y(t)$ as

$$y(t) = \frac{1}{2\pi j} \int_{-j\infty}^{j\infty} Y(s)e^{st}\, ds \tag{A.2}$$

Substituting Equation A.2 in Equation A.1, we obtain

$$I = \frac{1}{2\pi j} \int_{-\infty}^{\infty} \int_{-j\infty}^{j\infty} x(t)\, Y(s)e^{st}\, ds\, dt \tag{A.3}$$

Interchanging the order of integration, we obtain

$$I = \frac{1}{2\pi j} \int_{-j\infty}^{j\infty} Y(s) \int_{-\infty}^{\infty} x(t)e^{st}\, dt\, ds \tag{A.4}$$

Noting that the integral $\int_{-\infty}^{\infty} x(t)e^{st}\, dt$ can be written as $X(-s)$, we obtain as the expression for the original integral (Equation A.1)

$$I = \frac{1}{2\pi j} \int_{-j\infty}^{j\infty} X(-s)\, Y(s)\, ds \tag{A.5}$$

In particular, if $y(t) = x(t)$, expression A.1 gives the integral squared value of $x(t)$ as the following

$$\int_{-\infty}^{\infty} x^2\, dt = \frac{1}{2\pi j} \int_{-j\infty}^{j\infty} X(s)X(-s)\, ds \tag{A.6}$$

Some Remarks on the Bilateral Laplace Transformation

The Laplace transformation is usually defined in the following way.

$$F(s) \triangleq \int_0^\infty f(t)e^{-st}\, dt \tag{B.1}$$

The inverse transformation is given by the relationship

$$f(t) = \frac{1}{2\pi j} \int_{c-j\infty}^{c+j\infty} F(s)e^{ts}\, ds \tag{B.2}$$

where the value of c in Equation B.2 is taken to be greater than the real part of the poles of $F(s)$. For example, the Laplace transformation of the function $f_1(t) = e^{-at}$ ($a > 0, t > 0$) is $1/(s + a)$, defined in the region $Re[s] > -a$; the value of c in Equation B.2 must then be taken to be greater than $-a$.

The Laplace transformation may also be defined in a bilateral form, in the following way.

$$F(s) = \int_{-\infty}^\infty f(t)e^{-st}\, dt \tag{B.3}$$

with the definition of the inverse transformation remaining the same as given in Equation B.2. This implies that two different time functions may correspond to a single $F(s)$; in fact the integral (Equation B.2) may, as will be shown later, give different results for different values of c.

As the transform of the sum of two functions is equal to the sum of the separate transforms, the bilateral transformation (Equation B.3) can be expressed as the sum of two unilateral transforms as follows.

$$F(s) = \int_{-\infty}^0 f(t)e^{-st}\, dt + \int_0^\infty f(t)e^{-st}\, dt \tag{B.4}$$

The second term is the ordinary unilateral transformation as given in Equation B.1. The first term can be rewritten in terms of a variable $u = -t$, as follows:

$$\int_{-\infty}^0 f(t)e^{-st}\, dt = \int_0^\infty f(-u)e^{-(-s)u}\, du \tag{B.5}$$

234

This shows that the Laplace transformation of the negative-time portion of the function can be obtained by the following steps.

1. Reflect the function about the vertical axis [that is, form $f(-u)$].
2. Take the ordinary unilateral Laplace transformation of the function so obtained.
3. Replace s by $-s$ in the function obtained in step 2.

For example, consider the function $f_2(t) = e^{bt}$ ($b > 0, t < 0$), as shown in Fig. B.1a. After reflection about the vertical axis we obtain the function e^{-bt}, as shown in Fig. B.1b, whose Laplace transformation is $1/(s + b)$, defined for $Re[s] > -b$. On replacing s by $-s$ we obtain the Laplace transformation of this function to be

$$F_2(s) = \frac{1}{b - s} \quad \{Re[s] < b\} \tag{B.6}$$

The same result can be obtained by evaluating the first integral on the right side of Equation B.4. The bilateral Laplace transformation of the function defined by

$$f(t) = \begin{matrix} e^{-at} & (t > 0) \\ e^{bt} & (t < 0) \\ (a > 0, b > 0) \end{matrix} \tag{B.7}$$

is therefore

$$F(s) = \frac{1}{s + a} - \frac{1}{s - b} \tag{B.8}$$

defined in the region $-a < Re[s] < b$.

The function $f(t)$, as defined by Equation B.7, is shown in Fig. B.2. The poles of $F(s)$ are shown on the complex s plane in Fig. B.3, with the region of definition of $F(s)$ shown shaded.

If the line integration represented by Equation B.2 is performed along a line for which $-a < c < b$, for $F(s)$ as defined by Equation B.8, the result will be $f(t)$

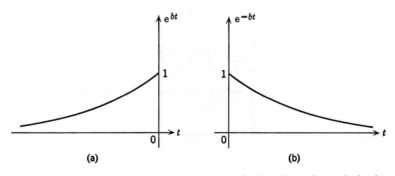

Fig. B1. (a) $f_2(t)$. (b) The same function after reflection about the vertical axis.

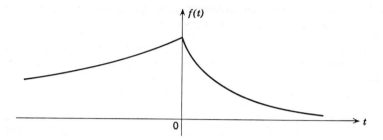

Fig. B.2. The function $f(t)$ defined by equation B.7.

as defined by Equation B.7. It should be noted that, as we proceed along the line of integration, the pole corresponding to the positive-time function e^{-at} is on the left, whereas the pole corresponding to the negative-time function e^{bt} is on the right. On the other hand, if we evaluated the integral (Equation B.2) along a line for which $c > b$, we would obtain the positive-time function $e^{-at} - e^{bt}$, as in the ordinary unilateral transformation, as both poles would be to the left. Similarly, if we evaluated the integral (Equation B.2) along a line for which $c < -a$, we would obtain a function in negative time only. The basic point required for the work in Chapter 3 is that if we are considering the time function obtained by inverting the Laplace transformation by line integration (Equation B.2) along the real axis (that is, with $c = 0$), poles in the left-half plane correspond to functions which exist only in positive time, while poles in the right-half plane correspond to functions which exist only in negative time.

The above remarks are intended to provide only the background material on the unilateral Laplace transformation required for the understanding of Chapter 3. For a more detailed discussion of the relevant properties of the Laplace transformation, the reader should consult the references listed below.

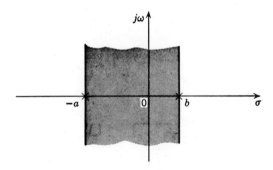

Fig. B.3. The poles of $F(s)$ and the region of definition of the transformation.

References

[1] Van der Pol, B., and H. Bremmer, *Operational Calculus Based on the Two-Sided Laplace Integral*, 2nd ed., Cambridge University Press, Cambridge, 1955.
[2] Truxal, J. G., *Automatic Feedback Control System Synthesis*, McGraw-Hill, New York, 1955.
[3] Newton, G. C., Jr., L. A. Gould, and J. F. Kaiser, *Analytical Design of Linear Feedback Controls*, Wiley, New York, 1957.

Some Relationships Involving Autocorrelation Functions and Spectral Densities

C.1 A SIGNAL WITH TWO COMPONENTS

The autocorrelation function of a signal with two components may be found as follows. Consider a signal $x(t)$ which is made up of two components $y(t)$ and $z(t)$. The autocorrelation function of $x(t) = y(t) + z(t)$ may be written as

$$\phi_{xx}(\tau) = \overline{x(t)x(t + \tau)} = \overline{[y(t) + z(t)][y(t + \tau) + z(t + \tau)]} \qquad \text{(C.1)}$$

which can be expanded in the form

$$\phi_{xx}(\tau) = \overline{y(t)y(t + \tau)} + \overline{z(t)z(t + \tau)} + \overline{y(t)z(t + \tau)} + \overline{z(t)y(t + \tau)} \qquad \text{(C.2)}$$

Expressing Equation C.2 in the notation of correlation functions, we have

$$\phi_{xx}(\tau) = \phi_{yy}(\tau) + \phi_{zz}(\tau) + \phi_{yz}(\tau) + \phi_{zy}(\tau) \qquad \text{(C.3)}$$

In particular, if the two components y and z are uncorrelated with each other, meaning that $\phi_{yz}(\tau)$ and $\phi_{zy}(\tau)$ are both identically zero, the autocorrelation function of x is simply the sum of the autocorrelation functions of the two components. That is

$$\phi_{xx}(\tau) = \phi_{yy}(\tau) + \phi_{zz}(\tau) \qquad \text{(C.4)}$$

C.2 THE AUTOCORRELATION FUNCTION AND SPECTRAL DENSITY OF THE OUTPUT OF A LINEAR SYSTEM

Consider the linear system shown in Fig. C.1, with a random input $x(t)$ whose statistical properties are known. The output $y(t)$ can be found from the convolution integral as follows:

$$y(t) = \int_{-\infty}^{\infty} x(t - u)w(u) \, du \qquad \text{(C.5)}$$

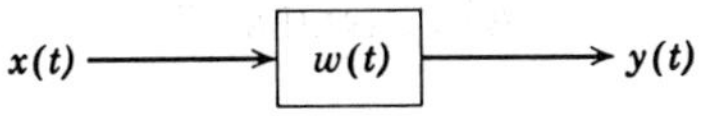

$$x(t) \longrightarrow \boxed{w(t)} \longrightarrow y(t)$$

Fig. C.1. A linear system with random input $x(t)$.

The autocorrelation function of $y(t)$ is by definition given by:

$$\phi_{yy}(\tau) \triangleq \overline{y(t)y(t + \tau)} \tag{C.6}$$

Substituting Equation C.5 in Equation C.6, we obtain

$$\phi_{yy}(\tau) = \overline{\int_{-\infty}^{\infty} x(t - u)w(u)\, du \int_{-\infty}^{\infty} x(t + \tau - v)w(v)\, dv} \tag{C.7}$$

Interchanging the operations of integration and averaging, we obtain

$$\phi_{yy}(\tau) = \int_{-\infty}^{\infty} \int_{-\infty}^{\infty} w(u)w(v)\overline{x(t - u)x(t + \tau - v)}\, du\, dv \tag{C.8}$$

Inserting correlation notation, we obtain the expression for the autocorrelation function of the output

$$\phi_{yy}(\tau) = \int_{-\infty}^{\infty} \int_{-\infty}^{\infty} w(u)w(v)\phi_{xx}(\tau + u - v)\, du\, dv \tag{C.9}$$

SPECTRAL DENSITY OF THE OUTPUT

By definition, we have

$$\Phi_{yy}(s) \triangleq \int_{-\infty}^{\infty} \phi_{yy}(\tau)e^{-s\tau}\, d\tau \tag{C.10}$$

Substituting Equation C.9 into Equation C.10, we have

$$\Phi_{yy}(s) = \int_{-\infty}^{\infty} \int_{-\infty}^{\infty} \int_{-\infty}^{\infty} w(u)w(v)\phi_{xx}(\tau + u - v)e^{-s\tau}\, du\, dv\, d\tau \tag{C.11}$$

Multiplying and dividing by e^{su} and e^{sv}, we have

$$\Phi_{yy}(s) = \int_{-\infty}^{\infty} \int_{-\infty}^{\infty} \int_{-\infty}^{\infty} w(u)w(v)\phi_{xx}(\tau + u - v)e^{-s(\tau + u - v)}e^{su}e^{-sv}\, du\, dv\, d\tau \tag{C.12}$$

$$= \int_{-\infty}^{\infty} w(u)e^{su}\, du \int_{-\infty}^{\infty} w(v)e^{-sv}\, dv \int_{-\infty}^{\infty} \phi_{xx}(\tau + u - v)e^{-s(\tau + u - v)}\, d\tau \tag{C.13}$$

$$= W(s)W(-s)\Phi_{xx}(s) \tag{C.14}$$

This is the frequency-domain relationship corresponding to Equation C.9.

APPENDIX D

Table of Integrals

The following table of integrals is part of a table originally published by Booton, Mathews, and Seifert [1], and is reproduced by permission of the authors. The entire table of integrals, including the description of the method of derivation, can also be found in reference [2].

The integral I_n is defined as follows.

$$I_n = \frac{1}{2\pi j} \int_{-j\infty}^{j\infty} \frac{c(s)c(-s)}{d(s)d(-s)} \, ds \tag{D.1}$$

where

$$c(s) = \sum_{k=0}^{n-1} c_k s^k \tag{D.2}$$

$$d(s) = \sum_{k=0}^{n} d_k s^k \tag{D.3}$$

and $d(s)$ has zeros in the left-half plane only. Although in most applications $c(s)$ has zeros in the left-half plane only, this is not a necessary condition.

REFERENCES

[1] Booton, R. C., Jr., M. V. Mathews, and W. W. Seifert, "Nonlinear Servomechanisms with Random Inputs," Report No. 70 (August 20, 1953), Dynamic Analysis and Control Laboratory, Massachusetts Institute of Technology.
[2] Newton, G. C., Jr., L. A. Gould, and J. F. Kaiser, *Analytical Design of Linear Feedback Controls*, Wiley, New York, 1957.

TABLE D.1

$$I_1 = \frac{c_0^2}{2d_0d_1}$$

$$I_2 = \frac{c_1^2d_0 + c_0^2d_2}{2d_0d_1d_2}$$

$$I_3 = \frac{c_2^2d_0d_1 + (c_1^2 - 2c_0c_2)d_0d_3 + c_0^2d_2d_3}{2d_0d_3(-d_0d_3 + d_1d_2)}$$

$$I_4 = \frac{c_3^2(-d_0^2d_3 + d_0d_1d_2) + (c_2^2 - 2c_1c_3)d_0d_1d_4 + (c_1^2 - 2c_0c_2)d_0d_3d_4 + c_0^2(-d_1d_4^2 + d_2d_3d_4)}{2d_0d_4(-d_0d_3^2 - d_1^2d_4 + d_1d_2d_3)}$$

$$I_5 = \frac{1}{2\Delta_5}[c_4^2m_0 + (c_3^2 - 2c_2c_4)m_1 + (c_2^2 - 2c_1c_3 + 2c_0c_4)m_2 + (c_1^2 - 2c_0c_2)m_3 + c_0^2m_4]$$

where

$$m_0 = \frac{1}{d_5}(d_3m_1 - d_1m_2) \qquad m_3 = \frac{1}{d_0}(d_2m_2 - d_4m_1)$$

$$m_1 = -d_0d_3 + d_1d_2 \qquad m_4 = \frac{1}{d_0}(d_2m_3 - d_4m_2)$$

$$m_2 = -d_0d_5 + d_1d_4 \qquad \Delta_5 = d_0(d_1m_4 - d_3m_3 + d_5m_2)$$

$$I_6 = \frac{1}{2\Delta_6}[c_5^2m_0 + (c_4^2 - 2c_3c_5)m_1 + (c_3^2 - 2c_2c_4 + 2c_1c_5)m_2 + (c_2^2 - 2c_1c_3 + 2c_0c_4)m_3 + (c_1^2 - 2c_0c_2)m_4 + c_0^2m_5]$$

where

$$m_0 = \frac{1}{d_6}(d_4m_1 - d_2m_2 + d_0m_3) \qquad\qquad m_4 = \frac{1}{d_0}(d_2m_3 - d_4m_2 + d_6m_1)$$

$$m_1 = -d_0d_1d_5 + d_0d_3^2 + d_1^2d_4 - d_1d_2d_3 \qquad m_5 = \frac{1}{d_0}(d_2m_4 - d_4m_3 + d_6m_2)$$

$$m_2 = d_0d_3d_5 + d_1^2d_6 - d_1d_2d_5 \qquad\qquad \Delta_6 = d_0(d_1m_5 - d_3m_4 + d_5m_3)$$

$$m_3 = d_0d_5^2 + d_1d_3d_6 - d_1d_4d_5$$

Answers to Problems

Chapter 2

1. $K = 2J(M)^{2/3}$, $\quad B = 2J(M)^{1/3}$
2. $K = J$, $\quad B = J\sqrt{2}$
3. $T = 1.118$ seconds $\quad$ /. /2 2
4. $a = 1.366$
5. (a) $K = 0.481$, $\quad$ I.S.E. $= 3.248$
   (b) $K = 2.805$, $\quad$ I.S.E. $= 1.522$

Chapter 3

1. (a) $\phi_{xx}(\tau) = \dfrac{A^2(\omega^2 + a^2)}{2} \cos \omega\tau$

   (b) $\phi_{xy}(\tau) = \dfrac{A^2\sqrt{\omega^2 + a^2}}{2} \cos \left(\omega\tau - \tan^{-1}\dfrac{\omega}{a}\right)$

2. (a) $\overline{e^2(t)} = (p^2 + q^2 + 1)\phi_{xx}(0) + 2pq\phi_{xx}(u) - 2p\phi_{xx}(u + v) - 2q\phi_{xx}(v)$
   (b) $p = -1/3$, $\quad q = 2/3$
3. Transfer function is $e^{-\tau}$ (a pure gain constant)
4. (a) $T = 0.414$, $\quad$ M.S.E. $= 1.000$

   (b) $W(s) = \dfrac{0.5}{1 + s}$, $\quad$ M.S.E. $= 0.375$

5. $K = 1.000$

6. $W(s) = \dfrac{0.146s + 0.450}{(s + 1.732)(s + 1.414)}$

Chapter 4

1. (a) $\dfrac{dx_1}{dt} = \left(\dfrac{-1}{R_1C}\right)x_1 - \left(\dfrac{1}{C}\right)x_2 + \left(\dfrac{1}{R_1C}\right)u$

   $\dfrac{dx_2}{dt} = \left(\dfrac{1}{L}\right)x_1 - \left(\dfrac{R_2}{L}\right)x_2$

(b) $\dfrac{dx_1}{dt} = -\left[\dfrac{1}{R_2C}\left(\dfrac{R_2}{R_3}+1\right)\right]x_1 + \left(\dfrac{1}{R_2C}\right)u$

$\dfrac{dx_2}{dt} = \left(\dfrac{-R_1}{L}\right)x_2 + \left(\dfrac{1}{L}\right)u$

(c) (a) is always controllable

(b) is controllable unless $R_1R_2R_3C = (R_2 + R_3)L$

2. Let $x_1 = $ angular position of J_1

$x_2 = \dot{x}_1$

$x_3 = $ angular position of J_2

$x_4 = \dot{x}_3$

State equations:

$\dot{x}_1 = x_2$

$\dot{x}_2 = \dfrac{-K_1}{J_1}x_1 + \dfrac{K_1}{J_1}x_3$

$\dot{x}_3 = x_4$

$\dot{x}_4 = \dfrac{K_1}{J_2}x_1 - \dfrac{K_1 + K_2}{J_2}x_3 + \dfrac{K_2}{J_2}u$

3. (a) $\dot{x}_1 = x_2$ $\dot{\mathbf{x}} = \begin{bmatrix} 0 & 1 & 0 \\ 0 & 0 & 1 \\ 0 & -2 & -3 \end{bmatrix}\mathbf{x} + \begin{bmatrix} 0 \\ 0 \\ 1 \end{bmatrix}u$

$\dot{x}_2 = x_3$

$\dot{x}_3 = -2x_2 - 3x_3 + u$

(b) $\lambda_1 = 0,$ $\lambda_1 = -1,$ $\lambda_2 = -2$

$\mathbf{\theta}^1 = \begin{bmatrix} 1 \\ 0 \\ 0 \end{bmatrix}$ $\mathbf{\theta}^2 = \begin{bmatrix} 1 \\ -1 \\ 1 \end{bmatrix}$ $\mathbf{\theta}^3 = \begin{bmatrix} 1 \\ -2 \\ 4 \end{bmatrix}$

(c) $\begin{bmatrix} 1 & 1.5 - 2e^{-t} + 0.5e^{-2t} & 0.5 + 0.5e^{-2t} - e^{-t} \\ 0 & 2e^{-t} - e^{-2t} & e^{-t} - e^{-2t} \\ 0 & 2e^{-2t} - 2e^{-t} & 2e^{-2t} - e^{-t} \end{bmatrix}$

(d) $\begin{bmatrix} 0.5 + 0.5e^{-2t} - e^{-t} \\ e^{-t} - e^{-2t} \\ 2e^{-2t} - e^{-t} \end{bmatrix}$

4. State equations:

$\dot{v}_1 = \dfrac{1}{RC}(-3v_1 + v_2)$

$\dot{v}_2 = \dfrac{1}{RC}(v_1 - 2v_2 + v_3)$

$\dot{v}_3 = \dfrac{1}{RC}(v_2 - 3v_3)$

Eigenvalues: $\lambda_1 = -1,$ $\lambda_2 = -3,$ $\lambda_3 = -4$

Eigenvectors: $\boldsymbol{\theta}^1 = \begin{bmatrix} 1 \\ 2 \\ 1 \end{bmatrix}$ $\boldsymbol{\theta}^2 = \begin{bmatrix} 1 \\ 0 \\ -1 \end{bmatrix}$ $\boldsymbol{\theta}^3 = \begin{bmatrix} 1 \\ -1 \\ 1 \end{bmatrix}$

Transition Matrix exp $(\mathbf{A}t)$:

$$\frac{1}{6} \begin{bmatrix} e^{-t} + 3e^{-3t} + 2e^{-4t} & 2e^{-t} - 2e^{-4t} & e^{-t} - 3e^{-3t} + 2e^{-4t} \\ 2e^{-t} - 2e^{-4t} & 4e^{-t} + 2e^{-4t} & 2e^{-t} - 2e^{-4t} \\ e^{-t} - 3e^{-3t} + 2e^{-4t} & 2e^{-t} - 2e^{-4t} & e^{-t} + 3e^{-3t} + 2e^{-4t} \end{bmatrix}$$

5. (a) State equations:

$$\dot{x}_1 = x_2$$

$$\dot{x}_2 = \frac{-x_1}{LC} - \frac{Rx_2}{L} = -2x_1 - 3x_2$$

Eigenvalues: $\lambda_1 = -1,$ $\lambda_2 = -2$

Eigenvectors: $\boldsymbol{\theta}^1 = \begin{bmatrix} 1 \\ -1 \end{bmatrix}$ $\boldsymbol{\theta}^2 = \begin{bmatrix} 1 \\ -2 \end{bmatrix}$

Phase-plane trajectories:

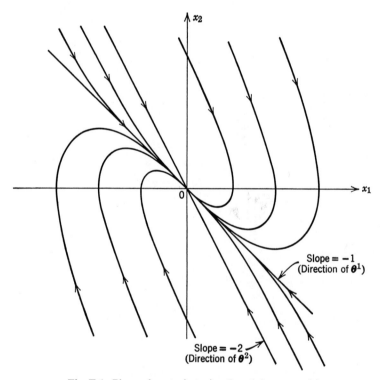

Fig. E.1. Phase-plane trajectories, $L = 1$ (not to scale).

(b) $\lambda_1 = -2/3, \qquad \lambda_2 \to -\infty$

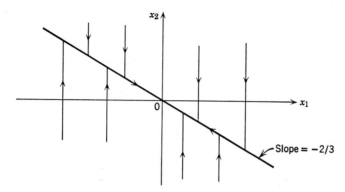

Fig. E.2. Phase-plane trajectories, $L = 0$ (not to scale).

(c)

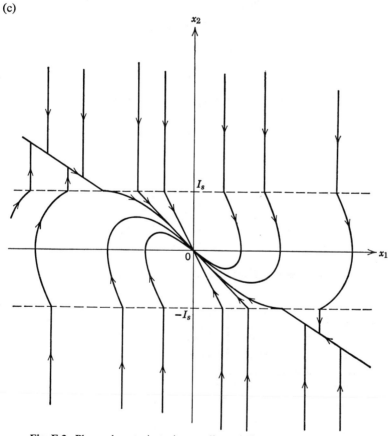

Fig. E.3. Phase-plane trajectories, nonlinear inductance (not to scale).

6. The isocline corresponding to trajectory slope m is the horizontal line whose equation is

$$x_2 = \frac{1}{m + a}$$

Sample trajectories are shown in Fig. E.4. Other trajectories are obtained by displacing the sample trajectories horizontally. As the magnitude of x_2 becomes very large, the slopes of the trajectories approach $-a$.

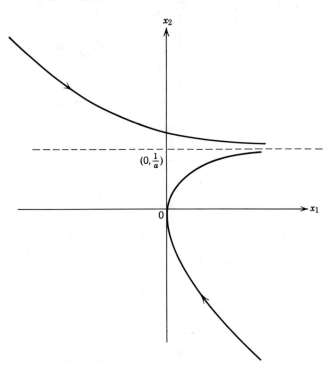

Fig. E.4. Sample trajectories (not to scale).

7. (a)

$$\dot{x} = \begin{bmatrix} -2 & 1 & 1 \\ 1 & -3 & 2 \\ 1 & 2 & -3 \end{bmatrix} x + \begin{bmatrix} 0 \\ 1 \\ -1 \end{bmatrix} u$$

where $x_1 = v_{AD}$, $x_2 = v_{BD}$, $x_3 = v_{CD}$.

(b) $\lambda_1 = 0$, $\lambda_2 = -3$, $\lambda_3 = -5$

$$\theta^1 = \begin{bmatrix} 1 \\ 1 \\ 1 \end{bmatrix} \qquad \theta^2 = \begin{bmatrix} 2 \\ -1 \\ -1 \end{bmatrix} \qquad \theta^3 = \begin{bmatrix} 0 \\ 1 \\ -1 \end{bmatrix}$$

(c)
$$\exp(\mathbf{A}t) = \tfrac{1}{6}\begin{bmatrix} 2 + 4e^{-3t} & 2 - 2e^{-3t} & 2 - 2e^{-3t} \\ 2 - 2e^{-3t} & 2 + e^{-3t} + 3e^{-5t} & 2 + e^{-3t} - 3e^{-5t} \\ 2 - 2e^{-3t} & 2 + e^{-3t} - 3e^{-5t} & 2 + e^{-3t} + 3e^{-5t} \end{bmatrix}$$

Final steady values $x_1 = x_2 = x_3 = 10$

(d) (i) No

(ii) Yes; AD, BD, or CD

(e) (i) No

(ii) Resistor connected between points B and D or C and D

8. (a) $\mathbf{A} = \begin{bmatrix} 0 & 1 \\ -2 & -3 \end{bmatrix}$ $\quad \mathbf{b} = \begin{bmatrix} 1 \\ \alpha - 3 \end{bmatrix}$ $\quad \mathbf{c}' = [1 \quad 0]$

$\mathbf{F} = \begin{bmatrix} 0 & 1 \\ -2 & -3 \end{bmatrix}$ $\quad \mathbf{g} = \begin{bmatrix} 0 \\ 1 \end{bmatrix}$ $\quad \mathbf{h}' = [\alpha \quad 1]$

(b) $\mathbf{T} = \begin{bmatrix} 0 & -\frac{1}{2} \\ 1 & 1\frac{1}{2} \end{bmatrix}$ $\quad \mathbf{T}^{-1} = \begin{bmatrix} 3 & 1 \\ -2 & 0 \end{bmatrix}$

(c) First form is observable but not controllable
Second form is controllable but not observable

9. (a) $\mathbf{f}(k + 1) = \begin{bmatrix} \frac{1}{2} & \frac{1}{2} \\ 1 & 0 \end{bmatrix}\mathbf{f}(k)$

where $f_1(k) = F(k)$, and $f_2(k) = F(k - 1)$

Eigenvalues are $\quad \gamma_1 = 1, \quad \gamma_2 = -\frac{1}{2}$

Eigenvectors are $\quad \boldsymbol{\theta}^1 = \begin{bmatrix} 1 \\ 1 \end{bmatrix} \quad \boldsymbol{\theta}^2 = \begin{bmatrix} 1 \\ -2 \end{bmatrix}$

(b) $\mathbf{G}^k = \tfrac{1}{3}\begin{bmatrix} 2 + (-\frac{1}{2})^k & 1 - (-\frac{1}{2})^k \\ 2 - 2(-\frac{1}{2})^k & 1 + 2(-\frac{1}{2})^k \end{bmatrix}$

The limit of $\mathbf{G}^k$, as k approaches infinity, is $\begin{bmatrix} \frac{2}{3} & \frac{1}{3} \\ \frac{2}{3} & \frac{1}{3} \end{bmatrix}$

(c) 10.000

Chapter 5

1. (a) $u^*(t) = -0.157e^t + 1.157e^{-t};$ $\quad I = 1.313$

(b) $u^*(t) = 0.1195e^t - 0.8805e^{-t};$ $\quad I = 0.761$

(c) $u^*(t) = -e^{-t} \quad (0 \leqslant t < \infty);$ $\quad I = 1.000$

2. (a) $u^*(t) = -0.152e^{1.414t} - 0.442e^{-1.414t};$ $\quad I = 0.593$

(b) $u^*(t) = 0.0243e^{1.414t} - 0.410e^{-1.414t};$ $\quad I = 0.387$

(c) $u^*(t) = -0.414e^{-1.414t} \quad (0 \leqslant t < \infty);$ $\quad I = 0.414$

3. $x(t) = 1.414e^{-0.707t} \sin\left(0.707t + \frac{\pi}{4}\right)$

$u^*(t) = 1.414e^{-0.707t} \sin\left(0.707t - \frac{\pi}{4}\right)$

4. Fig. 5.8: $u^*(t) = -x(t)$

Fig. 5.9: $u^*(t) = -0.414x(t)$

Fig. 5.10: $u^*(t) = -x_1 - 1.414x_2$

5. $u^*(t) = 0.5625t - 1.375;$ $\quad I = 1.94$

6. Let $x_1 = \theta,$ $x_2 = \omega$

State equations are: $\dot{x}_0 = (u - x_2)^2$

$$\dot{x}_1 = x_2$$
$$\dot{x}_2 = -x_2 + u$$

Optimal control input $u^*(t) = 9t^2 + 8t - 9$

7. $u(t) = 0.563ke^t$

8. $x = R(\theta - \sin\theta)$

$y = R(\cos\theta - 1)$

The optimal curve is a cycloid, with R the radius of the generating circle. This is a variation of the brachistochrone problem, which is discussed in most books on the calculus of variations.

Chapter 6

1. $u(t) = -1.1$ for $0 \leqslant t \leqslant 0.3131$ seconds

$u = -0.1625e^t - 1.2005e^{-t}$ for $0.3131 \leqslant t \leqslant 1$ seconds

Value of $I = 1.318$

2. $u(t) = -1,$ $0 \leqslant t \leqslant 1$

$u(t) = \frac{2}{3}t - \frac{5}{3},$ $1 \leqslant t \leqslant 4$

$I = 2.00$

3.

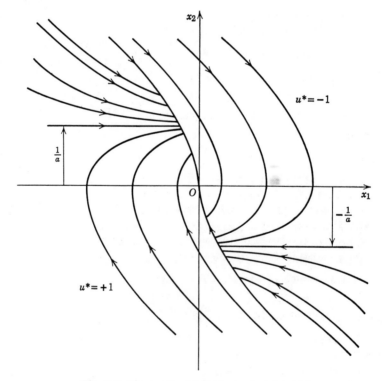

Fig. E.5. Time-optimal trajectories (not to scale).

4. $\dot{x} = \begin{bmatrix} 0 & 1 \\ -1 & 0 \end{bmatrix} x + \begin{bmatrix} 1 & 0 \\ 0 & 1 \end{bmatrix} u$

(a) Input vector **u** changes from one vertex of the admissible square to another, at intervals of $\pi/2$ seconds, as shown in Fig. E.6.

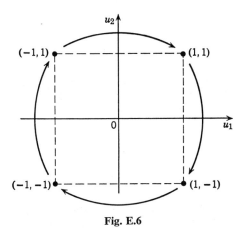

Fig. E.6

The switching curves and optimal trajectories are as shown in Fig. E.7 (sections of switching curves are quarters of circles of radius $\sqrt{2}$ units).

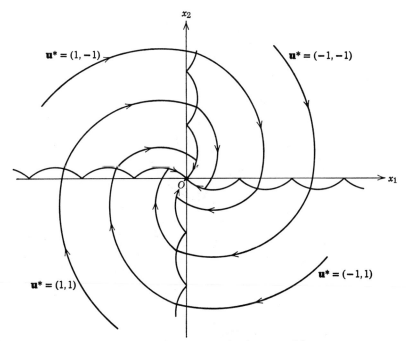

Fig. E.7. Optimal trajectories (not to scale).

(b) Input vector **u** again changes from one vertex to another of the admissible square, at intervals of $\pi/2$ seconds, as shown in Fig. E.8.

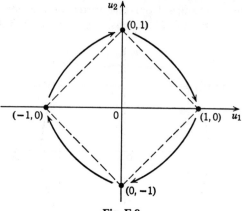

Fig. E.8

Switching curves and optimal trajectories are as shown in Fig. E.9 (sections of switching curves are quarters of circles of unit radius, placed along a 45° line).

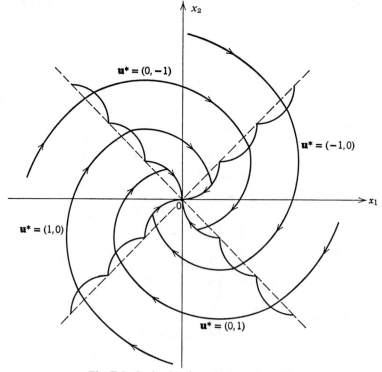

Fig. E.9. Optimal trajectories (not to scale).

(c) Control inputs: $u_1(t) = -\cos(t - \phi)$

$u_2(t) = \sin(t - \phi)$

Solutions of differential equations:

$$x_1(t) = -(t - \phi)\cos(t - \phi)$$
$$x_2(t) = (t - \phi)\sin(t - \phi)$$
$$x_1^2(t) + x_2^2(t) = (t - \phi)^2$$

State reaches the origin at $t = \phi$

An optimal trajectory (for $t < \phi$) is shown in Fig. E.10.

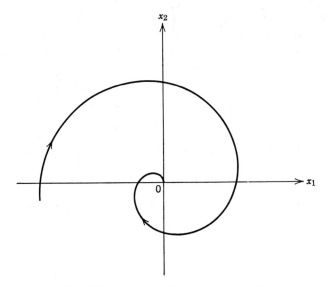

Fig. E.10. Optimal trajectory (not to scale).

5. The control input has one of the following two forms:

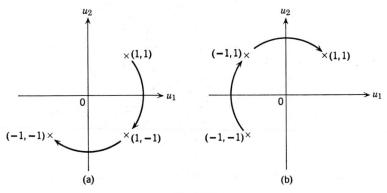

Fig. E.11

The optimal trajectories have the form:

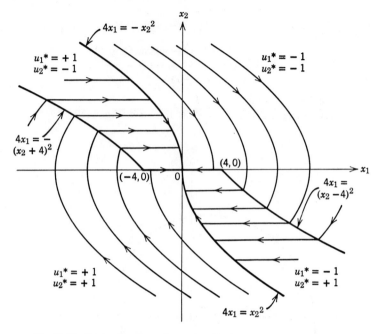

Fig. E.12. Optimal trajectories and switching curves (not to scale).

6. (a)

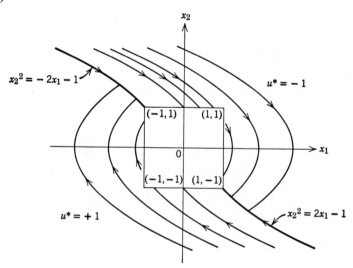

Fig. E.13. Optimal trajectories and switching curves (not to scale).

(b)

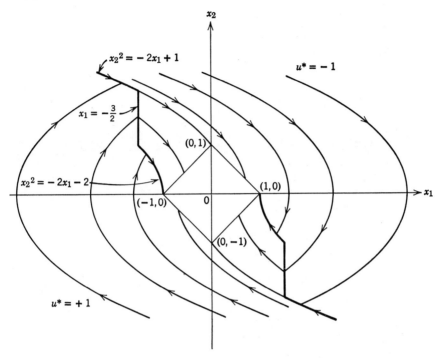

Fig. E.14. Optimal trajectories and switching curves (not to scale).

7. (a) $\dot{\mathbf{x}} = \begin{bmatrix} -1 & 0 \\ 0 & -1 \end{bmatrix} \mathbf{x} + \begin{bmatrix} 1 & -1 \\ 0 & 1 \end{bmatrix} \mathbf{u}$

  (b) Yes
  (c) (i) No. (ii) No.
  (d) Minimum-time transition from $(1, 0)$ to $(0, 0)$ can be achieved in three
    ways, namely:

   (i) $\mathbf{u} = \begin{bmatrix} -1 \\ -1 \end{bmatrix}$ for 0.405 seconds, followed by $\mathbf{u} = \begin{bmatrix} -1 \\ 1 \end{bmatrix}$ for 0.288
     seconds

   (ii) $\mathbf{u} = \begin{bmatrix} -1 \\ 1 \end{bmatrix}$ for 0.288 seconds, followed by $\mathbf{u} = \begin{bmatrix} -1 \\ -1 \end{bmatrix}$ for 0.405
     seconds

   (iii) $\mathbf{u} = \begin{bmatrix} -1 \\ 0 \end{bmatrix}$ for 0.693 seconds

    The total time is the same for all three cases.

Chapter 7

1. (a) (i) $\dfrac{c}{\sqrt{30}}, \quad \dfrac{2c}{\sqrt{30}}, \quad \dfrac{3c}{\sqrt{30}}, \quad \dfrac{4c}{\sqrt{30}}.$

    (ii) $c, 0, 0, 0$

   (b) (i) $0, 0, 0, c$

    (ii) $\dfrac{12c}{25}, \quad \dfrac{6c}{25}, \quad \dfrac{4c}{25}, \quad \dfrac{3c}{25}.$

2. $u(0) = \dfrac{c}{\sqrt{85}}, \qquad u(1) = \dfrac{2c}{\sqrt{85}}, \qquad u(2) = \dfrac{4c}{\sqrt{85}}, \qquad u(3) = \dfrac{8c}{\sqrt{85}}.$

3. (a) $W_N - S_{N-1} = S_{N-1} + 1$

    Hence (i) $S_N = 3S_{N-1} + 1$

    (ii) $W_N = 3W_{N-1}$

   (b) 1, 3, 9, 27 units; 40 units

4. (a) For $N = 3$: $u(0) = -1.168$

    $u(1) = -0.964$

    $u(2) = -0.868$

    $S_3(1) = 1.5012$

   (b) For $N = 3$: $u(0) = -0.523$

    $u(1) = -0.248$

    $u(2) = 0$

    $S_3(1) = 0.8563$

5. (a) For $N = 3$: $u(0) = -0.540$

    $u(1) = -0.531$

    $u(2) = -0.640$

    $S_3(1) = 0.7883$

   (b) For $N = 3$: $u(0) = -0.268$

    $u(1) = -0.120$

    $u(2) = 0$

    $S_3(1) = 0.5590$

6. (a) $S_1(x) = x^2;$ $u = 0$

    $S_2(x) = 1.5x^2;$ $u = -0.5x$

    $S_3(x) = 1.6x^2;$ $u = -0.6x$

    $S_4(x) = 1.615x^2;$ $u = -0.615x$

   (b) $S_\infty(x) = 1.618x^2;$ $u = -0.618x$

   (c) $S_\infty(x) = 1.051x^2;$ $u = -0.951x$

7. $u(t) = 0.200 \sinh (1.414t - 1.414)$

   $x(t) = 0.200 \cosh (1.414t - 2.294)$

Index